Environmental Trends

Council on Environmental Quality
Executive Office of the President
Washington, D.C.

Cosponsored by the

Interagency Advisory
Committee on
Environmental
Trends

1989

Contents

Acknowledgments

Environmental Trends is a publication of the Council on Environmental Quality (CEQ) within the Executive Office of the President. Throughout production of this sourcebook the Council consisted of Mr. A. Alan Hill, Chairman, and Dr. William L. Mills and Ms. Jacqueline E. Schafer, Members. This edition was initiated by Dr. Harvey Doerksen, the first Project Manager, through his ideas on environmental data, indicators, and monitoring and through his efforts to activate and involve the Interagency Advisory Committee on Environmental Trends and to procure contractual support. He was succeeded by Ms. Carroll Curtis who provided the majority of the impetus to develop the book to its final stages and the persistence to see it through difficult times. Major John C. Jens assumed overview to publish the book; however, Ms. Curtis, then of the Virginia Institute of Marine Science within the College of William and Mary, Williamsburg, Virginia, continued to put the book in camera-ready copy for the printer. Contract managerial assistance was provided by Lucinda Low Swartz and Lynn Grant Mohr.

The research and development of the book was directed by Carroll Curtis. Other research assistance was provided by NUS Corporation, Gaithersburg, Maryland, under contract. Final data files and computer-generated graphs and charts were prepared under contract by Lori Hidinger and George Clark of SRA Technologies, Inc., Alexandria, Virginia. Additional data entry was provided by Todd Ornett and Steve Russell, summer interns at CEQ.

Lawrence Fahey, Meridian Maps, Dunn Loring, Virginia, compiled the maps, which were required to be hand drawn, and created the page layout format. Dr. Ethan T. Smith, U.S. Geological Survey, Reston, Virginia, supplied the computer-generated water and other resources maps.

The text was drafted by Carroll Curtis from published sources. Thomas E. Dahl, U.S. Fish and Wildlife Service, Washington, D.C., prepared the text for Chapter 5.

Editing was accomplished by David Johnston (under contract), Carroll Curtis, John C. Jens, and Leota Kane and the editorial staff of the Office of Scientific and Technical Information, U.S. Department of Energy, Oak Ridge, Tennessee.

Typesetting for the final camera-ready copy was done also at the Office of Scientific and Technical Information. Steve Jewell, Government Printing Office, assisted in printing preparations.

The Council wishes to thank the Interagency Advisory Committee on Environmental Trends, which was established to provide the outline and guidance for this book. Many of these agencies contributed data and/or funding to support this project. The Advisory Committee members are: Dr. Richard M. Parry, Jr. (Agricultural Research Service, Department of Agriculture), Dr. John Miranoski (Economic Research Service, Department of Agriculture), David E. Ketcham and Lambert N. Wenner, alternate (Forest Service, Department of Agriculture), Tom George (Soil Conservation Service, Department of Agriculture), Jacob Silver (Bureau of the Census, Department of Commerce), Larry Pugh (National Atmospheric and Oceanic Administration, Department of Commerce), Dr. John Belshe (U.S. Army Corps of Engineers, Department of Defense), Ted Williams and Richard Ball, alternate (Office of Environmental Analysis, Department of Energy), Cindy Kelly (Environmental Protection Agency), David Williams (Bureau of Land Management, Department of the Interior), Thomas E. Dahl (Fish and Wildlife Service, Department of the Interior), Dr. Albert G. Green, Jr. (National Park Service, Department of the Interior), Dr. Harvey Doerksen (Office of Policy Analysis, Department of the Interior), Dr. Ethan T. Smith (U.S. Geological Survey, Department of the Interior), Dr. Robert Watson (National Aeronautics and Space Administration), Dr. Julian P. Shedlovsky (National Science Foundation), Suzanne Butcher (Department of State), Robert Johnson and Dennis Ryan, alternate (Tennessee Valley Authority), and Fred Skaer (Federal Highway Administration, Department of Transportation). The Committee will continue to advise CEQ on environmental data and monitoring policy questions.

In addition, representatives of the Bureau of Mines, National Acid Precipitation Assessment Program, Association of State and Interstate Water Pollution Control Administrators, Association of American Railroads, Transportation Policy Associates, International Joint Commission, and Canada Wildlife Service provided data and assistance on this project. And a final thanks to the many persons who helped on this project in many ways to make it a success but whose names are not listed here.

Introduction

The Council on Environmental Quality is required, by the National Environmental Policy Act of 1969, to report on the status and condition of the environment; current and foreseeable trends in the quality, management, and utilization of the environment; and the effects of environmental trends. The Council reports to Congress in an annual report and maintains an archive of national environmental statistics, which it updates and publishes periodically in the annual report as statistical tables and in environmental trends reports as charts, graphs, and maps.

Environmental Trends updates the Council's 1981 report by that name. This sourcebook contains 367 graphics, most of which are computer generated and indicate current conditions and trends in the environment of the United States. The statistical series for *Environmental Trends* was compiled from data available through government agencies, private studies, or the literature of each discipline. The data were reviewed and verified by experts at various federal agencies. National data are used wherever possible, with breakdowns shown when especially meaningful. The text is drawn from the published sources cited.

An Interagency Advisory Committee on Environmental Trends was convened by the Council to assist in the preparation of *Environmental Trends*. The Advisory Committee selected the list of environmental indicators and identified the data sources that best described each of the indicators. In selecting indicators, the Advisory Committee reviewed the 1981 report for usefulness and adequacy of statistics and applied the following criteria in its evaluation: (1) reflects a meaningful condition or variation in environmental quality, likened to environmental or human health consequences; (2) allows for aggregation of data to display national trends in environmental quality as well as disaggregation to show local/regional conditions; and (3) is measurable and of sufficient time series coverage to reveal conditions and trends. In applying the criteria, the Advisory Committee was mindful of the kinds of questions that the indicators could address, such as: Are environmental conditions getting better or worse? What aspects of the environment are most improved, most degraded? Where do environmental conditions pose a health hazard? Are the data monitored sufficiently to give confidence in making accurate assessments? Have environmental legislation and programs resulted in any measurable improvements? In what areas is change most noticeable?

Environmental Trends consists of nine chapters: minerals and energy, water, climate and air quality, land resources, wetlands and wildlife, protected areas, population, transportation, and environmental risks and hazards. The graphs and charts were generated and enhanced for final output using commercial database management and graphics software. The numerical data are published in tabular form in *Environmental Quality 1987/1988—The Eighteenth Annual Report of the Council on Environmental Quality* together with *The President's Message to Congress.* Interested individuals will be able to confirm statistical trends information depicted in graphs and charts herein by consulting that report. Computer-generated maps were produced using a commercially available mapping software package; the remaining maps and figures were compiled by a cartographer.

What does the information in *Environmental Trends* tell us? In the first chapter it tells us that more metals and nonmetals (sand, gravel, and phosphate rock) have been mined domestically and more energy sources have been tapped in this Nation in the last 50 years than in all preceding time since settlement. Despite this increase, the mining and energy industries have made great strides in recent years to reduce environmental pollutants and impacts. However, some challenge areas still persist, including land reclamation, acid mine drainage, air emissions, and effluent discharges.

With regards to water quantity and quality, the trend data confirm that competing demands continue for available surface and ground water as sources of public and rural water supply, irrigation and industrial water, electric power generation, recreation, and fish and wildlife habitat. Despite severe drought, chronic water shortage, overdrafting of ground water, saltwater intrusion, and reduction in water quality in certain areas, water supplies are sufficient to accommodate competing uses in most regions of the Nation.

Perhaps the greatest progress has been made in controlling air and water pollution where concentrations of many pollutants are showing measurable decline. Emissions of total suspended particulates, sulfur dioxide, nitrogen oxides, volatile organic compounds, carbon monoxide, and lead from various sources have been reduced in the past decade as a result of pollution controls. Concentrations of suspended solids, oxygen-demanding wastes, and phosphorus are declining in many waterways. There has been a marked reduction in environmental levels of DDT and other persistent organochlorine pesticides; polychlorinated biphenyls (PCB); vinyl chloride; benzene; asbestos; and mercury, lead, and other heavy metals. Concentrations of these and other chemicals in human and wildlife tissues have also declined. Although pollutant loads are being reduced, they are being dispersed over long distances and deposited hundreds of miles away from the source.

Nevertheless, pollution concerns remain. Shellfish-growing waters in many estuaries remain closed to harvest because of pollution. On a global scale, concentrations of carbon dioxide and other "greenhouse" gases continue to increase. Other forms of contamination, such as radon and toxic substances, are proving to be more serious than once believed. For many of these concerns, statistical trends data are limited or are not available.

Wetlands, forests, native grasslands, estuarine habitats, and other representative natural habitats have been and continue to be lost as a result of agricultural conversion, urbanization, transportation system development, and increased demand for recreation sites. Fish and wildlife populations, which are dependent on these natural systems, are being adversely impacted by the losses. The rate of habitat loss may be slowing in some natural areas but increasing in others.

In the past 10 years, many new national parks and refuges have been established, wilderness areas and wildlife and scenic rivers designated, and certain marine and estuarine areas given additional protection. However, the natural condition of some protected public lands has begun to decline because of visitor impact, including vandalism, pollution, and reduced air quality.

The farmland and cropland situation is also changing. Since the 1930s, the trends in number of farms and farm size have been toward fewer but larger farms. The amount of prime farmland in the Nation's agricultural base continues to decline; much of the farmland is being converted to urban and residential use or submerged by water impoundments. Soil erosion continues to be a challenge in places, especially where conservation measures are not used. In recent years, however, millions of acres of highly erodible and marginal cropland have been taken out of production and placed in conservation reserves, which are usually planted with trees. This trend is also reflected in reforestation statistics, which show a continuing increase in the forest acres planted with seedlings or direct seeded. The amount of fertilizer applied to cropland on the national level has declined, mostly a reflection of cropland diversion. The use of insecticides has declined, whereas the use of herbicides has increased. Total water use for irrigation increased steadily for the first seven decades of this century but has since begun to decrease. On a regional scale, irrigated acres have declined in some areas but increased in others. As the charts suggest, there has been a slow, but gradual, improvement in the condition of grazing lands in the United States. The forests of the United States continue to be plagued by insect pests, disease, and wildfire but remain productive.

There continues to be a loss in biological diversity worldwide. Although very few species of vertebrates have been officially declared extinct during the past 30 years, many species have been declared threatened or endangered. Much is being done to identify plants, animals, and habitats that need protection; the survival rate of some protected species is even showing signs of improvement.

Patterns of land use in the United States are changing dramatically. Human settlements, recreation sites, industry, and energy exploration are being located in many areas that were once avoided because they were too hot, too cold, too dry, too risky (from natural hazards, such as earthquakes, floods, and hurricanes), too wild, or too remote (such as steep mountain slopes, isolated coasts, and the underwater continental shelf). The effects of this expansion are apparent with regards to increased fuel consumption for cooling and heating, water shortages, loss of lives and property, loss of fish and wildlife habitat, and spills of oil and hazardous wastes. These trends also reflect many of the remaining environmental concerns, such as changing rural life, which influence the extent, location, and quality of the remaining natural areas of the country.

Population characteristics and economic conditions in the United States greatly influence environmental quality. The total population—its growth, age structure, migration and settlement patterns, and awareness of environmental concerns—greatly influences how the Nation's land and resources are used. The prevailing economic situation affects the ability of industries, municipalities, and individuals to invest in pollution abatement controls and conservation measures.

Since settlement, dramatic changes in the major modes of transportation in the United States have generally deteriorated environmental conditions. Emissions, noise, land disturbance, and accidents involving hazardous materials are continuing environmental concerns.

Waste is an inevitable by-product of our society, and the challenge of waste disposal—whether the waste is solid, liquid, or gaseous, hazardous or benign—has reached critical dimensions in recent years. The most significant waste disposal challenges today are municipal and industrial solid and sludge disposal, control of hazardous wastes, cleanup of uncontrolled hazardous waste sites, and disposal of radioactive waste.

The prognosis for improvements in environmental quality and reduction of human health risk is good. Pollution controls and environmental safeguards put into place over the past two decades have resulted in measurable changes in many aspects of the environment. Increased public awareness of environmental risks and hazards and more attention to conservation and protection of available resources have also helped improve the quality of the Nation's environment. But there is still more to do. The purpose of *Environmental Trends* is to bring this awareness of past accomplishments and future challenges to the citizens of the United States.

Chapter 1
Minerals and Energy

1-1
Geologic regions

The geologic formations of the United States reflect the results of geologic processes that have occurred throughout the history of the earth. These rock units are categorized according to their type and age and are grouped to define geologic regions. The differences between these rocks, how they are formed, and where they are located help geologists interpret the earth's history. Geologic maps record rock formations exposed at the earth's surface or just under the soil cover.

Quaternary and Tertiary rocks are the youngest, less than 100,000 years old and between 100,000 and 65 million years old, respectively. They each include two distinct rock types—sedimentary rocks, which are formed from layers of accumulated sand, gravel, and finer deposits under moderate pressure, and hard or igneous rocks such as basalts, which are created by extrusive or volcanic events. The intrusive and plutonic rocks of Tertiary and Mesozoic ages (the latter are from 65 to 225 million years old) in the western United States and Paleozoic age (225 to 570 million years old) in the eastern United States are predominately granites. These rocks result from molten magma in the earth's interior which has solidified beneath the surface; they can be seen only where uplift and erosion have uncovered them. Mesozoic rocks include mostly sedimentary sandstones and shales. These sedimentary rocks are composed of rock fragments or mineral grains brought together by the processes of weathering, erosion, transportation, and deposition. Along with solidification of magma, consolidation of sediments, and metamorphism, these processes form a rock cycle. Sandstones are formed from deposits of sediments that make up beaches, deltas, floodplains, and deserts. Shales are formed from layers of particles finer than sand.

Paleozoic rocks include thick layers of limestone, dolomite, and sandstone. Upper Paleozoic rocks are 225 to 345 million years old, while Lower Paleozoic rocks are 345 to 570 million years old. Limestones originate either from the accumulation of remains of living marine organisms (primarily corals and algae, which remove calcium carbonate from seawater and incorporate it into reef structures) or from the chemical precipitation of calcium in warm seas, hot springs, saline lakes, and limestone caves. Dolomite rock is generally believed to be formed by replacement of calcite by dolomite in limestone before it is deeply buried by other sediments.

Precambrian rocks are 570 million years old and older. These ancient rocks are formed from sedimentary and igneous or other metamorphic rocks by processes involving extreme heat, pressure, or both. Metamorphic processes occur at considerable depths within the earth and change the texture or mineral composition of the rocks. As a result, many Precambrian rocks are conspicuously bent and folded.

Geologic regions by rock type

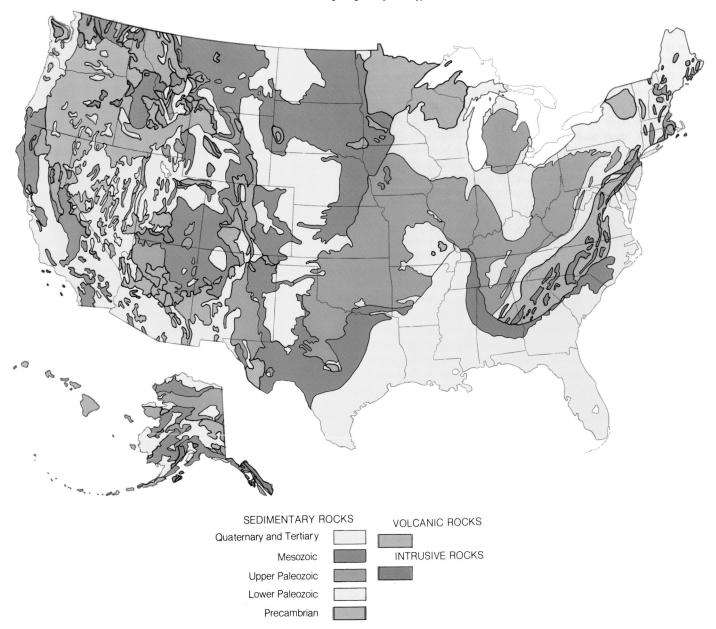

SEDIMENTARY ROCKS
Quaternary and Tertiary
Mesozoic
Upper Paleozoic
Lower Paleozoic
Precambrian

VOLCANIC ROCKS

INTRUSIVE ROCKS

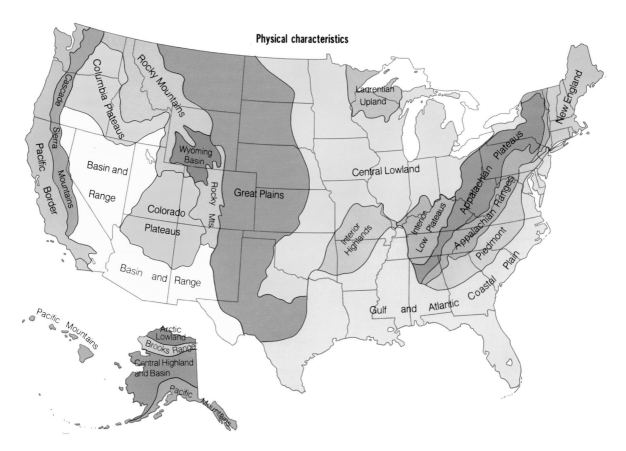

Physical characteristics

1-2
Physical characteristics

The physical characteristics of the United States reflect landform, or surface topography, and underlying geologic structure. Landforms can be depositional or erosional. Differences in landform result not only from rock types and their orientation but also from climate and length of time exposed. Areas of similar surface and geologic structure are delineated as provinces. Each province is unique with regard to its developmental history and contemporaneous features.

The Continental Shelf is the submerged margin of the continent. On the Atlantic and Gulf coasts it is wide and gently sloping, and on the Pacific coast it is narrow and irregular.

The Gulf and Atlantic Coastal Plains are composed of undeformed sedimentary rocks that presumably overlie eroded metamorphic and intrusive (granitic) rocks. The Coastal Plain grades from flat, marshy lowlands along the coast to gently rolling, well-drained uplands. The lower Coastal Plain, which is protected by barrier islands and beaches, contains extensive, meandering rivers and tidal estuaries. The sediments of the lower Coastal Plain are marine in origin and consist of sand, silt, and clay, with the exception of the Mississippi Valley with its broad plain and delta formed from gravel, sand, and mud deposited by the river.

The Appalachian Highland Region was once a great, elongated basin of deposition that was later folded, faulted, and uplifted to form a mountain range. The eastern side of the mountain range is dominated by igneous and metamorphic rocks, and the western side is composed mainly of sedimentary rocks that are only mildly faulted. Those igneous and metamorphic rocks testify to a mountain chain even older than the current Appalachian Range. In the southern Appalachians, metamorphic rocks at

low elevations form the Piedmont; similar rocks at higher elevations form the Blue Ridge Mountains. The adjacent Ridge and Valley Province is formed from sedimentary rocks that are mildly deformed in broad open folds. In the northern Appalachians, rocks are mainly igneous and metamorphic.

The interior of the conterminous United States, composed of the Great Plains, Central Lowlands, Interior Highlands, and Laurentian Upland, is the Central Stable Region, the part of the continent between the eastern and western mountain ranges. This region is mostly low-lying and covered by a veneer of flat-lying sedimentary rocks and in the northern and eastern halves by glacial deposits. In the north central portion of the interior, the sedimentary cover is thin, and ancient metamorphic rocks of the Laurentian Shield are exposed. In the western portion, the elevation increases on to the Great Plains, which is a broad belt of young sediments shed from the Rocky Mountains and deposited along its front.

The Interior Highlands, or Ozark Region, is composed of the Ozark Plateaus and the Ouachita Mountains. The Ozark Plateaus contain a number of basins and domes where faulting is minor, folds are very gentle, and igneous rocks are rarely exposed. The Arbuckle and Ouachita Mountains, on the other hand, include strongly faulted rocks in areas of southern Oklahoma and Arkansas.

The Cordilleran Mountain Region extends from the Great Plains Region westward to the Pacific coastline. A great variety of rock types and diversity of landform are found throughout this region. Like the Appalachian Range, the Rocky Mountains were formed primarily by uplifting and associated faulting. They are younger and appear to be more complex. Rocks in the eastern part of the northern Rockies are folded and thrusted, whereas those in the western part of the northern Rockies are intrusive.

These sections are similar to the western part of the Appalachians; however, the rest of the Rocky Mountains are different. In Wyoming, the middle Rockies are uplifted primarily by faulting with many intermontane basins and plains. Large sedimentary basins occur on the Wyoming Plateau between the mountain ranges. The Basin and Range Province contains mostly isolated ranges separated by wide desert plains and many lakes, ancient lake beds, and alluvial fans. The southern portion of the Rockies is made up of very high, complex mountains.

The Colorado Plateau is an unusual structural feature because of its fairly thick accumulation of flat-lying, relatively undeformed sedimentary rock at high elevation. This plateau is known for its deeply entrenched meandering streams and rivers, of which the Grand Canyon is the most famous. Abruptly bounding this province and the Basin and Range Province is the Sierra Nevada Range, which, like the northern Rockies, is a series of large granitic intrusions.

The Pacific Coast Province is a geologically young and active, but very complex, area. Much of the seismic activity and the only active volcanoes in the conterminous United States occur here where the North American crustal plate grinds past the Pacific crustal plate in the south and over it in the north. The Coast Ranges, consisting of complexly folded and faulted rocks, form the western part, or Pacific Border. The Great Valley lowland grades into the Sierra Nevada Mountains to the southeast and the Cascade Range to the northeast. The Cascade Range is composed of volcanic and continental sedimentary rocks capped by very young, high volcanoes. To the east of the Cascade Range is the Columbian Province, which consists of deep, extensive lava flows of varying ages and is entrenched by rivers similar to but not as numerous as those of the Colorado Plateau.

Alaska, mostly highlands and mountains, is considered to be a part of the western Cordillera. The Hawaiian Islands are a series of volcanoes formed from lava outpouring through a fissure zone in the ocean floor.

1-3
Distribution of mineral resources

Many of the minerals that form the crust of the earth are useful to man. The major mineral resources mined in the United States include lead, zinc, copper, bauxite (for aluminum), gold, silver, iron ore, sand, gravel, building stone, and phosphate rock. Deposits of these minerals are scattered unevenly across the United States and are found above and below ground.

Lead deposits are concentrated primarily in the lower Mississippi Valley in a western extension of a historic Missouri lead belt. A significant increase in domestic lead reserves was realized over the last two decades from discovery and development of deposits in this district and, more recently, in Alaska. Additional lead reserves are located in Idaho and Colorado and occur with zinc and silver deposits in Alaska.

Zinc deposits are found in Alaska; from Maine southward through the Appalachian Mountains; in Tennessee, Missouri, and other parts of the Mississippi Valley; and in the Rocky Mountain states. About 60% of the zinc in these deposits occurs in ores associated with other minerals such as lead, copper, and/or precious metals. The remaining zinc reserves are ores in which zinc is the principal component.

More than 90% of the domestic copper deposits are located in five states—Arizona, Utah, New Mexico, Montana, and Michigan—and nearly all of the reserves are in mines where copper is the principal product. Sizeable deposits in Alaska and Minnesota hold promise for future development.

Most of the world's aluminum is produced from the mineral bauxite. The principal domestic deposits of bauxite for primary aluminum are in central Arkansas, whereas deposits in Alabama and Georgia are the source of refractory and chemical bauxites. Bauxite is also found in Missouri and Illinois and in alunite deposits in Colorado and Utah.

Gold and silver deposits are found throughout the western half of the conterminous United States and in Alaska. The largest producers of gold are the states of California, Colorado, South Dakota, Nevada, Alaska, Utah, and Montana. Most silver is produced

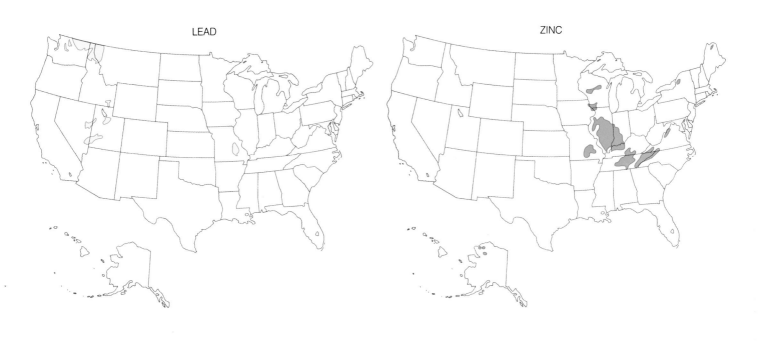

LEAD   ZINC

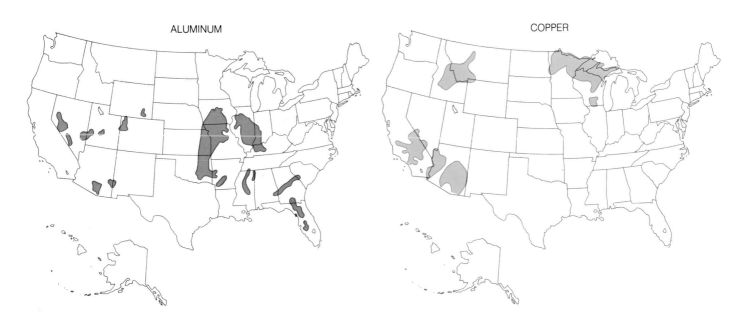

ALUMINUM   COPPER

IRON

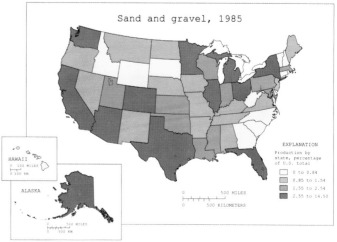

Sand and gravel, 1985

EXPLANATION
Production by
state, percentage
of U.S. total

0 to 0.84
0.85 to 1.54
1.55 to 2.54
2.55 to 14.50

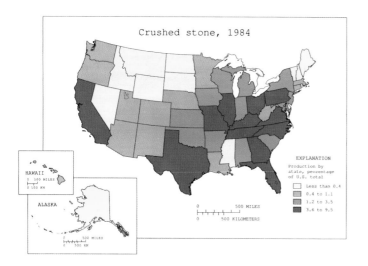

Crushed stone, 1984

EXPLANATION
Production by
state, percentage
of U.S. total

Less than 0.4
0.4 to 1.1
1.2 to 3.5
3.6 to 9.5

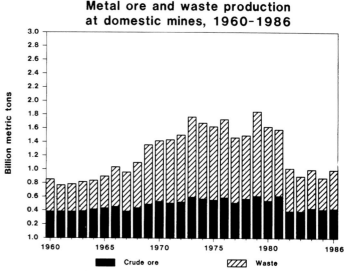

Metal ore and waste production
at domestic mines, 1960-1986

Crude ore   Waste

as a by-product of copper, lead, and zinc, although significant silver deposits are found in Idaho, Montana, Nevada, Utah, and Arizona.

More than 95% of the domestic iron ore reserves are located in the Lake Superior area, mainly in Minnesota and Michigan. Missouri, Texas, and Wyoming account for the remaining iron ore reserves.

Construction grade sand and gravel are produced in all 50 states. Because of the low unit cost, sand and gravel are produced near the point of use. The industry, therefore, is concentrated in large, rapidly expanding urban areas and, on a transitory basis, in areas where highways, dams, and other large-scale projects are being constructed. Leading the states in volume mined in 1986 were California, Texas, Michigan, Arizona, Ohio, Alaska, New York, Colorado, Illinois, and Minnesota. The crushed stone industry is also widespread, with mining occurring in every state except Delaware and North Dakota.

Most of the Nation's industrial grade sand is produced east of the Mississippi River. Top producing states are Illinois, Michigan, and New Jersey in the East and California and Texas in the West.

Phosphate rock deposits are found in onshore and offshore marine phosphorite deposits. Onshore mining in Florida yields most of the phosphate rock produced in the United States, although production from North Carolina, Idaho, Utah, Montana, and Tennessee is also significant.

1-4
Domestic mine ore and waste production

More metals and nonmetals have been mined in this country in the last 50 years than in all preceding time. In recent years, however, domestic production of major commodities such as lead, zinc, copper,

bauxite, iron ore, and phosphate rock has declined. The decline is attributable to a number of factors, including chronically depressed world metal prices, overproduction in foreign nations that rely on the export of monomineralic commodities, the strong value of the dollar relative to that of other currencies, relatively high domestic labor and operating costs compared with those of developing nations, and the replacement of metals with industrial minerals such as carbon fibers, glass fibers, and plastics in certain products. The mines that continue to operate have had to modernize mining and processing operations (including the use of environmental controls) in order to survive.

Other economic factors affect mine production, including the grade of ore mined, its mineral content, and the amount of spoil material that must be handled to recover a marketable product. The general trends for most metals mined at domestic

Nonmetal ore and waste production at domestic mines, 1960-1986

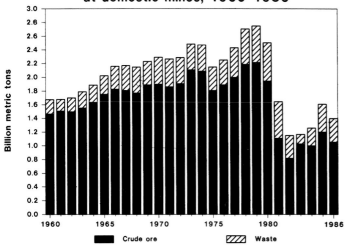

Total ore production at domestic mines, 1960-1986

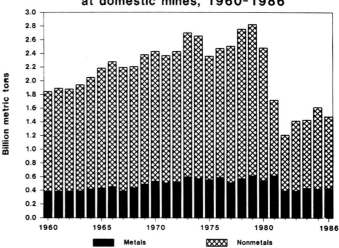

mines are ones of declining grades of ores and increasing ratios of ore mined to marketable product extracted. In contrast, the ratio of material handled to marketable product yield has declined because mining and processing operations have become more efficient. For most nonmetal minerals, however, there is no discernable trend in the ratio of ore mined to marketable product (the ratio is usually around 1 to 1), whereas the trend in ratio of material handled to marketable product yield has been increasing.

In 1986, total domestic ore output was approximately 1.5 billion tons, half of that produced in peak-year 1979. Copper and iron ore accounted for more than half of the metal ore mined, while phosphate, sand and gravel, and stone accounted for almost all of the nonmetal output. To produce these quantities of crude ore, over 909 million tons of mine waste (soil and rock generated while gaining access to the ore or mineral) was produced. This represents 51% of the waste generated in 1979. The largest quantities of mine waste are generated by copper, iron, and phosphate.

The volume of wastes handled at surface and underground mines in the United States more than

doubled during the 1970s. The large increase resulted primarily from increased activity in low-grade copper ore and phosphate rock mining, although iron ore production also contributed significantly to this trend. In recent years, the amount of waste handled has declined, principally because less waste can be economically handled at lower commodity prices.

Wastes are generated at several points during mining operations. Rock and soil may need to be removed in order to gain access to the ore during preproduction stripping and mine development as well as during the actual extraction of the ore. This material represents over one-half of the total volume of mining waste and is generally discarded in waste piles located at the mine site. The remaining wastes are generated during processing of the ores. Nearly one-third of this waste results from onsite leaching operations while the other two-thirds are produced during physical or chemical beneficiation. These wastes, called tailings, are typically slurried to waste impoundments. A small fraction of waste is used for backfilling the mines and for offsite construction and other purposes.

More material is handled at nonmetal mines than at metal mines, but less of it is waste. During the

1970s, metal mines generated almost twice as much waste as crude ore produced.

Surface mining produces most of the Nation's crude ore and most of the material handled. For example, in 1984, surface mining produced 94% of the crude ore and 99% of total material handled. The percentage of surface mining activities has steadily increased over the past 15 years, despite the overall reduction in domestic mining.

1-5
Lead production

Lead is the most corrosion resistant of the common metals. Its major uses are in storage batteries and television tubes, in materials for construction and metalworks industries and, until recently, as an antiknock additive to gasoline. The United States has less than 15% of the world's reserves of lead but is the world's most efficient recycler of lead, meeting over 40% of the Nation's lead demands in most years from recycling scrap.

The United States started mining lead in the mid-1800s. Domestic mine production peaked after World War I and again in the early 1970s and declined in postwar years and during economic

Lead production at domestic mines, 1900-1986

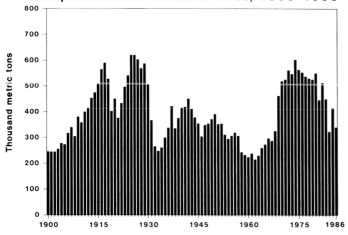

Bauxite production at domestic mines, 1900-1986

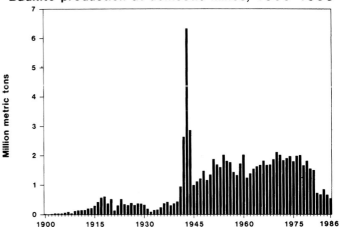

recessions. Between 1963 and 1983, domestic mine output doubled but has since declined despite increasing demand for lead. Use of other metals and plastics in building construction materials and in packing containers has hurt the lead market in recent years.

Lead is mined primarily underground. Except for wastes and tailings from mines, most of the environmental problems associated with the lead industry occur at smelters and refineries. Pollution controls, now in place for various postmine phases of lead production, have reduced particulate lead and sulfur dioxide emissions, toxic water discharges, and occupational exposure. Storage and disposal of hazardous wastes that can originate from smelter slags, scrap battery cases, settling pond solids, and treatment plant sludges at smelters are current issues of concern.

1-6
Zinc production

Zinc is used as protective coating on steel, die castings, alloying metal with copper to make brass, and a chemical compound in rubber. Zinc-coated steel is extensively used in buildings, bridges, ships, off-road machinery, and transmission and communication towers.

The domestic zinc industry began in the mid-1800s, and until the middle 1960s, the United States was the world's principal producer. In the last two decades, domestic mine and smelter production has declined substantially. This decline is attributable to mine closures resulting from high production and labor costs and, in some cases, depleted ore reserves; reduced investment in zinc mining and smelting because of low metal prices and strict environmental standards; and smelter closures for a number of reasons, including foreign competition, declining domestic mine production, environmental regulations, and high production costs associated with older energy- and labor-intensive technology. Recovery of zinc coproducts (lead, copper, gold, and silver) and by-products (cadmium, germanium, thallium, and indium—the domestic supply of which is mainly recovered in processing zinc ores and concentrates) has declined accordingly.

Zinc is an essential element in plant and animal nutrition, although excessive amounts are toxic. To minimize environmental contamination, zinc mines and mills have installed water control systems to reduce zinc and other element levels in effluent discharges, and dust and fume collection equipment to reduce atmospheric emissions. Waste dumps, mill tailings, and excavations, although still an area of concern, are increasingly subject to public scrutiny. Some additional environmental concerns in the zinc industry are associated with coproducts lead, cadmium, and sulfur.

1-7
Copper production

Growth of the domestic copper industry is intimately linked with its use in electrical and electronic equipment and wiring, although copper has a variety of other applications, including use in roofing, plumbing, heat exchangers, artillery shell casings, household utensils, jewelry, and coinage. In addition to metallic copper, copper ores are the source of the country's entire primary production of arsenic, rhenium, selenium, tellurium, platinum, and palladium, as well as significant quantities of gold, silver, molybdenum, nickel, uranium, iron, lead, zinc, and sulfur.

Since the turn of the twentieth century, when domestic copper production became significant, copper mining has been affected by major events in the history of the United States. Principal among these are world wars and other foreign conflicts (1917–1919, 1950–1953, and 1965–1973), strategic stockpile purchases (1953 to 1958) and releases (1965 to 1973), economic recessions (in the early 1920s and 1930s, between 1956–1958 and 1975–1977, and in 1982), and labor strikes (in 1954, 1959, 1967, 1971–1973, and 1980). Since the mid-1970s, a persistent oversupply on the world market, coupled with weak demand and escalating costs of energy, capital investment, and environmental controls, has hurt the domestic copper industry.

Copper is one of the most extensively recycled metals, and scrap is a significant part of the domestic copper supply. Two types of scrap are used by industry—new scrap that is generated during the fabrication of copper products, and old scrap that consists of worn-out, discarded, or obsolete copper products.

Environmental concerns related to copper mining include stream pollution from tailings, waste disposal, and mine reclamation. The smelter phases emit sulfur dioxide and arsenic into the air and produce sulfuric acid, which must be discarded. Energy is consumed in all production phases. Major improvements in emission control and energy use have been made in recent years, at great expense to copper mine and plant owners. Companies without the financial strength to implement productivity improvement and environmental compliance technology have closed or have changed ownership. Those that remain will continue to give special attention to improved environmental compliance devices, energy-saving features, and minimal material loss technology.

1-8
Bauxite production

Bauxite is the principal ore of aluminum. World reserves of bauxite are abundant, but domestic ores are nearing depletion. Opportunities for expanding domestic supply lie in the development of nonbauxitic aluminum-bearing deposits and the recovery of aluminum from scrap.

Open pit mining accounts for all of the bauxite mined in the United States, since underground mining ceased in 1976, and these operations are subject to environmental regulations. Standards exist for vapor and dust emissions from blasting, loading, and hauling of ore and overburden, acid mine drainage, and waste disposal and land reclamation when mining is completed.

The bauxite refining process to alumina (aluminum oxide) produces solid, liquid, and gaseous wastes. For each ton of alumina produced, a ton or more of solids is discharged as a caustic red mud slurry. The slurry is impounded in open lakes until the material solidifies sufficiently to permit land reclamation. During impoundment, leakage through the retaining dikes may occur, requiring acid neutralization.

Emissions of sulfur dioxide from the refinery boiler house and dust containing lime, bauxite, and alumina particles from the ore crushers are controlled with absorbent filters and electrostatic precipitators. At primary aluminum smelters, hood systems and wet and dry scrubbers are used to reduce

Copper production at domestic mines, 1900-1986

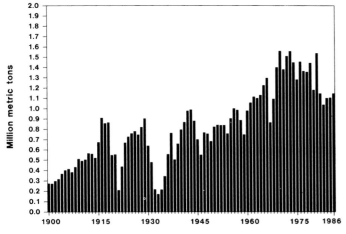

Zinc production at domestic mines, 1900-1986

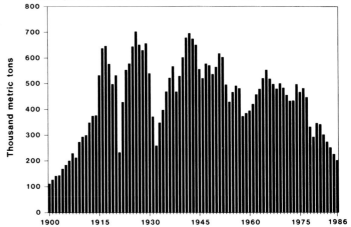

emissions of fluoride particulates and gases, which are harmful to plant and animal life in high concentrations. The efficiency of fluoride removal varies, but at most plants, it is over 80%. Recovered fluorides are recycled.

1-9
Gold production

Gold mining in the United States began about 1800; however, an 1848 discovery in California was of special significance because of its influence on development in the West and on the amount of gold produced.

Over three-quarters of the domestic production comes from gold ore; the rest is a by-product of copper and other base metal mining. Recovery of secondary gold from current manufacturing operations and from discarded jewelry, dental materials, used plating solutions, and junked electronic equipment also yields economical quantities of the metal.

Domestic gold production has generally fluctuated in response to variations in gold price and costs of production. During the early years of World War II, most of the domestic mines were closed so that equipment, supplies, and skilled labor could be used on mining more strategic metals. Few mines reopened after the war, and nearly 20 years elapsed before any new large mines were developed in the United States. Since 1980, increased gold prices have rekindled the fervor of gold exploration, and as a result new mines have opened in the West. Domestic mine output increased from 0.96 million ounces in 1979 to 3.7 million ounces in 1986.

About 15% of domestic mine production comes from underground mines and the rest from open pit mines and placer (stream) deposits. Placer mining, once an important source of gold, is fraught with environmental problems associated with dredging large alluvial or marine deposits, diverting large amounts of water, and stream pollution resulting from sediments placed in suspension during the mining process. It should be noted, however, that in Alaska, many of the streams contain significant amounts of naturally induced particles, such as glacial rock flour and other sediment.

Gold is recovered from ores by leaching with cyanide, amalgamation with mercury, flotation on air bubbles, gravity concentration, smelting, or a combination of these processes. Because of the danger of mercury poisoning, the use of mercury amalgamation in large gold operations has virtually disappeared. In mines using the cyanidation process, special precautions and monitoring procedures are employed to avoid contaminating the surrounding environment with cyanide. The exact fate and transport of cyanide in the environment are sometimes difficult to predict. Many of the current management controls emphasize source elimination by various steps, including treatment of the leachate by alkaline chlorination to destroy the cyanide or treatment of the leached ore heap with neutralizing hypochlorite solutions. Other potential pollutants that may be associated in gold deposits are tellurium, bismuth, antimony, and thallium. Abandoned waste dumps, mill tailings, excavations, and other forms of land disturbance may also be environmental concerns; many of these sites, however, are the consequence of geological reconnaissance and the search for new mineral deposits.

1-10
Silver production

Silver is used in nonindustrialized countries principally for jewelry and sterling-ware, whereas in industrial countries it is used primarily for nondecorative, utilitarian purposes. The most important of the latter uses are in photographic materials and in electrical and electronic products.

Domestic silver mine production has remained stable for the past 20 years but is expected to increase in the future, though at a slower rate than demand. The increase in annual mine production during the period 1981-1983 was due in part to the silver price increases of 1979-1983, while recent declines in production are due to a lowering of silver prices and temporary closure of a number of mines.

Silver is not toxic, except in large doses, yet silver mining and processing can present potential environmental problems because other materials that may be present in the ore or are used to recover the silver may be toxic. These potential problems are being handled through available technology.

Silver is mined using open pit and underground methods, and nearly all silver-bearing ores are crushed by grinding and then processed by flotation or cyanidation. Processing plants use ponds and impoundments to contain process waters and avoid polluting downstream waters with fine solids from flotation procedures. Other retention devices are used to stabilize accumulated tailings. In cyanidation, solution collection systems for returning the leachate to the storage tanks must be adequate to prevent contamination of ground water, nearby surface waters, and surrounding land areas.

Achieving adequate sulfur dioxide emission control and disposing of slag and other wastes, especially iron and silica, are the problems encountered at the smelter. Refining presents little environmental concern because the bulk of noxious impurities is removed during the smelting step; however, spent solutions from electrolytic refining are a disposal problem because of toxic materials in the solutions.

1-11
Iron ore production

Iron ore is the source of primary iron for the world's iron and steel industries. Regular production of iron ore started in the United States around 1645 and, by the 1840s, most of the bog iron deposits in the northeast were all but exhausted, causing many mining operations to shut down. When high grade ores were discovered in Michigan and Wisconsin in the late 1800s, many steel companies acquired iron ore properties in the Great Lakes area, consolidated smaller mines, and organized the iron ore industry into the structure that exists today.

By the 1950s, higher grade domestic ores had been depleted, and lower, less desirable grade ores were being mined. The reduction in ore quality coupled with rising import volumes led to the closing of hundreds of mines and a drop in iron ore production. This downward trend became acute when a severe recession developed in 1982.

Environmental factors in the iron ore industry include disposal of solid wastes such as overburden, waste rock, and plant tailings; reclamation of mined land, tailings disposal areas, and process water; elimination of dust from mines, processing plants, and shipping facilities; reduction of noise, particularly in crushing plants and blasting operations; and control of seismic shock from blasting.

More than 97% of domestic ore output is from open pit mines, and at most mines, large quantities of overburden and waste rock must be stripped in

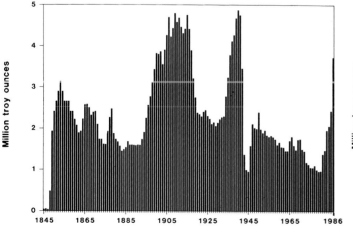

Gold production at domestic mines, 1845-1986

Million troy ounces

Silver production at domestic mines, 1860-1986

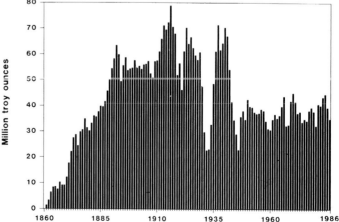

Million troy ounces

Iron ore production at domestic mines, 1900-1986

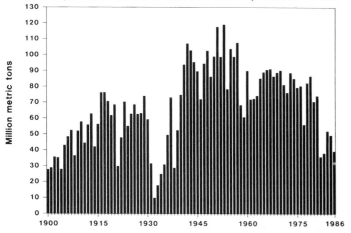

Nickel production at domestic mines, 1950-1986

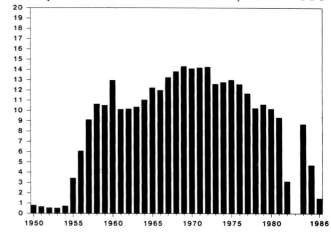

order to mine the crude ore. Reclamation of disturbed land and tailings areas by seeding and fertilizing is now common practice at iron ore mines. Abandoned pits usually fill with ground water and are sometimes developed into recreational lakes, but no economical way is available to return large open pits to original land contours.

Water is required for producing iron ore pellets, at roughly 12,000 gallons per ton of ore produced. All but 5% of this volume is reclaimed or recycled. State regulations usually require strict monitoring of the quality of processing water discharged into streams and lakes.

Large expenditures have been made by the industry for dust control in all phases of iron ore production. Blasting operations are now designed to minimize dust, air and ground shock, and are conducted only under specific atmospheric conditions.

1-12
Nickel production

Nickel is vital to the stainless steel industry and plays a key role in the chemical and aerospace industries. Nickel's greatest value is in alloys with other elements, where it adds strength and corrosion resistance over a wide range of temperatures.

Nickel reserves in the United States are very limited. In the mid-1980s, domestic mine production declined because of worldwide economic recession. The remaining domestic mine (in Oregon) closed in 1982, reopened in late 1983, and closed again in May 1986. Since then, most of the nickel consumed in the United States, other than the small quantities of nickel produced as a coproduct of copper and platinum metals and recycled from scrap, comes from imports, principally from Canada.

The United States possesses reserves of nickel that could be used if technological and environmental problems were resolved. Domestic reserves in Oregon, California, and Minnesota are situated in environmentally sensitive regions. Ocean nodules offer a potential source of nickel, but the success of mining ocean nodules is dependent upon the development of reliable recovery systems and environmental safeguards. A shift from traditionally mined nickel-bearing sulfide ores to laterites also has

potential; some laterites were being mined in the mid-1980s.

Nickel is mined by both underground and open pit methods. The most serious environmental problem identified in the mining and processing of nickel-bearing sulfide ores is the sulfur dioxide that is released in smelting sulfide ores. Under currently installed technology for sulfur removal at the mill and smelter, sulfur dioxide emissions have been reduced.

Nickel carbonyl toxicity is another environmental problem. Humans are exposed to small concentrations of nickel in water and food with no apparent effects; however, nickel may be toxic to plants in relatively low doses. To workers in nickel smelters and refineries, the risk of respiratory carcinogenesis has been reduced by technological improvements.

1-13
Sand and gravel production

Sand and gravel have many uses. They are used as concrete aggregate for highways, buildings, airports, and dams; for road base and covering; as asphaltic concrete aggregates and other bituminous mixtures; as construction fill; for concrete products such as blocks, bricks, and pipes; in plaster and gunite sands; and various miscellaneous and unspecified uses (railroad ballast, snow and ice control, road stabilization).

The United States is self-sufficient in sand and gravel, producing enough to meet all domestic needs and to be a small net exporter, mainly to Canada. At the beginning of the 20th century, the production of sand and gravel was relatively small and its uses limited. In the 1980s, however, annual production ranked second only to crushed stone in the nonfuel minerals industry. Most (95% in 1986) is used for construction purposes, mainly as an aggregate in concrete, as road base material, and as fill. Smaller, but important, quantities of silica sand are mined for industrial purposes, principally for glassmaking, foundry, and abrasive industries.

Construction sand and gravel usually occur in the same deposit but in varying proportions to each other. The two basic mining methods are open pit excavations on land and dredging for submerged

deposits. Open pit operations have four major steps: (1) site clearing—removing trees and vegetation, stripping overburden and topsoil, and transporting, redepositing, or stockpiling it at or off the site; (2) mining—removing the sand and gravel; (3) processing—screening, washing, blending, and stockpiling the mined material; and (4) reclaiming the extraction area. Mining submerged deposits involves dredging with a suction or bucket-type dredge.

In surface mining for sand and gravel, considerable acreage is disturbed and much is left in an unreclaimed state. Noise, dust, and storage of wastes are environmental problems now being addressed by many states and localities. Permits, wastewater control, and site reclamation are required.

Industrial-grade sand is mined primarily from open quarries (one underground operation exists). The major environmental considerations in the industrial sand industry are emissions of particulate matter (especially silica dust), discharge of processing water, and noise abatement. Both wet and dry methods of dust control are now being used. Increasingly sophisticated but expensive methods of treating process waters are being employed to remove clay suspensions, which result from washing and screening silica sand. Noise and vibrations produced by blasting and movement of heavy trucks have been reduced both inside and outside of mining and processing sites.

1-14
Crushed stone production

Crushed stone is rock that has been broken, crushed, or ground after quarrying. It is used in a wide variety of industrial applications including construction, chemical, metallurgical, and agricultural.

The crushed stone industry in the United States grew rapidly between 1928 and 1979, mainly because of increasing demands for crushed stone for railroad, highway, and other construction work. Even with recent declines in mine production, the volume of crushed stone produced is greater than that of any other mineral mined in the United States. Furthermore, recycling of crushed stone from concrete and asphalt road surfaces is increasing, especially in

Sand and gravel production at domestic mines
1900-1986

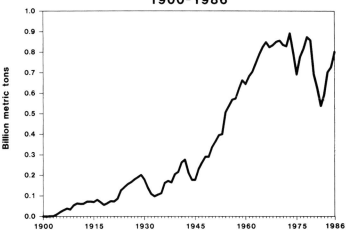

Crushed stone production at domestic mines
1920-1986

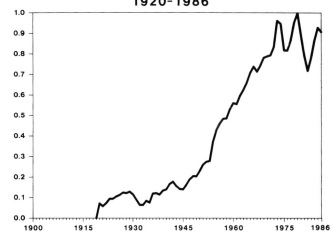

response to legislative incentives, local scarcity of raw materials, and mining waste disposal problems.

Most crushed stone is mined from open quarries, and there are relatively few (140 out of 4000) mines that are underground. The environmental problems that crushed stone producers must deal with include land disturbance, dust emissions, water pollution, noise, traffic, and vibration. Many complaints arise because a great number of stone quarries and processing plants are located in suburban areas near the major crushed stone markets. However, significant progress has been made in these areas of environmental concern.

1-15
Asbestos production

Asbestos is adaptable to more than 2000 uses. It is a fibrous mineral, and because of its high tensile strength and high temperature resistance, it is used in rockets and missiles, although the construction industry is the largest consumer of asbestos products. Major industrial uses are for insulation, fireproof textiles, asbestos cement products, and various fillers and linings.

Domestic production of asbestos fiber has declined dramatically since 1973 in response to environmental and economic problems, and relatively few domestic asbestos mines and mills remain active. Asbestos minerals are widespread in the earth's crust, however, and some nonasbestos mine and mill operations present a risk of low level asbestos exposure during processing.

Asbestos is associated with various health hazards. Prolonged occupational exposure to heavy concentrations of asbestos dust, in the absence of personal protective devices, may increase the chance of lung cancer, asbestosis (a pneumoconiosis), and mesothelioma (a rare type of cancer).

Since 1981, a spate of actions has been taken to minimize the hazards of asbestos exposure. At the mine site, capping or containment of the waste piles and wet processing and dust control during crushing and blasting operations occur.

Interest in finding substitutes for asbestos is great, but other materials generally fail to compete with asbestos in terms of quality, versatility, and costs. Glass fiber and mineral wool are the most successful substitutes, particularly for thermal insulation.

1-16
Phosphate rock production

Over 90% of the phosphate rock mined in the United States is used to make fertilizer, and the balance is smelted in electric furnaces to produce elemental phosphorus. Mine production grew nearly six-fold between 1950 and 1980 to a record high of 54.4 million metric tons in response to growing demands for phosphates in fertilizer and animal feed supplements. Since then, domestic production has fluctuated. Worldwide reduction in demand for agricultural products and increased competition from foreign sources have resulted in mine closures, reduced production schedules, and consolidation of operations.

Environmental standards have been established to address air and water quality, solid waste disposal, and land reclamation at phosphate mines. A major issue is managing the clay fraction (slimes) produced during the beneficiation of phosphate ores. Other problems relate to reclamation of wetlands disturbed by mining operations, water and energy consumption, and phosphogypsum disposal.

Asbestos production at domestic mines
1900-1986

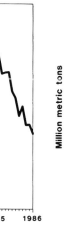

Phosphate rock production at domestic mines
1900-1986

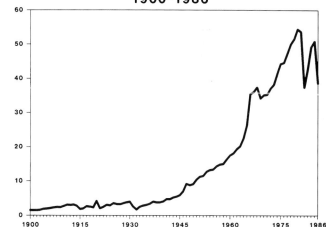

Coal fields

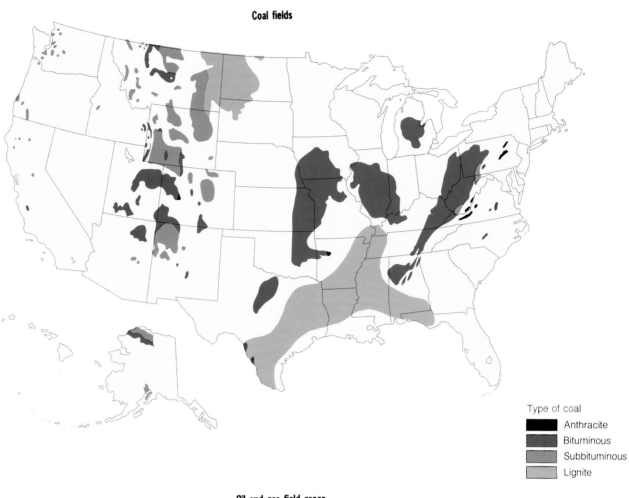

Type of coal

■ Anthracite
■ Bituminous
■ Subbituminous
□ Lignite

Oil and gas field areas

■ Natural gas and petroleum fields

Phosphate mine wastes are characterized by large volumes of low-percent-solids slurries and low radioactivity in product and waste fractions. A risk to human health in confined areas is from radionuclides, which exist as radon gas. The radon gas, a decay product of radon, occurs naturally in the phosphate matrix (mineral zone). Measures, including sealing residential home foundations from rising gas and reventilating closed spaces, are used to mitigate the effects of radionuclides.

Water is used by the phosphate rock industry as the medium for conveying phosphate ore to the mill; attritioning the ore; and separating clay, sand, and pebble-sized fractions in the washing plant. Water is also used as the medium for size classification, floating or depressing the concentrate, and carrying the waste clay and sand tailings from the mill to the disposal site. Ninety percent of this water is commonly recycled.

Energy is used in all phases of mining and processing. Electricity is used to power draglines, shovels, pumps, and other processing equipment. Diesel oil is consumed by bulldozers and portable mining equipment. Dryers are usually gas- or fuel oil-fired. Energy consumption is a function of material handling requirements and, therefore, depends upon the deposit's stripping ratio (cubic yards of waste per ton of product), the ore's concentration ratio (tons of matrix per ton of product), distance from mine to beneficiation plant, and water content prior to drying.

A phosphate rock product—sodium tripolyphosphate—is a principal detergent builder, but it contributes to the eutrophication of streams, lakes, estuaries, and other receiving waters. In recent years, detergent phosphate levels have been reduced; in many areas, phosphate-containing detergents are banned.

1-17
Distribution of energy resources in the United States

Much of the energy used in the United States is derived from domestic sources. The principal energy sources are coal, oil, and natural gas, although nuclear, hydroelectric, geothermal, wood, and solar energy sources are also utilized.

The Nation is fortunate to have large supplies of several of the energy-producing resources it uses. Reserves of some fuels—notably, coal and uranium—are very large compared to current levels of use, and even reserves of oil and natural gas are substantial compared to those in most other industrialized countries. Most of the Nation's energy reserves are located underground on public and private lands and on the outer continental shelf.

Coal, oil, and natural gas are fossil fuels that originate from once-living material and are combusted to release energy. It takes millions of years and increased temperature and pressure (due to burial) to form these energy-containing products. Nuclear power comes from the fission, or splitting of the nuclei, of plutonium or uranium-235 into lighter elements, which releases energy in the process. Other sources of energy depend directly or indirectly on the sun to drive climatic and hydrological processes, which produce wind, water, and thermal energy, and to promote fuelwood growth and production of other biomass energy sources.

Coal comes from plant material that has accumulated at the bottom of swampy areas as peat and has been compacted by the weight of overlying sediments. The first stage of compaction produces lignite coal which is low in sulfur content. Further pressure produces bituminous coal, the most abundant of coal types, and even more pressure produces anthracite, the hardest coal and the one with the highest heat content. To produce reasonably pure coal, little other sediment can be accumulating in the swamp at the same time.

There are major coal producing areas of the United States for each type of coal. Coal reserves in the East are generally deeper underground than those in the West, where they can be mined at the earth's surface.

Petroleum products come primarily from oil-forming organic material that has accumulated in marine sediments, primarily shale. In stagnant bottom waters, these organic materials do not readily decompose and build up over time. As with coal, deep burial, some heat, and much time are necessary to produce oil and gas. Once formed, the petroleum products migrate very slowly from the shale source rock to more permeable rock reservoirs where, if trapped beneath an impermeable rock cap, they are economically recoverable by drilling. Oil and

natural gas fields are located primarily in Texas, Oklahoma, and Louisiana and on the outer continental shelf of the Gulf, Pacific, and Alaskan coasts.

1-18
Production of energy by source

Total energy production in the United States nearly doubled from 1950 through 1970, declined through the mid-1970s, and then rose slightly to relatively stable production levels in the 1980s.

In aggregate, the pattern of domestic energy production has changed significantly over time. The basic fuel type of principal use changed from wood to coal to crude oil and then to natural gas. Since the Arab oil embargo of 1973–1974, coal production and nuclear-based energy generation have increased in importance whereas natural gas production and petroleum production have declined.

Historically, the three fossil fuels—coal, crude oil, and dry natural gas—have accounted for the bulk of domestic energy production, which by 1986 totaled 64 quadrillion Btu. Coal accounted for the largest share (41%) of domestic energy production in 1949-1951 and, after a long hiatus, again in 1984-1986. In the interim, first crude oil and then natural gas dominated domestic production. In 1986, coal production totaled 19.5 quadrillion Btu, crude oil totaled 18.4 quadrillion Btu, and dry natural gas production totaled 16.5 quadrillion Btu. Natural gas plant liquids accounted for another 2 quadrillion Btu.

Nuclear power generation began in the early 1960s and increased rapidly to account for 13% of the nation's electricity production in 1984 and over 7% of its total energy production by 1986. Since the mid-1970s, coal and nuclear fuels have provided increasing shares of fuel input for power generation, displacing substantial quantities of both petroleum and natural gas.

Hydroelectric generation accounted for over 1 quadrillion Btu of electricity in 1949 and since the 1970s has provided about 3 quadrillion Btu per year. Other sources of renewable energy provide only a small part of domestic energy supplied. Geothermal energy, which is produced from hot dry rock, steam, or hot water, has historically provided between 0.1 and 0.3% of the domestic production of electricity.

Production estimates for other renewable energy sources such as solar, wind, and waste products are less well-defined. One measure of solar energy pro-

Zinc production at domestic mines, 1900-1986

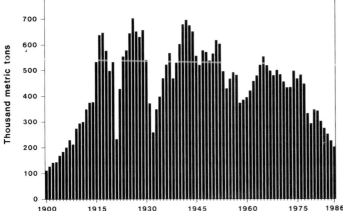

1-18b
Energy equivalents

One quadrillion Btu equals approximately

  50 million metric tons of coal production
  66 million metric tons of oven-dried hardwood
   1 trillion cubic feet of dry natural gas
170 million barrels of crude oil
470 thousand barrels per day of crude oil for one year
293 billion kilowatt-hours of electricity converted to heat
  27 days of petroleum imports to the United States
  26 days of United States motor gasoline usage
  28 hours of world energy consumption (1986)

NOTE: one quadrillion = 1,000,000,000,000,000 (one thousand trillion)

Coal production by rank at domestic mines 1900-1986

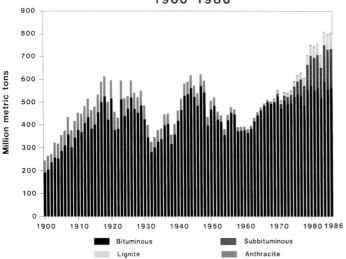

Million metric tons

Bituminous   Subbituminous
Lignite   Anthracite

Coal production by source at domestic mines 1915-1986

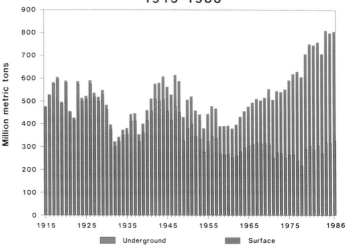

Million metric tons

Underground   Surface

duction in the United States is the sale of solar thermal collectors. The annual quantity of medium temperature, special, and other collectors shipped by producers increased steadily from less than one-half million square feet in 1974 to almost 12 million square feet in 1985 but then dropped to 1.1 million square feet in 1986 after federal tax credit expired at the end of 1985. Annual shipments of low temperature collectors increased to over 12 million square feet by 1980 but have since declined to less than 4 million square feet in 1986. Solar thermal collectors are used primarily for pool heating, domestic hot water, and space heating.

Wood and other biomass fuels had almost ceased to be used as energy sources prior to the 1973 oil shock, but since then they have begun to make a comeback. Industries with ready access to wood and wood products, such as the paper and lumber industries, rely heavily on wood as an energy source. Domestic wood use for residential heating has nearly doubled from the low values of the mid-1970s to account for more than 10% of the market and about 4% of total energy production.

The Nation's pursuit of energy independence through the development of new energy technologies and the enhanced recovery and utilization of traditional energy resources has impacted environmental quality in the United States. The extraction and processing of energy encompasses a wide range of technologies, and each energy source and production cycle impacts land, air, and water resources in different ways. Since the beginning of the environmental decade of the 1970s, a myriad of federal laws has been promulgated to ensure adequate environmental protection in all phases of energy development and utilization. The success of these efforts can be seen in reductions in levels of most pollutants associated with energy production and consumption, improvements in reclamation of lands disturbed by mining activities, and better management of solid and hazardous waste disposal.

1-19
Production of coal by rank and by source

Except for the wartime increase in the 1940s, coal's share of domestic energy production had been de-

clining since the 1920s because of competition from cleaner burning oil and natural gas. In recent years, however, the trend has reversed somewhat as the volume of domestic coal production increased in response to higher prices for alternative energy sources. In the mid-1980s, the market share of coal produced in the United States was 30% of total domestic energy production.

Production of anthracite coal has steadily declined since World War I to a current production rate of around 4.3 million tons per year (0.48% of total coal volume in 1986), whereas production of bituminous and lower rank coals has increased. Despite its superior burning qualities, anthracite, mined primarily in Pennsylvania, accounts for a diminishing share of total coal production. Lower rank coals are primarily used in electric power production, accounting for 85% of domestic coal use in 1986. Production of subbituminous and lignite coal, mainly from the western United States, has increased from 13 million tons in 1969 to 265 million tons, or 30% of total coal volume, in 1985. (Subbituminous and lignite production figures were included with bituminous figures prior to 1969.)

The amount of coal mined underground in the United States exceeded that of coal mined on the surface until the 1970s, when the trend was reversed. Now, over one-half of domestic coal is mined at the surface using techniques such as area mining, mountaintop removal, and contour mining. Surface mining has increased in both the western and eastern United States, partly as a result of the economic advantages of large-scale mechanization to surface mining. The growing importance of surface coal mining, where productivity is generally higher than for underground mining, led to increases in average productivity during the mid-1980s. In recent years, underground production has increased, but only to the same levels produced in the 1950s and mid-1960s.

Both underground mining and surface mining can harm the environment, but the consequences of surface mining are often more visible. Surface mining removes earth to recover underlying minerals. When early miners used primitive digging tools to remove the overlying soil and rocks, damage to the environment was minimal. But when miners began using bulldozers and earth-moving machinery that could

remove 130 cubic yards of earth with one scoop, the potential for damaging land and water increased to great proportions.

A major problem associated with surface mining is erosion, which causes siltation of streams and rivers. Silt alters the chemical balance of the water, buries plants and animals, impacts feeding and spawning habits, and suffocates fish by coating their gills. Silt also reduces the channeling capacity of streams and rivers and reduces the flood storage capacity of reservoirs. Acid drainage and toxic materials may leach from the disturbed land.

Today, federal regulations require surface coal miners to use appropriate measures to reduce or prevent erosion and the formation of acid water. Treatment ponds must be used to ensure that all water released to receiving streams meets stringent environmental requirements. After mining is completed, the land must be reclaimed—toxic material buried and the land returned to its approximate original contour, planted in soil-binding grasses, and in some cases, overplanted with trees and wildlife shrubs. But "orphan" mines, those that were abandoned before any regulations were passed, remain a primary concern because reclamation of these areas is proceeding at a very slow pace.

There are other environmental problems associated with coal mining. As coal is mined, transported, and processed for combustion, small amounts of sulfur, nitrogen, and carbon are oxidized as SO_2, NO_x, HC, and carbon monoxide. The major form of air pollution from the extraction and processing of coal, however, is dust. The chemical constituents of coal dust vary according to coal types: some are more caustic than others. About one-half of the total coal mined in the United States is prepared or cleaned prior to utilization to remove some of the noncombustible materials. Coal cleaning is usually done at or near the minehead, and the resulting waste consists of rocks and mineral matter, such as clays, quartz, pyrites, marcasites, as well as residual coal and unidentified matter. The rejected material represents, on the average, about 20% of the raw coal by weight. Coal cleaning is receiving more attention as a means of reducing coal sulfur content and, thus, the amount of sulfur oxides released by combustion of coal.

1-20
Petroleum production

Petroleum production includes extraction of crude oil and production of natural gas liquids from natural gas plants. Until recently, oil production in the United States supplied well over one-half of the domestic oil demand. By 1986, nearly 41% of the United States petroleum needs were met with imports, primarily oil.

Domestic production of crude oil increased steadily from 1940 to 1970 to reach a peak of 9.5 million barrels a day. During much of the 1950s and 1960s, production capacity exceeded demand to such an extent that mechanisms such as production prorationing and import ceilings were implemented to protect domestic production. By the 1970s, however, petroleum demand had increased, and production neared 100% of capacity. The average productivity of wells began to decline, and oil production leveled off. Increases in Alaskan production at the end of the decade and through 1986 counteracted declines in lower-48 production. Nevertheless, by 1986 daily domestic production had declined to 8.7 million barrels. Of total domestic production, 86% came from onshore wells and 14% from offshore in 1986.

The trend in natural gas plant liquids production has followed that of dry natural gas from which it is derived. Production increased steadily from 1950 through 1972 and has remained fairly stable since then.

Oil production disturbs very little land in comparison to other fuel extraction activities. Exploratory and production drilling on land require site preparation by clearing, creation of holding ponds for circulating fluids and brine, and construction of access roads, pipeline right-of-ways, and separation facilities. Once production has ended, a site can be restored in a relatively short period of time. In some areas, petroleum extraction results in subsidence of the land.

Petroleum extraction wastes include drilling muds and cuttings and production water or brines. Drilling mud is a dense fluid that is pumped down the inside of the drill bit to lubricate and coat the bit and to free it of cuttings, which are then carried up to the surface of the drilling operation. The basic drilling fluid used is a water-based clay suspension to which various additives are added to obtain desired properties. Some of these additives contain materials considered to be toxic.

The environmental impact of drilling mud and cutting disposal is of some concern. Drilling mud is continually circulated after removal of the cuttings, and only a portion of the fluid is lost to the environment in the borehole. After completion of a well, however, there may be some 50 tons of mud to dispose of, and a production platform in its main drilling phase may have to dispose of some 400 tons of mud per year. After use, the water-based muds may contain a percentage of oil that cannot be separated. Although attempts are made to remove oil from the cuttings, the final oil content may be 10%. The quantities of oil in mud and cuttings are small on an annual basis, and it is usual for them to be discharged to the sea in offshore exploration. Because of the fixed position of offshore drilling platforms, it is possible to monitor the effects of the discharged muds and cuttings. On land, the drilling muds and cuttings are spread over land surface areas or settled in a diked area, holding pond, or pit.

Production water or brines are brackish waters that are produced in association with crude oil in underground reservoirs. Water is always present with the oil produced from a well and in amounts that vary with production stage. (Amounts increase as the oil reservoir is depleted.) Production water is separated from the oil and, particularly in the later stages of production, may be reinjected into the reservoir to augment production. Otherwise it is treated to minimize oil content and reinjected into the oil-bearing reservoir, evaporated in a manner similar to the drilling fluids, or discharged to the sea, as in the case of offshore production.

1-21
Dry natural gas production

Dry natural gas has been used as a source of fuel in the United States for over 150 years, although early use was localized. An increase in production, as well as end use consumption, has occurred over the past 30 years. Much of this increase is due to increased pipeline construction, development of new markets (such as in the petrochemical and fertilizer industries), and, more recently, demand for low-sulfur fuels.

Dry natural gas production generally occurs in the same areas as oil drilling. Gross production of dry natural gas from oil wells increased moderately from 2.9 trillion cubic feet in 1950 to 4.9 trillion cubic feet in 1986, whereas dry natural gas production from gas wells increased from 5.6 trillion cubic feet in 1950 to a peak of 19.4 trillion cubic feet in 1973 and then declined, as average well productivity declined, to 14.2 trillion cubic feet in 1986.

Natural gas is extracted onshore and offshore, and the environmental effects associated with the extraction process are similar to those described for petroleum production. After hydrogen sulfide is removed, the natural gas is distributed to storage facilities by pipeline or is cooled to a liquid state and transported in specially designed tankers and trucks. The main concern with the liquified natural gas is tank rupture because the liquified natural gas would vaporize quickly, posing a threat of explosion or fire.

1-22
Hydroelectric energy production

Water has a long history of service in the United States, first as a supplier of mechanical power and then as a supplier of energy for production of electricity. Early settlers in the United States, especially in New England, exploited streams of sufficient streamflow and hydraulic head to supply mechanical power. Waterwheels were connected to grindstones, saws, and other industrial equipment. Significant technological breakthroughs occurred during the late 19th century which led to a change in water use from providing mechanical power to supplying electric power. The first hydroelectric power station in the United States was built in Appleton, Wisconsin, in 1882. From that point on, many new sites were developed, and older mechanical plants were converted to produce electric power.

Petroleum production at domestic wells 1940-1986

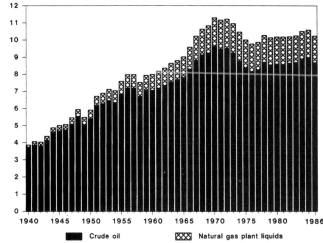

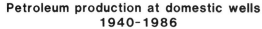

Marketed natural gas production at domestic wells 1900-1986

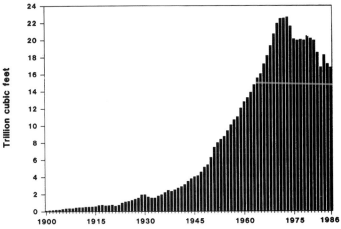

Most hydroelectric power sites were privately owned before 1930. This trend reversed between 1930 and 1970, when many large-scale public water resource projects, which included hydroelectric facilities, were undertaken. Now, private and public interests have about equal shares in the Nation's total conventional hydroelectric power capacity.

Hydroelectric generating capacity and energy production have increased steadily throughout this century. Annual fluctuations in generation occur because of water availability. The rate of increase in conventional generating capacity was greatest during the period from 1950 through the mid-1960s. Since then, pumped storage capacity has increased along with conventional capacity. Pumped storage utilizes off-peak electricity from the generation source to pump water uphill. The water is then released during peak demand periods to generate electricity. Pumped storage contributes negatively to net energy generation because some energy is lost in the cycle of pumping and regeneration. However, it allows electricity to be made available during periods of peak demand. Net energy generation reached a peak of 332 billion kilowatt-hours in 1983. Since then, it has declined to 250 billion kilowatt-hours in 1986.

The rate of expansion of hydroelectric power has declined since the late 1960s. By the 1960s, the most favorable sites for dams had been developed. Moreover, expansion of oil and gas industries and forecasts concerning nuclear technologies resulted in decreased interest in further development of hydroelectric power generating capabilities.

The major adverse environmental impacts of hydroelectric power as an energy source are the loss of traditional land use and wildlife habitat, disturbance of fisheries habitat and elimination of spawning runs, and noise pollution. The positive aspects, on the other hand, relate to the electric energy generated, water supply, flood control, and increased recreational opportunities.

1-23
Uranium production

On average, economic reserves of uranium ore in the United States contain about 3 pounds of uranium oxide per ton of uranium ore. A 1000-megawatt nuclear reactor requires about 250 tons of uranium for each refueling, approximately every 18 months.

From 1949 through 1967, most of the domestic uranium production was for military purposes. Spurred by incentives, domestic production grew from 0.4 million pounds of uranium oxide in 1949 to 35 million pounds in 1960. As stockpiles began to accumulate, demand declined and annual production fell to 23 million pounds in 1967.

In the late 1960s, the decline was reversed when orders for new nuclear electricity-generating plants led to higher projections of demand and increased domestic production. During the late 1970s, however, as planned units were cancelled or postponed, projected demand fell. Buildups of inventories at electric utilities and competition from foreign suppliers also contributed to the second major decline in domestic production, which stood at 14 million pounds in 1986.

Historically, domestic producers have faced competition from low-cost uranium imports. From 1949 through 1960, net imports actually exceeded domestic production. In 1966, imports were suspended by curtailing enrichment services for foreign uranium intended for use in domestic facilities, and no uranium was imported from 1968 through 1974. With the gradual removal of these restrictions during the 1977-to-1983 period, foreign uranium deliveries to the United States increased.

Nuclear power to generate electricity was first used commercially in 1957. Nuclear power's contribution to electricity generation in the United States has increased almost every year from the mid-1960s through 1986; the exceptions were 1979 and 1980. In 1986, 414 billion net kilowatt-hours (18% of total U.S. generation) came from nuclear power. Net summer capability, a measure of the steady hourly output that generating equipment is expected to supply to the system, also increased every year, to reach 85 million kilowatts by the end of 1986.

Nuclear power generation came on line around the time that the environmental problems caused by burning increasing amounts of coal were becoming more apparent. At that time, nuclear energy was perceived to be an economically, environmentally benign method for generating energy. Contrary to early beliefs, however, nuclear power produces its own environmental problems. Among these are thermal discharges from a nuclear plant (which are much greater than those from a comparably sized coal-fired plant) and the release of radiation, which may occur at all stages of the nuclear fuel cycle.

Residues from mining and milling uranium contain low concentrations of naturally occurring radioactive elements. Uranium mill tailings are generated in large volumes, and over 100 million metric tons are now stored at various sites of mining and milling operations. Because tailings emit the carcinogenic radon-222 gas, protection of these piles from water and erosion is of great concern.

Release of radiation may also occur during the uranium enrichment and fuel fabrication phases of production, at the nuclear reactor, at the spent fuel reprocessing plant, or at the waste disposal site. Release may occur through mishandling of materials or accident. Federal regulations require treatment, control, and monitoring of radioactive releases to the air and water.

1-24
Energy consumption by fuel type and end user

Energy consumption has increased more than 30-fold since 1850. In 1978, consumption levels peaked at 78.9 quadrillion Btu.

There was a steady and rapid increase in domestic energy consumption after World War II—for almost 3 decades—as the economy prospered on cheap and plentiful supplies of oil. During the 1949-to-1973 period, energy consumption more than doubled, increasing from 30 quadrillion Btu in 1949 to 74 quadrillion Btu in 1973. The domestic energy market was dominated by rapid growth in petroleum and natural gas consumption, which more than tripled during the period. After the 1973 oil price shock, energy consumption fluctuated, rising to a peak of 79 quadrillion Btu in 1979 before returning in the mid-1980s to about the same level as in

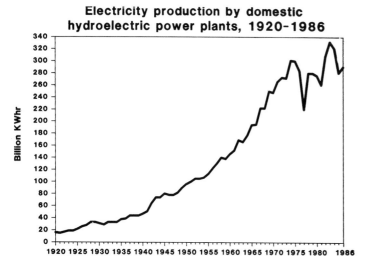

Electricity production by domestic hydroelectric power plants, 1920-1986

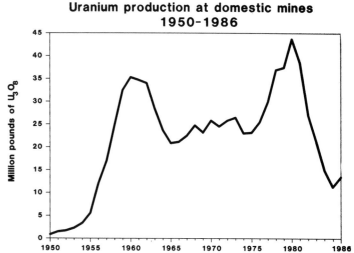

Uranium production at domestic mines 1950-1986

Domestic energy consumption by source
1950-1986

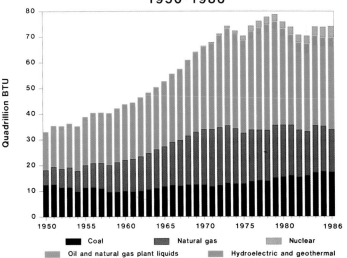

Domestic energy consumption by end-user sector
1950-1986

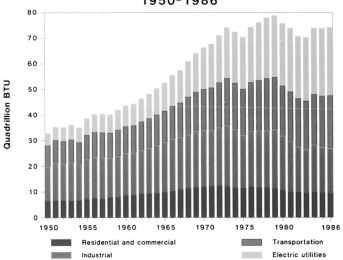

1973. Reductions in energy consumption between 1978 and 1983 are partly the result of energy conservation measures, including more efficient use of energy sources and reduction in per capita consumption. Since then, consumption has increased.

The composition of demand after 1973 reflects a shift away from petroleum and natural gas toward electricity generated by other fuels. In 1973, petroleum and natural gas accounted for 77% of total energy consumption; by 1986, their share had declined to 66%. Reductions in domestic oil consumption are due, in part, to economic recessions following oil price increases after 1973. Improvements in the efficiency with which oil is used and substitutions of other fuels for oil are additional reasons for the reduction. The decline in natural gas consumption in the United States from 1973 to 1985 resulted in a decline in production over the same period. Coal is the major fuel used in electricity generation, although the industrial sector, primarily the iron and steel industry, is also a large consumer. Significant amounts of coal are still consumed by the residential sector. Further substitution of coal for oil is expected in industry, but this is likely to be a slow process, and little substitution is expected in the transport or residential/service sectors in the foreseeable future.

Industrial sector consumption proved to be the most responsive to the turmoil in energy markets during the 1970s and 1980s. Consumption fluctuated after 1973 but in 1986 was considerably below the sector's peak consumption in 1979. Increases in efficiencies in industrial operation and expansion in the service trades were primarily responsible for the decline.

Growth in electric utility consumption continued during the 1970s and 1980s despite rising energy prices. In 1986, that sector's consumption reached 27 quadrillion Btu. However, only around 8 quadrillion Btu were sold to consumers; the remainder was used to generate, transmit, and distribute the electricity.

The transportation and residential and commercial sectors accounted for most of the growth in energy consumption during the 1949-1986 period. Residential and commercial consumption leveled off in response to higher energy prices, but, when prices⟋

fell in 1986, grew to a record level of almost 28 quadrillion Btu. Transportation sector consumption grew more slowly over the 39-year period but also attained a record level (21 quadrillion Btu) in 1986.

There have been significant improvements in the efficiency with which energy is used in all the major energy sectors—residential, service, transport, and industry. In the residential sectors, factors such as higher levels of thermal insulation and weatherization of buildings and more efficient appliances (such as stoves and refrigerators) have reduced the amount of energy required to satisfy household needs. Thus, despite increases in room temperatures during winter and decreases during summer, and in spite of more widespread use of various appliances (for example, freezers, microwaves, coffeemakers), energy use per household in the United States declined from 1972 to 1982. Since then, however, per household consumption has increased. The potential for further improvements in household energy use is substantial and attainable as the most energy-efficient technologies commercially available are introduced to replace the older, less efficient ones.

In the service sector, which includes commercial and public sector buildings, improvements similar to those in the residential sector have taken place, and further improvements are technically and economically feasible. In the transportation sector, there is further scope for improving the fuel economy of automobiles and light trucks, both by increasing engine and drive train efficiency and by reducing vehicle weight and aerodynamic and rolling resistances. There has also been a trend toward greater efficiency in air travel, and further reduction in fuel intensity of passenger aircraft appears feasible.

Industrial energy efficiency trends are harder to assess because of the greater heterogeneity and complexity of energy use in this sector. As in the other sectors, efficiency improvements may come from energy saving measures or new energy conversion systems, but they have also arisen from new technological processes for producing a given product (for example, steel) and from product changes. Regardless of the end user and the energy saving measures that have been instituted recently in the United States, it is somewhat disconcerting to realize that at least three-fourths and probably 90%

of all the energy associated with the fossil fuels burned over the past 200 years has been wasted as useless heat.

Overall, the environmental impacts of energy consumption are far-reaching, potentially affecting air and water quality, land use, and public health. The impacts vary considerably by the type of fuel utilized and the fuel cycle. Coal use and nuclear energy are the two most problematic fuel cycles with respect to pollution. Coal combustion contributes most of the air quality pollutants attributable to energy production—total suspended particulates, sulfur dioxide, and nitrogen oxides—as well as substantial amounts of trace elements. Utilization of coal also gives rise to a myriad of solid waste disposal problems including coal ash and char residuals from combustion, inorganic solids and sludges from air and water pollution control devices and acid gas removal, tars and oil sludges produced in several coal conversion processes, biosludges (degradation product of organics in coal conversion waters), and spent catalysts used in coal gasification and liquefaction processes. Nuclear energy impacts of concern include airborne radioactive elements from emissions, disposal of radioactive wastes, and accidental release of radioactive elements into the air and water systems.

Solid and hazardous wastes are generated by all energy industries. Disposal of such materials is associated with several environmental problems, chief among which are contamination of ground water by leachates from disposal ponds and landfills, release of toxic organics into the air, and surface water contamination from overflow or runoff.

Environmental statutes and regulations have had significant effects on reducing the impacts of increased fossil fuel and nuclear energy use. Stringent requirements are in place, or proposed, to affect emissions and effluent loadings, waste disposal and containment, and facilities siting and expansion. Technologies to control particulate air emissions are now highly advanced; some are capable of removing more than 99.9% of particulates. Sulfur dioxide controls are not as efficient as particulate emission controls, and nitrogen oxide controls are even less efficient. Efficient control technologies for carbon dioxide emissions from fossil fuel combustion have yet to be developed.

Treatment of wastewater before discharge into publically owned wastewater treatment plants and surface waters of the United States is required of all energy facilities, and methods of industry solid and hazardous waste disposal are under increasing scrutiny and control.

1-25
World energy consumption by region and per capita

The United States uses one-third of all the energy used in the world in any given year. This is more than any other country. Per capita use of energy in the United States is among the highest of industrialized countries.

The United States and Canada use relatively more energy for transportation than other industrialized countries. By comparison, Japan and European countries have fewer and smaller cars which use less fuel and are driven fewer miles. On the other hand, Japan and European countries use relatively more energy in the industrial, commercial, and residential sectors.

Throughout the 1960s and early 1970s, the growth of end-use energy consumption in the United States was greater than the growth in population. Per capita consumption rose between 1960 and 1973. Thereafter, per capita consumption trended downward. This reduction is attributed to the adoption of energy conservation measures and more efficient use of energy sources. Total energy use and consumption per capita for most other countries has changed only slightly since 1960.

1-26
Land utilized and reclaimed by the mining industry

During the 51-year period 1930–1980, over 5 million acres (0.25% of the total U.S. land mass) was used to meet the Nation's fuel and nonfuel mineral needs. Of this total, over two-thirds of the acreage was used for excavations associated with surface mining, and the rest was used for the disposal of overburden waste from surface mining (16%), processing waste (10%), and waste from underground mines (3%). Two percent of the land surface area was subsided or disturbed as a result of underground

workings. Excluded from the total are areas used for haul roads, freshwater reservoirs, railroads and public highways at the edge of mining properties, and streams affected by acid mine drainage and sedimentation.

Nearly half the land utilized by the mining industry between 1930 and 1980 has been restored to some degree, although lands restored prior to 1977 may not have been restored to current standards. Fifty-three percent of the land has not been reclaimed. Some of the unreclaimed land has been restored to other productive uses such as for farming or grazing, highways, recreation, industrial and residential complexes, and demonstration reclamation projects, but much of it remains abandoned.

The trend in land reclamation is increasing, especially in light of Federal and State laws governing reclamation of lands disturbed by mining activities and various demonstration and abandoned mine reclamation projects. Strip mining is prohibited anywhere the land cannot be subsequently reclaimed, as is the creation of "orphan banks"—tons of unstable earth and rock pushed down mountainsides or stacked in large conical piles. Provisions for reclaiming the thousands of mines that were previously

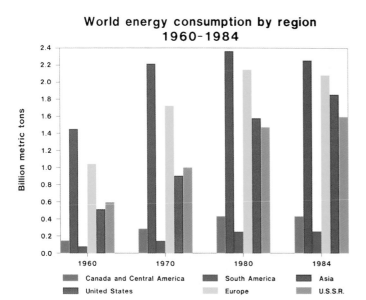

World energy consumption by region 1960-1984

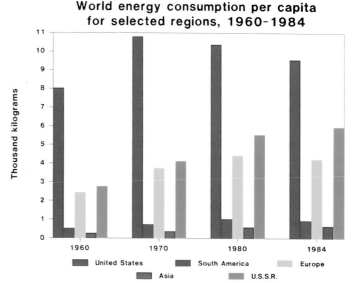

World energy consumption per capita for selected regions, 1960-1984

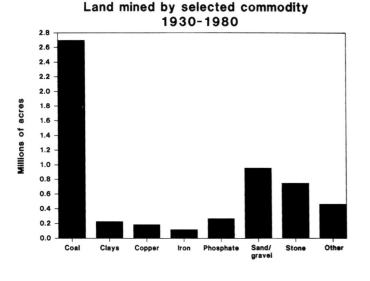

Land mined by selected commodity 1930-1980

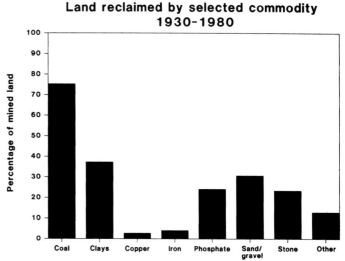

Land reclaimed by selected commodity 1930-1980

abandoned and that are either inadequately reclaimed or totally unreclaimed are provided by law. Recent changes in the legislation closed a loophole that had allowed surface mining without reclamation on sites of 2 acres or less.

Coal lands are required to be reclaimed before noncoal sites, and situations that endanger public health, safety, and general welfare must be remedied before environmental problems can be treated. Some of the people-related problems being addressed include flooding, pollution of water supplies, underground mine subsidence, mine fires, hazardous abandoned mining equipment or facilities, dangerous earth slides and high-walls, and dangerous open shafts and portals. Acid mine drainage and erosion of raw, unvegetated mine-spoils are the most serious environmental problems of abandoned mine lands. Damage to land that once produced agriculture, forest, and wildlife benefits affects local land bases and economies, aesthetics, and related amenities.

1-27
Acid mine drainage

Acid mine drainage is generated by the oxidation of iron sulfides in mine spoil, producing water that is acidic, with high concentrations of iron, sulfate, and other objectionable constituents, including manganese, aluminum, suspended and dissolved solids, color, and hardness. Sulfuric acid and dissolved metals lower the pH of water, making it corrosive and unable to support many forms of aquatic life. Acid waters also corrode piers, bridges, and industrial equipment. Contamination of ground water may occur as rainwater percolates through coal storage and refuse piles, leaching and carrying acids and other toxic ions into ground-water reservoirs.

Acid drainage from underground coal mines and coal refuse piles is one of the most persistent mining problems in the United States. Twenty years ago, 10,500 miles of streams were significantly degraded by coal mine drainage, and approximately half was affected by acid mine drainage. Current water quality data indicate that little improvement has occurred since then. This is due primarily to acid water flowing from abandoned mines and spoil piles, not from active mines, which are required by law to eliminate or treat acid mine drainage. Drainage from deep underground mines remains a major environmental concern, whereas surface mine drainage is somewhat easier to control.

Research is continuing on methods to reduce acid mine drainage, such as neutralizing by addition of alkaline minerals. Mine sealing is supposed to limit acid production in abandoned mines, but this technique has been only marginally successful because of problems with maintenance, natural deterioration, vandalism, and mine reopening. Other methods, such as water diversion, bacterial inhibition, waste capping, improved drainage control, and techniques for reclaiming polluted streams are being investigated. A less conventional but promising approach featuring constructed wetlands to treat acid mine drainage by removing pollutants is also being explored.

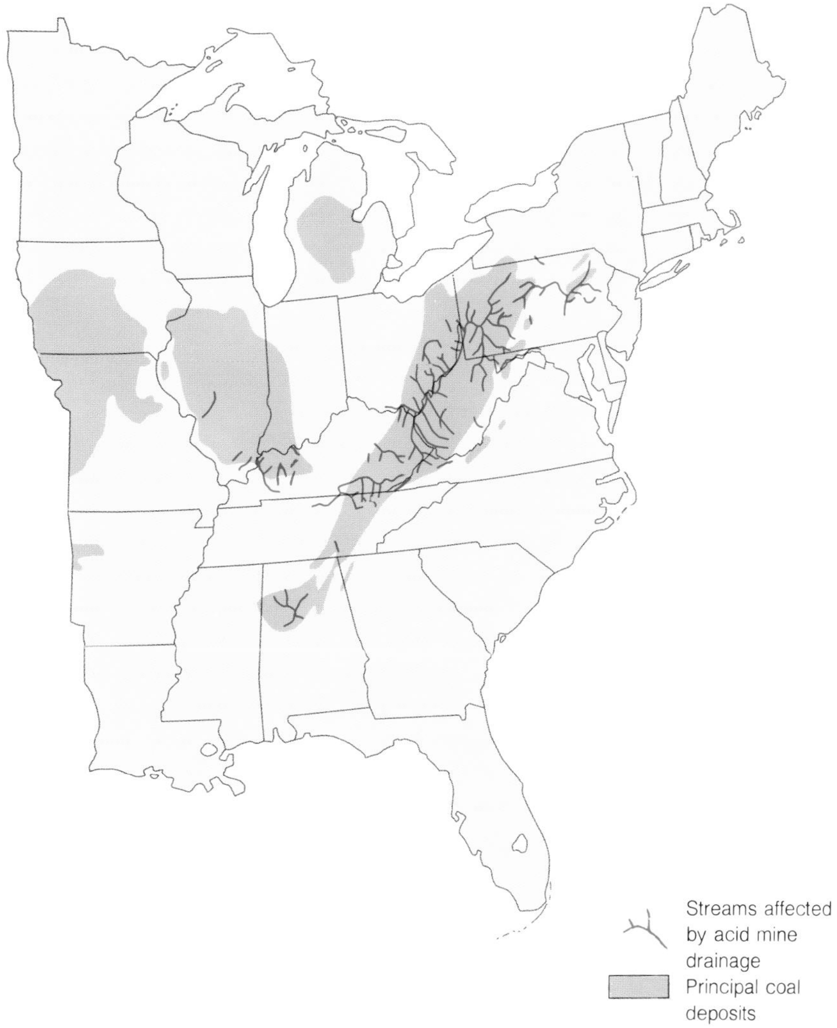

Sources and technical notes

1-1
Geologic regions

1-1
Geologic regions by rock type

Meridian Maps. 1987. After "Geology," pp. 74-75, in *The national atlas of the United States of America*, U.S. Department of the Interior, Geological Survey. 1970 (Washington, D.C.).

The geologic map of the United States pictured here is highly generalized as are the descriptions of geologic regions. The rock types described for various ages are not mutually exclusive but occur throughout the geologic record. The publications of the U.S. Geological Survey should be consulted for more detailed information.

1-2
Physical characteristics

1-2
Physical characteristics

Meridian Maps. 1987. After "Physical subdivisions," p. 61, in *The national atlas of the United States of America*, U.S. Department of the Interior, Geological Survey. 1970 (Washington, D.C.).

The 17 provinces shown on the map are generalized from more than 80 such physiographic provinces of the conterminous United States. They can be further grouped into 6 regions.

1-3
Distribution of mineral resources

1-3a
Lead

1-3b
Zinc

1-3c
Aluminum

1-3d
Copper

1-3e
Iron

Medlin, T. 1987. Generalized from W. W. Tooker. 1980. Maps showing areas favorable for the occurrence of selected mineral resources. U.S. Department of the Interior, *Geological Survey Open File Report 79-576* (Reston, Va.).

1-3f
Sand and gravel

Streams affected by acid mine drainage

Principal coal deposits

1-3g
Crushed stone

Tepordei, V. V., and L. L. Davis. 1986. *Sand and gravel production data*, table 2, 1985 construction sand and gravel production by state (preliminary). U.S. Department of the Interior, Bureau of Mines, Branch of Industrial Minerals Rock Reports (Washington, D.C.).

Tepordei, V. V. 1984. *1984 crushed stone data*, table 1, 1984 crushed stone production by state (estimated). U.S. Department of the Interior, Bureau of Mines, Branch of Industrial Minerals Rock Reports (Washington, D.C.).

1-4
Domestic mine ore and waste production

1-4a
Metal ore and waste production at domestic mines, 1960–1986

1-4b
Nonmetal ore and waste production at domestic mines, 1960–1986

U.S. Department of the Interior, Bureau of Mines. *Minerals Yearbook,* annual issues (Washington, D.C.).

1-5
Lead production

1-5
Lead production at domestic mines, 1900–1986

U.S. Department of the Interior, Bureau of Mines. 1987. *U.S. salient lead production* (Washington, D.C.). Data compiled by W. D. Woodbury, BOM.

Woodbury, W. D. 1985. "Lead," pp. 433-452, in *Minerals Facts and Problems,* U.S. Department of the Interior, Bureau of Mines (Washington, D.C.).

1-6
Zinc production

1-6
Zinc production at domestic mines, 1900–1986

U.S. Department of the Interior, Bureau of Mines. *Minerals Yearbook,* annual issues (Washington, D.C.). Data compiled by J. H. Jolly, BOM.

Jolly, J. H. 1985. "Zinc," pp. 923-940, in *Minerals Facts and Problems,* U.S. Department of the Interior, Bureau of Mines (Washington, D.C.).

1-7
Copper production

1-7
Copper production at domestic mines, 1900–1986

U.S. Department of the Interior, Bureau of Mines. *Minerals Yearbook,* annual issues (Washington, D.C.). U.S. and world copper mine production historical series data compiled by J. L. W. Jolly, BOM.

Jolly, J. L. W. 1985. "Copper," pp. 197-222, *Minerals Facts and Problems* U.S. Department of the Interior, Bureau of Mines (Washington, D.C.).

1-8
Bauxite production

1-8
Bauxite production at domestic mines, 1900–1986

U.S. Department of the Interior, Bureau of Mines. *Minerals Yearbook,* annual issues (Washington, D.C.). Crude bauxite production (dry equivalent) data compiled by L. Baumgardner, BOM.

McCawley, F. X., and L. H. Baumgardner. 1985. "Aluminum," pp. 9-32, in *Minerals Facts and Problems* U.S. Department of the Interior, Bureau of Mines (Washington, D.C.).

1-9
Gold production

1-9
Gold production at domestic mines, 1845–1986

U.S. Department of Commerce, Bureau of the Census. 1976. *Historical statistics of the United States: Colonial times to 1970* (Washington, D.C.), part 1, series M 268.

U.S. Department of the Interior, Bureau of Mines. 1979. *Minerals in the U.S. economy: Ten-year supply profiles for mineral and fuel commodities* (Washington, D.C.), p. 34.

U.S. Department of the Interior, Bureau of Mines. 1986. *Nonferrous metals supply/demand data, 1974–1984* (Washington, D.C.), p. 25.

U.S. Department of the Interior, Bureau of Mines. 1987. *Mineral commodity summaries* (Washington, D.C.), p. 62.

U.S. Department of the Interior, 1988. *Gold and silver, monthly. Mineral industrial surveys* (Washington, D.C.), p. 3.

Lucas, J. M. 1985. "Gold," pp. 323-338, in *Minerals Facts and Problems* U.S. Department of the Interior, Bureau of Mines (Washington, D.C.).

1-10
Silver production

1-10
Silver production at domestic mines, 1860–1986

U.S. Department of Commerce, Bureau of the Census. 1976. *Historical statistics of the United States: Colonial times to 1970* (Washington, D.C.), part 1, series M 269.

U.S. Department of the Interior, Bureau of Mines. 1979. *Minerals in the U.S. economy: Ten-year supply profiles for mineral and fuel commodities* (Washington, D.C.), p. 79.

U.S. Department of the Interior, Bureau of Mines. 1986. *Nonferrous metals supply/demand data, 1974–1984* (Washington, D.C.), p. 47.

U.S. Department of the Interior, Bureau of Mines. 1987. *Mineral commodity summaries* (Washington, D.C.), p. 144.

Reese, R. G., Jr. 1985. "Silver," pp. 729-740, in *Minerals Facts and Problems* U.S. Department of the Interior, Bureau of Mines (Washington, D.C.).

1-11
Iron ore production

1-11
Iron ore production at domestic mines, 1900–1986

U.S. Department of Commerce, Bureau of the Census. 1976. *Historical statistics of the United States: Colonial times to 1970* (Washington, D.C.), part 1, series M 205.

U.S. Department of the Interior, Bureau of Mines. 1979. *Minerals in the U.S. economy: Ten-year supply profiles for mineral and fuel commodities* (Washington, D.C.), part 1, p. 43.

U.S. Department of the Interior, Bureau of Mines. 1986. *Ferrous metals supply/demand data, 1974–1984* (Washington, D.C.), p. 11.

U.S. Department of the Interior, Bureau of Mines. 1987. *Mineral commodity summaries* (Washington, D.C.), p. 78.

Klinger, F. L. 1985. "Iron Ore," pp. 385-404, in *Minerals Facts and Problems,* U.S. Department of the Interior, Bureau of Mines (Washington, D.C.).

1-12
Nickel production

1-12
Nickel production at domestic mines, 1950–1986

U.S. Department of Commerce, Bureau of the Census. 1976. *Historical statistics of the United States: Colonial times to 1970* (Washington, D.C.), part 1, series M 231.

U.S. Department of the Interior, Bureau of Mines. 1979. *Minerals in the U.S. economy: Ten-year supply profiles for mineral and fuel commodities* (Washington, D.C.), p. 57.

U.S. Department of the Interior, Bureau of Mines. 1986. *Ferrous metals supply/demand data, 1974–1984* (Washington, D.C.), p. 19.

U.S. Department of the Interior, Bureau of Mines. 1987. *Mineral commodity summaries* (Washington, D.C.), p. 108.

Sibley, S. F. 1985. "Nickel," pp. 535-552, in *Minerals Facts and Problems*, U.S. Department of the Interior, Bureau of Mines (Washington, D.C.).

1-13
Sand and gravel production

1-13
Sand and gravel production at domestic mines, 1900–1986

U.S. Department of Commerce, Bureau of the Census. 1976. *Historical statistics of the United States: Colonial times to 1970* (Washington, D.C.), part 1, series M 193.

U.S. Department of the Interior, Bureau of Mines. 1979. *Minerals in the U.S. economy: Ten-year supply profiles for mineral and fuel commodities* (Washington, D.C.), p. 75.

U.S. Department of the Interior, Bureau of Mines. 1986. *Industrial minerals supply/demand data, 1974–1984* (Washington, D.C.), p. 67.

U.S. Department of the Interior, Bureau of Mines. 1987. *Mineral commodity summaries* (Washington, D.C.), p. 136.

U.S. Department of the Interior, Bureau of Mines. 1988. Preprint from the *1987 Minerals Yearbook* (Washington, D.C.), p. 1.

Davis, L. L., and V. V. Tepordei. 1985. "Sand and gravel," pp. 689-704, in *Minerals Facts and Problems* U.S. Department of the Interior, Bureau of Mines (Washington, D.C.).

1-14
Crushed stone production

1-14
Crushed stone production at domestic mines, 1900–1986

U.S. Department of Commerce, Bureau of the Census. 1976. *Historical statistics of the United States: Colonial times to 1970* (Washington, D.C.), part 1, series M 194.

U.S. Department of the Interior, Bureau of Mines. 1979. *Minerals in the U.S. economy: Ten-year supply profiles for mineral and fuel commodities* (Washington, D.C.), p. 81.

U.S. Department of the Interior, Bureau of Mines. 1986. *Industrial minerals supply/demand data, 1974–1984* (Washington, D.C.), p. 75.

U.S. Department of the Interior, Bureau of Mines. 1988. Preprint from the *1987 Minerals Yearbook* (Washington, D.C.), p. 1.

Tepordei, V. V. 1985. "Stone, crushed," pp. 757-769, in *Minerals Facts and Problems* U.S. Department of the Interior, Bureau of Mines. 1985. (Washington, D.C.). 956 pp.

1-15
Asbestos production

1-15
Asbestos production at domestic mines, 1900–1986

U.S. Department of the Interior, Bureau of Mines. *U.S. salient asbestos statistics* (Washington, D.C.). Data compiled by R. L. Virta, BOM.

U.S. Department of the Interior, Bureau of Mines. 1979. *Minerals in the U.S. economy: Ten-year supply profiles for mineral and fuel commodities* (Washington, D.C.), p. 10.

U.S. Department of the Interior, Bureau of Mines. 1986. *Industrial minerals supply/demand data, 1974–1984* (Washington, D.C.), p. 5.

U.S. Department of the Interior, Bureau of Mines. 1987. *Mineral commodity summaries* (Washington, D.C.), p. 14.

U.S. Department of the Interior, Bureau of Mines. 1988. Preprint from the *1987 Minerals Yearbook* (Washington, D.C.), p. 1.

Clifton, R. A. 1985. "Asbestos," pp. 53-64, in *Minerals Facts and Problems* U.S. Department of the Interior, Bureau of Mines (Washington, D.C.).

1-16
Phosphate rock production

1-16
Phosphate rock production at domestic mines, 1900–1986

U.S. Department of Commerce, Bureau of the Census. 1976. *Historical statistics of the United States: Colonial times to 1970* (Washington, D.C.), part 1, series M 303.

U.S. Department of the Interior, Bureau of Mines. 1979. *Minerals in the U.S. economy: Ten-year supply profiles for mineral and fuel commodities* (Washington, D.C.), p. 65.

U.S. Department of the Interior, Bureau of Mines. 1986. *Industrial minerals supply/demand data, 1974–1984* (Washington, D.C.), p. 57.

U.S. Department of the Interior, Bureau of Mines. 1987. *Mineral commodity summaries* (Washington, D.C.), p. 116.

Stowasser, W. F. 1985. "Phosphate rock," pp. 579-594, in *Minerals Facts and Problems,* U.S. Department of the Interior, Bureau of Mines. 1985 (Washington, D.C.). 956 pp.

1-17
Distribution of energy resources in the United States

1-17a
Coal fields

Executive Office of the President, Council on Environmental Quality. 1981. *Environmental trends* (Washington, D.C.), figure 9-14, Coal fields, p. 194.

1-17b
Oil and gas field areas

Executive Office of the President, Council on Environmental Quality. 1981. *Environmental trends* (Washington, D.C.), figure 9-19, Natural gas and petroleum fields, p. 194. Updated by J. Roen, USGS.

1-18
Production of energy by source

1-18a
Domestic energy production by source, 1950–1986

U.S. Department of Energy, Energy Information Administration. 1988. *Annual energy review 1987* (Washington, D.C.), table 2, p. 9.

U.S. Department of Energy, Office of Environmental Programs. 1981. *Energy and land use* (Washington, D.C.).

U.S. Department of Energy, Office of Environmental Programs. 1981. *Energy and solid/hazardous waste* (Washington, D.C.).

U.S. Department of Energy. 1981. *Energy and air quality* (Washington, D.C.).

1-18b
Energy equivalents

U.S. Department of Energy, Energy Information Administration. 1988. *Annual energy review 1987* (Washington, D.C.), appendix B3, Energy equivalents, p. 282.

1-19
Production of coal by rank and by source

1-19a
Coal production by rank at domestic mines, 1900–1986

1-19b
Coal production by source at domestic mines, 1900–1986

U.S. Department of Commerce, Bureau of the Census. 1976. *Historical statistics of the United States: Colonial times to 1970* (Washington, D.C.), part 1, series 93, 94, 95, 123, 124, 125.

U.S. Department of Energy, Energy Information Administration. 1988. *Annual energy review 1987* (Washington, D.C.), table 75, p. 173.

1-20
Petroleum production

1-20
Petroleum production at domestic wells, 1940–1986

U.S. Department of Commerce, Bureau of the Census. 1976. *Historical statistics of the United States: Colonial times to 1970* (Washington, D.C.), part 1, series M 143, 138.

U.S. Department of Energy, Energy Information Administration. 1988. *Annual energy review 1987* (Washington, D.C.), table 46. p. 107.

U.S. Department of Energy, Office of Environmental Programs. 1981. *Energy and land use* (Washington, D.C.).

U.S. Department of Energy, Office of Environmental Programs. 1981. *Energy and solid/hazardous waste* (Washington, D.C.).

Cormack, D. 1983. *Response to oil and chemical marine pollution.* Applied Science Publishers (London & New York).

1-21
Dry natural gas production

1-21
Marketed natural gas production at domestic wells, 1900–1986

U.S. Department of Commerce, Bureau of the Census. 1976. *Historical statistics of the United States: Colonial times to 1970* (Washington, D.C.), part 1, series M 147.

U.S. Department of Energy, Energy Information Administration. 1988. *Annual energy review 1987* (Washington, D.C.), table 67, p. 153.

1-22
Hydroelectric energy production

1-22
Electricity production by domestic hydroelectric power plants, 1920–1986

U.S. Department of Commerce, Bureau of the Census. 1976. *Historical statistics of the United States: Colonial times to 1970* (Washington, D.C.), part 1, series M 37.

U.S. Department of Energy, Energy Information Administration. 1988. *Annual energy review 1987* (Washington, D.C.), table 83, p. 193.

U.S. Department of Defense, Army Corps of Engineers. 1983. *National hydroelectric power resources study* (Washington, D.C.).

1-23
Uranium production

1-23
Uranium production at domestic mines, 1950–1986

U.S. Department of Energy, Energy Information Administration. 1988. *Annual energy review 1987* (Washington, D.C.), table 94, p. 217.

U.S. Department of Energy, Office of Environmental Programs. 1981. *Energy and solid/hazardous waste* (Washington, D.C.).

1-24
Energy consumption by fuel type and end user

1-24a
Domestic energy consumption by source, 1950–1986

1-24b
Domestic energy consumption by end-user sector, 1950–1986

U.S. Department of Energy, Energy Information Administration. 1988. *Annual energy review 1987* (Washington, D.C.), table 3, p. 11 and table 4, p. 13.

1-25
World energy consumption by region and per capita

1-25a
World energy consumption by region, 1960–1986

1-25b
World energy consumption per capita for selected regions, 1960–1986

Statistical Office of the United Nations. *Energy statistics yearbook,* annual (New York).

World Resources Institute. 1987. *World Resources 1987.* Basic Books, Inc (New York), pp. 93-110.

1-26
Land utilized and reclaimed by the mining industry

1-26a
Land mined by selected commodity, 1930–1980

1-26b
Land reclaimed by selected commodity, 1930–1980

Johnson, W., and J. Paone. 1981. *Land utilization and reclamation in the mining industry, 1930-1980.* U.S. Department of the Interior, Bureau of Mines Information Circular 8862 (Washington, D.C.).

1-27 Acid mine drainage

1-27 Streams affected by acid mine drainage

Executive Office of the President, Council on Environmental Quality. 1981. *Environmental trends* (Washington, D.C.), figure 9-17, Streams affected by acid mine drainage, 1970s, p. 192.

Kim, A. G., V. S. Heisey, R. L. P. Kleinmann, and M. Deul. 1982. *Acid mine drainage: Control and abatement research.* U.S. Department of the Interior, Bureau of Mines Information Circular 8905 (Washington, D.C.).

Brodie, G. A., D. A. Hammer, and D. A. Tomljanovich. Manuscript, no date. *Constructed wetlands for acid drainage control in the Tennessee Valley.* Tennessee Valley Authority (Knoxville, Tenn.).

Chapter 2
Water

2-1
Hydrologic cycle

Water constantly circulates from the sea to the land, by way of the atmosphere in the form of precipitation, and eventually returns to the sea as ground-water and surface-water flow and to the atmosphere through evaporative processes. This movement of water and moisture is driven by energy from the sun, and the process is termed the "hydrologic cycle."

The magnitude of water transported by the hydrologic cycle in the conterminous United States is illustrated by a gross water budget. Long-term measurements indicate that approximately 40,000 billion

gallons of water vapor pass over the country each day, and, of this amount, 4,200 billion gallons fall as precipitation. About two-thirds of this precipitation (2,800 billion gallons) is returned to the atmosphere daily via evaporation and transpiration from surface-water bodies, land surfaces, and vegetation, and the rest is discharged into streams, lakes, or the ocean, or seeps underground.

In 1985, approximately 399 billion gallons of water per day were withdrawn from aquifers and streams for public water supply, rural use, irrigation, and industry. Much of this water (307 billion gallons per day) was eventually returned to its source (usually streams), whereas 92 billion gallons per day were consumed and incorporated into manufactured products, crops, and animal tissue and hence no longer available for immediate use.

Competing demands are put on available surface water and ground water for public and rural water supply, irrigation and industrial water, electric power, recreation, and fish and wildlife habitat. Water supplies are generally abundant in the United States, yet they are not evenly distributed across the land and may not be readily available when and where needed or of adequate quality for intended use. As water is transported through the hydrologic

cycle, the quantity and quality of water can change in response to meteorologic, climatic, geologic, and biologic conditions, and how the resource is developed and managed.

Precipitation is the source of nearly all the fresh water that occurs on and beneath the land surface, and is the single most important factor controlling the variability and availability of surface-water resources. Average annual precipitation in the United States is about 30 inches per year; however, the range varies from a few tenths of an inch per year in the desert areas of the Southwest to 400 inches or more per year at some locations in Hawaii. About one-third of the conterminous United States, mostly in the West and Midwest, receives less than 20 inches of precipitation during an average year. In any given year, departures from average conditions can be extreme.

Runoff is that portion of precipitation that falls on the land and does not evaporate directly or is not taken up by plants. Runoff flows from the land directly to local streams, lakes, ponds, or wetlands or infiltrates soil and rocks to recharge the ground-water reservoirs. The amount and character of runoff from a given amount of annual precipitation can vary considerably depending upon the season in

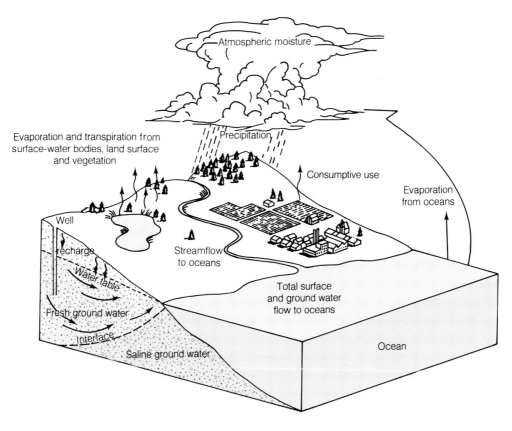

Hydrologic cycle

Average annual precipitation

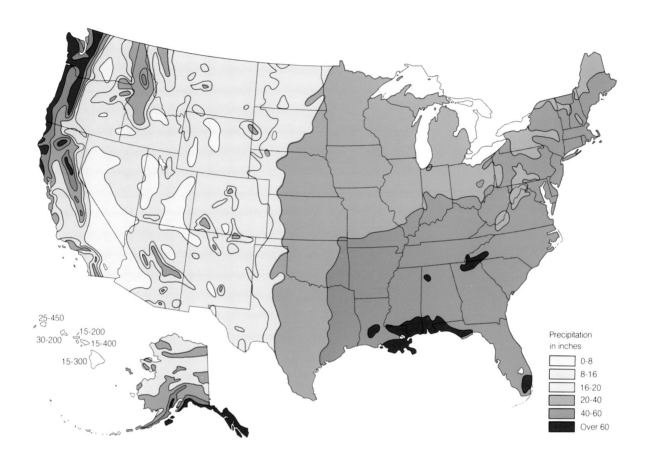

25-450
30-200
15-200
15-400
15-300

Precipitation
in inches

- 0-8
- 8-16
- 16-20
- 20-40
- 40-60
- Over 60

Average annual runoff

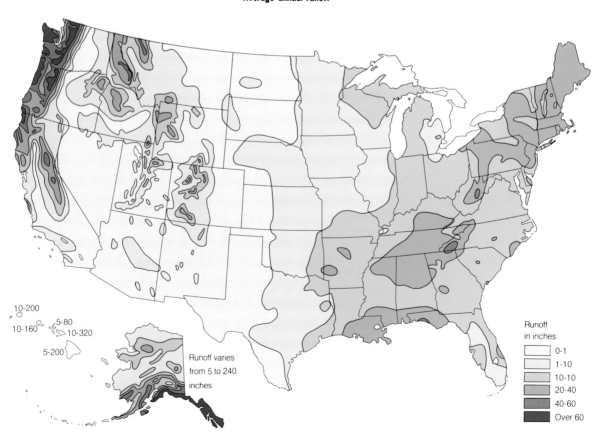

10-200
10-160
5-80
10-320
5-200

Runoff varies
from 5 to 240
inches

Runoff
in inches

- 0-1
- 1-10
- 10-10
- 20-40
- 40-60
- Over 60

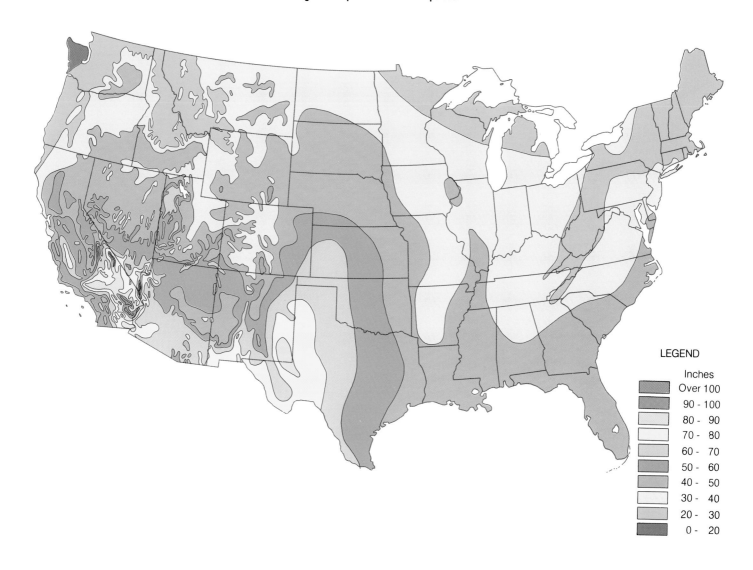

LEGEND

Inches

	Over 100
	90 - 100
	80 - 90
	70 - 80
	60 - 70
	50 - 60
	40 - 50
	30 - 40
	20 - 30
	0 - 20

which the major precipitation occurs and whether the precipitation is associated with a few large storms or with many small ones. Geologic and topographic characteristics of the area and land use patterns also affect runoff. In areas of low rainfall, runoff is generally only a very small percentage of the precipitation, whereas in humid areas, runoff is commonly more than one-half of the amount. The highest runoff rates occur in southeastern Alaska and western Washington, where annual runoff of many streams exceeds 60 inches, and for a few streams, it is as much as 240 inches. In semiarid and arid regions, such as parts of the Great Plains, the Great Basin of Nevada and Utah, and southern California, Arizona, and New Mexico, runoff is less than 1 inch per year.

Water loss through evaporation from land and surface-water bodies and by transpiration from plants are other factors that affect the availability of water resources. Evapotranspiration losses and the effects of these losses on runoff differ from basin to basin and from year to year within a basin.

Generally, climatic conditions that contribute to decreased precipitation tend to increase evaporation, whereas the converse usually is true. In semiarid regions, transpiration rates nearly equal precipitation rates and major evaporation losses occur shortly after precipitation; this results in low runoff. In a lake, evaporation can be a major short-term factor moderating a rise or fall in the elevation of the lake level and a corresponding increase or decrease in the area covered by the lake.

2-2
Flow of selected rivers

Streamflow varies from river to river across the country and over time. Each geographic region has a characteristic streamflow pattern that responds to the nature of the river basin and the seasonal distribution of high and low atmospheric pressure systems. Obvious variations in peak discharge occur from season to season, which result principally from climatic changes. Most rivers have distinct

periods of high flow followed by periods of low flow; however, the timing of high and low flows can differ from year to year. High flows result from storm runoff and snowmelt, whereas low flows result from periods of low precipitation and high evaporation.

Low temperatures in the basins of northern streams or those that drain mountain areas delay runoff by holding the precipitation as snow or ice until melting occurs during periods of higher temperatures. The snow-storage effect is illustrated by mean monthly discharge of the Boise River near Twin Springs, Idaho. Snow storage is most pronounced where temperatures remain below freezing for several months and winter precipitation is relatively abundant. This results in very low winter flows followed by high runoff when the snow and ice melt. In contrast, where temperatures seldom fall below freezing or do so for only short periods, monthly streamflow patterns closely correspond to monthly precipitation patterns.

Floods are natural and recurring hydrologic events, yet they are one of the most destructive

Flow of selected rivers

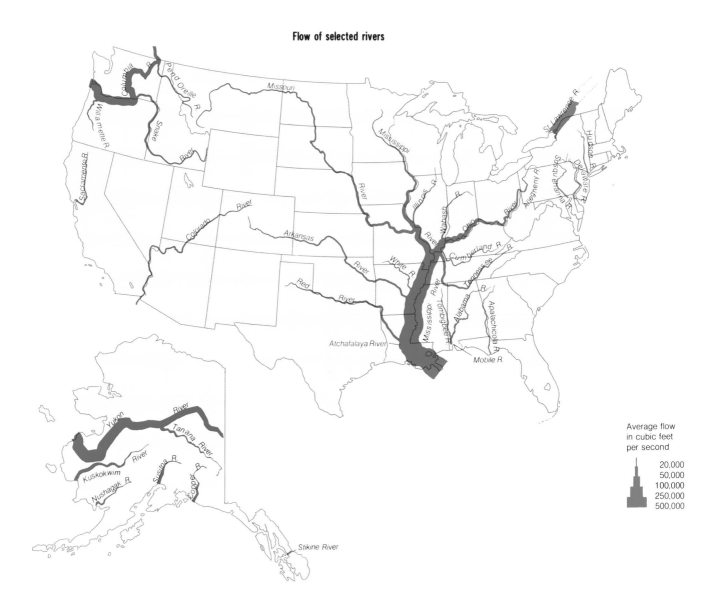

Average flow
in cubic feet
per second

20,000
50,000
100,000
250,000
500,000

natural hazards in the United States. Floods (excluding coastal flooding from high tides and storm surge) result from intense rains, rapid snowmelt, or a combination of the two. They range from fairly common high flows that barely overtop the natural stream banks and have only local effects to rare flows that crest well above the stream's confines and have extensive and severe impacts. Although floods are a hazard, the storms that cause floods nonetheless replenish soil moisture and recharge the ground-water systems, which supply aquifers and discharge into streams between storms.

In semiarid areas, such as the Middle Concho River in Texas, a small change in annual precipitation can have a large effect on runoff from the drainage basin. In these regions, the variability in the size of storms results in high variability among annual discharges.

Unusually long, dry periods or droughts are caused by a deficiency in precipitation and can reduce streamflow and lower ground-water tables. The severity of a drought depends upon the amount of water storage available from the preceding year,

the water demands relative to average flow, and the natural flow during a drought period. Multiyear droughts in the late 1920s and early 1930s in the Red River of the North at Grand Forks, North Dakota, for example, resulted in a prolonged reduction in streamflow.

Streamflow diversion and storage of surface waters can also change flow patterns. Flow conditions in some rivers have been artificially modified by dredging; rerouting and lining of channels; construction of locks, dikes, levees, dams, and reservoirs; and land conversions on the floodplains. These modifications are made to maintain and improve navigation on rivers, store water supplies, and provide flood protection to low-lying areas. The effects of water development on streamflow include changes in flood peaks, average annual discharge, and flow duration. Closure of the Kingsley Dam on the North Platte River at North Platte, Nebraska, illustrates the effects of water development on peak annual discharge.

The patterns of suspended-sediment concentrations discharged by rivers reflect such influencing

factors as climate (especially rainfall), the properties of the rocks and soil that are exposed to erosion, man-made structures (dams, reservoirs, levees), storms (particularly hurricanes), and catastrophic events (eruption of Mount St. Helens). On a national scale, the amount of sediment delivered to the oceans by rivers is only about 10% of the total eroded off the uplands of the country, and the remainder is stored somewhere between the erosion site and the sea. A fraction of this 90% is stored in reservoirs, but most of it is stored on hillsides, floodplains, and other parts of stream valleys where it can be mobilized during storm events.

2-3
Water levels in lakes

The Great Salt Lake is a modern remnant of a much larger lake that existed during most of the Pleistocene Epoch, which began about 1.6 million years ago and ended with the melting of the last glacial ice sheets between 11,000 and 12,000 years ago.

Mean monthly discharge
Boise River near Twin Springs, Idaho, 1951-1980

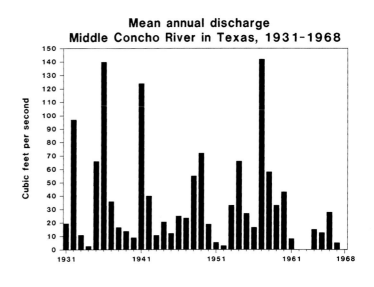

Mean annual discharge
Middle Concho River in Texas, 1931-1968

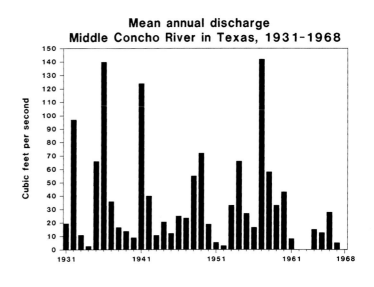

Mean annual discharge, Red River of the North
at Grand Forks, North Dakota, 1885-1986

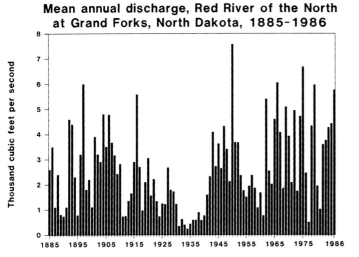

Peak annual discharge, North Platte River
at North Platte, Nebraska, 1895-1986

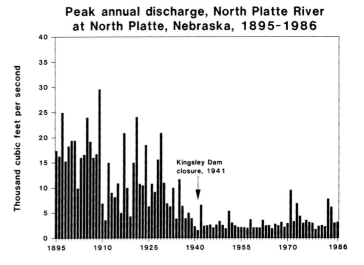

Annual suspended sediment discharge
Missouri River at Omaha, Nebraska, 1940-1976

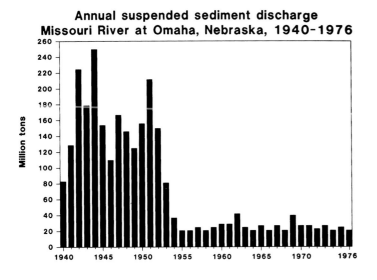

Annual suspended sediment discharge, Juniata
River at Newport, Pennsylvania, 1940-1983

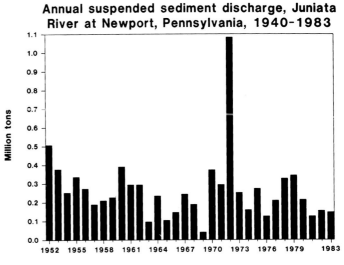

Water levels in the Great Salt Lake, Utah
1850-1986

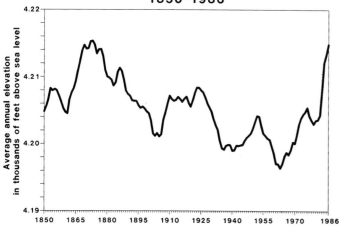

Water levels in the Great Lakes
1950-1986

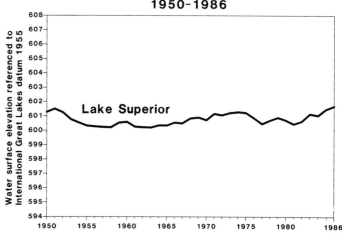

Great Salt Lake now occupies a low-lying desert area in western Utah. It has no natural outlet to the ocean. The lake's water level fluctuates seasonally and over the long term in response to changes in climate and the hydrology of the drainage system. Since the mid-1980s, the lake's water level has been rising.

The Great Salt Lake usually declines annually in the spring and summer when loss of surface water from evaporation is greater than the combined input from surface streams, ground water, and precipitation. The level begins to rise in the autumn when the temperature decreases, evaporation is reduced, and water input exceeds water loss. During dry years, the net water level declines and thus causes both a decrease in surface area and concentration of salts. Conversely, the lake's water level rises during wet years and thus causes an increase in surface area and dilution of the brine.

In response to above-average precipitation between 1982 and 1986, the water level in the Great Salt Lake rose a net 10.6 feet to the highest lake level since 1873. This increase caused flooding and resulted in extensive damage to roads, railroads, wildfowl-management areas, recreational facilities, and industrial installations that had been established since the last major lake level rise more than one hundred years ago.

The Great Lakes also have experienced recent high water levels. Water in the Great Lakes system flows through waterways from Lake Superior (elevation of 600.59 feet above sea level) to Lakes Michigan and Huron (578.27 feet) to Lake Erie (570.44 feet), to and over Niagara Falls and through Lake Ontario (244.71 feet), and through the St. Lawrence River into the Atlantic Ocean. Long-term fluctuations in Great Lakes water levels are caused by variations in inflow and outflow from the lakes.

Inflow to the lakes is from precipitation, runoff, ground-water discharge, and return flow from artificial diversions. Outflow occurs from evaporation, discharge into the St. Lawrence River, and diversions from the lakes. To provide adequate water depths for navigation and to assure dependable flows for the production of hydroelectric power, outflows from Lakes Superior and Ontario are regulated by control structures. Water levels in and outflows from Lakes Michigan, Huron, and Erie are determined by the discharge capacities of the rivers that drain them, and it is these lakes that have experienced the most significant rises in water level.

The enormous storage capacity of the Great Lakes generally absorbs most of the variations in water supply; however, the water levels of the lakes do fluctuate a few feet from year to year and from season to season. Precipitation and air temperature strongly influence the levels of the lakes. In the

Water levels in the Great Lakes
1950-1986

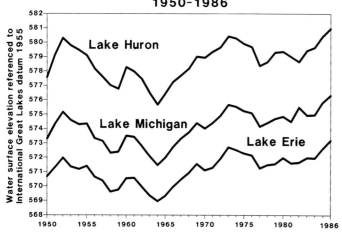

Water levels in the Great Lakes
1950-1986

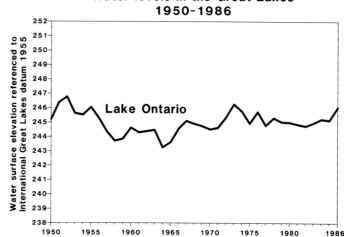

early 1960s, below-average precipitation led to record low lake levels, and since then above-average precipitation and below-average air temperatures (which result in more runoff for a given amount of precipitation because evaporation and transpiration are less) have caused lake levels to rise. Spring and fall storms, common in the Great Lakes area, coupled with the high water levels, have exacerbated flooding and erosion along shorelines.

Efforts to manipulate water levels in the Great Salt Lake and the Great Lakes through water diversions and control of outflows have helped alleviate problems caused by extremes in water levels, although fluctuations are expected to continue in response to climatic factors. Given the uncertainty of future lake levels and the effects of increased flooding if water levels continue to rise, the dynamics of these lakes will continue to be the subject of interest and study.

2-4
Surface-water development

Dams are used to regulate streamflow and create reservoirs that provide reliable supplies of surface water for a variety of purposes. Water stored during wet periods can be released from the reservoir into the river channel when needed downstream during dry periods, or it may be withdrawn directly from the reservoir and carried by pipe or canal to its destination. In either situation, a minimum streamflow must be maintained in the river to provide sufficient water for instream uses, such as navigation, fish and wildlife habitat, waste assimilation, or water temperature control. Some reservoirs are built for the single purpose of controlling floods whereas others are operated to provide storage for multiple purposes, including flood control, navigation, hydroelectric power, irrigation water supply, municipal and industrial water supply, fish and wildlife conservation, recreation, low flow augmentation, or pollution abatement.

The intensity of reservoir development varies across the Nation. Factors that influence whether a reservoir is constructed are the project purposes that must show benefits in excess of construction costs. Other considerations include the existence of suitable reservoir sites and various political, institu-

tional, and environmental considerations. The range in reservoir storage intensity varies on a regional basis from about 24 acre-feet of reservoir capacity per square mile of land area in the Great Basin water resource region to 366 acre-feet per square mile in the Upper Colorado region. (An acre-foot is the volume of water required to cover one acre of land to a depth of one foot; it is equivalent to 325,851 gallons).

By the mid-1980s, approximately 2,654 reservoirs and controlled natural lakes with capacities of 5,000 acre-feet or more existed in the United States and Puerto Rico. These reservoirs have a combined normal storage capacity of more than 479 million acre-feet. In addition, there are at least 50,000 smaller reservoirs with capacities ranging from 50 to 5,000 acre-feet and about 2 million smaller farm ponds used for water storage.

Many reservoirs are built to decrease the magnitude and frequency of downstream flooding. Between 1935 and 1985, over 600 federally funded flood-control dams were built. By 1986, the U.S. Army Corps of Engineers had constructed and/or controlled 681 flood-control projects. Water levels in flood-control reservoirs are usually kept low during the flood-prone season to provide as much storage space as possible for floodwaters. Releases are controlled by an operator through outlet structure or spillway. The effectiveness of these dams is a function of reservoir capacity compared to the area of the basin, the intensity of precipitation, the runoff characteristics of the basin, the availability of reliable real-time meteorological and stream gauge data, and reservoir operation. If reservoir storage is not reserved for the flood peak, the reservoir could fill and be ineffective in reducing the flood wave and possibly cause the dam to be overtopped. On the other hand, if water is released in anticipation of a flood and a flood does not occur, valuable water for other uses may be lost.

Dams and reservoirs typically bring about changes in the upstream and downstream environment. Although some positive benefits are created, some unfavorable environmental changes may occur. For example, impounded water may inundate wetlands or valuable fish and wildlife habitat may be lost. Some reservoirs trap sediment and reduce the amount of sediment in the river immediately downstream of the

dam. The river reacts to the reduction in sediment load by eroding its bed and banks to regain its normal sediment load. The river channel may deepen through disintegration and may become wider or smaller depending upon water discharges and local geologic conditions. Channel widening occurs through bank failure and erosion. Where the channel narrows, riparian vegetation commonly becomes established on the older parts of the streambed and a new floodplain is created. The increase in vegetation may block parts of the channel and impede the flow of water.

Trends in reservoir capacity can be viewed in two ways: storage volume capacity of active reservoirs and storage capacity per unit volume of dam material. The number of dams and thus the total reservoir storage volume capacity for U. S. Army Corps of Engineers dams has increased steadily since 1920. Much of the growth in capacity averaged about 80% per decade until the early 1960s. Since then, reservoir capacity has increased at a slower rate.

Much of the growth in active reservoir storage volume capacity, especially after 1930, took place with the construction of multipurpose reservoirs that provided economies of scale and combination of uses. This was made possible by a change in technology that increased the number of practical dam sites. Early dam builders sought streams that cut through narrow or "box" canyons of hard rock or broad lakes with narrow stream outlets. Over the years, however, less favorable sites have been developed.

The change in capacity–volume ratio for major reservoirs has been associated with a shift in the types of dams constructed. Prior to the 1920s, many reservoirs were larger and dams were constructed of reinforced concrete, whereas many of the newer sites required broad-based earth-filled dams. The percentage of masonry dams decreased from over 90% of the total number of dams built before 1930 to about 10% since 1960.

The rate of construction of reservoirs for municipal and industrial water supplies and irrigation has not kept pace with the growth in population. In 1960, the national average reservoir storage volume equaled 204 days of withdrawal (which is equivalent to withdrawal of 119 million acre-feet of water at

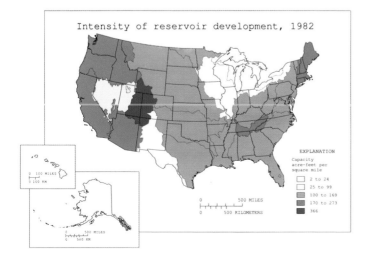

Intensity of reservoir development, 1982

EXPLANATION
Capacity
acre-feet per
square mile
2 to 24
25 to 99
100 to 169
170 to 273
366

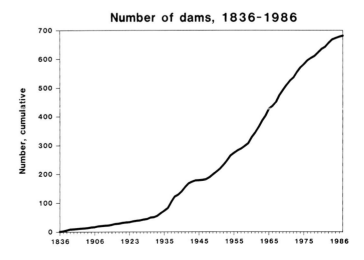

Number of dams, 1836-1986

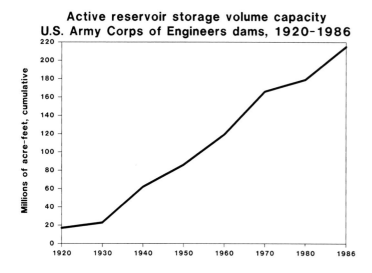

Active reservoir storage volume capacity U.S. Army Corps of Engineers dams, 1920-1986

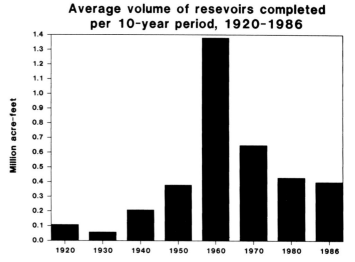

Average volume of resevoirs completed per 10-year period, 1920-1986

190 billion gallons per day). By 1970, storage had increased to 216 days of withdrawal, but by 1980, it had fallen to 201 days, which signifies the first decline in the six decades for which records are available. Data also show that from 1920 to 1970, reservoir storage capacity and water withdrawals were positively correlated, but in the decade 1970 to 1980, storage capacity did not keep up with increasing withdrawals. Nonetheless, in 1980, with-

drawals were less than 21% of the renewable water supply for the conterminous United States (which is 1,380 billion gallons per day).

2-5
Ground-water development

Ground water is the only, or dominant, source of drinking water for most rural areas. It is the largest

source of water for irrigation and other purposes in arid and most semiarid regions and provides supplemental irrigation needs in humid areas. Ground water is also an important source of water for urban and industrial purposes in humid areas.

The widespread use of ground water results not only from its general availability but also from economic and public-health considerations. From the standpoint of economics, ground water is commonly

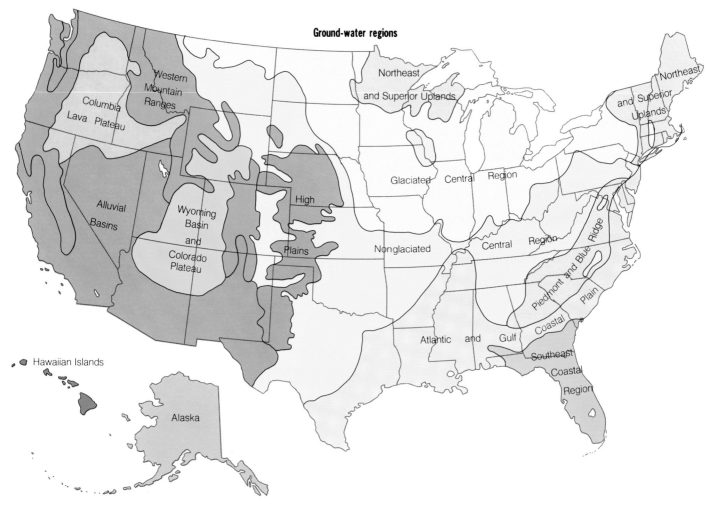

Ground-water regions

available at the point of need at relatively little cost and thus does not require the construction of distant reservoirs and long pipelines. It is usually of good quality, normally free of suspended sediments and free of bacteria and other disease-causing organisms, and thus does not require extensive treatment and filtration except in limited areas where it has been polluted. Ground water is saline in some places, however, and unfit for most uses.

Ground water occurs in openings in the rocks that form the earth's crust. The nature of the water-bearing openings in rocks depends to a large degree on the geologic age of the rocks as well as on the process that formed the rocks. Geologically young types of rocks—unconsolidated sedimentary deposits and extrusive igneous (volcanic) rocks—tend to have a larger volume of openings than do older rocks of the same type that have been consolidated and partially or completely filled by minerals or sediment. Intrusive igneous rocks and metamorphic rocks are among the oldest water-bearing rocks. At the time of their formation, they did not contain any appreciable openings, but over the course of geologic time, they could break along sets of vertical and horizontal fractures that then serve as water-bearing openings.

Part of the precipitation that reaches the land surface percolates underground to a zone in which interconnected rock openings contain only water. Saturated rock units whose capacity to transmit water is large enough to supply water in a usable quantity to a well or a spring are referred to as aquifers. The water table is the water level near the upper part of the saturated zone, and below the water table is ground water. The saturated zones are places where ground water is recharged. After reaching the saturated zone, water moves downward and laterally under hydraulic gradients to discharge areas. Generally, an equilibrium prevails in which the long-term recharge of the ground-water system is balanced by the long-term discharge from it. When recharge exceeds discharge, water accumulates in storage and the water table rises. Conversely, when withdrawal exceeds recharge, water is removed from storage and the water table drops.

The volume of ground water in the upper one-half mile of the earth's crust within the conterminous United States is estimated to be 50,000 cubic miles. Although ground water is available nearly everywhere in the United States, the quantity available and the conditions controlling its occurrence and development differ from one part of the Nation to another. For a concise description of ground-water conditions in the United States, it is necessary to divide the Nation into regions in which the conditions are generally similar. Because the presence and availability of ground water depend primarily upon geologic conditions, ground-water regions also are areas in which the composition, arrangement, and structure of rock units are similar. Hydrologic characteristics vary from one ground-water region to another as well as within regions, from one part to another. Patterns of ground-water development in the Nation reflect many of these variations.

Pumping of ground water has increased steadily over the past three decades. Overall, ground-water use has been increasing at a faster rate than that of surface water for irrigation purposes, rural and public water supplies (particularly in growing urban areas in the South and Southwest), and manufacturing and energy production (excluding thermoelectric power generation). Several factors could cause this trend to continue or accelerate in the future. The most cost-effective surface-water (reservoir) sites already have been developed, and the sustained yields are decreasing because of sedimentation and increasing withdrawals. In addition, the cost of storage at the remaining reservoir sites is becoming increasingly expensive. And finally, public opposition to new reservoir construction is increasing because of potential environmental damages.

States with the largest ground-water use are those in the western part of the conterminous United States—Arizona, California, Idaho, Kansas, Nebraska, and Texas—where irrigated agriculture is common. In the eastern part of the country, states that use large amounts of ground water for irrigation include Arkansas, Florida, Louisiana, and Mississippi.

Changes in water table levels in wells reflect changes in the amount of ground water in storage in aquifers. In certain areas, long-term withdrawals of large volumes of ground water, primarily for irrigation, have resulted in widespread declines in water levels by as much as 40 feet or more. In some of these areas, the decline in water level took place many years ago during the initial stages of ground-water mining, and the water table has since stabilized at a lower level. In other areas, reductions in water levels are recent events that are presently continuing.

The effect of ground-water overuse varies from place to place. In water deficient areas, such as southern Arizona and the southern High Plains region of Kansas, New Mexico, Oklahoma, and Texas, very large volumes of ground water have been and continue to be withdrawn to supply agricultural and municipal needs, but these withdrawals cannot be sustained indefinitely. A drawdown of the water table has occurred in these areas, and pumping has decreased as falling water levels cause well yields to decline and pumping costs to rise.

In wetter areas, such as Florida and the Atlantic Coastal Plain, ground-water development has redistributed natural flow patterns where ground water that originally discharged to streams is diverted to well fields. Ground-water depletion has been small but has caused sinkholes, saltwater intrusion, and land surface subsidence.

Ground-water mining in the San Joaquin Valley of California has resulted in sediment compaction and land subsidence. In the six-county area of metropolitan Chicago, on the other hand, which experienced water-level declines of more than 850 feet between 1864 and 1980, no major subsidence has occurred because the underlying rocks are consolidated and resist compaction when water is withdrawn.

In South Dakota, the lowered water table level represents a drawdown that occurred in the Dakota aquifer in the early part of the century when the aquifer was first developed for irrigation, water power, and municipal supplies. Use of water from the Dakota aquifer has decreased since 1970, and rural and municipal water systems have been constructed or developed from other sources.

Recent ground-water development trends suggest the need to conserve existing ground-water supplies and protect ground-water quality. These actions are critically important to the Nation's ability to meet present and future water needs.

Characteristics of ground-water regions

Region	Well yield, gal/min
Western Mountain Ranges	10 to 100
Alluvial Basins	100 to 5,000
Columbia Lava Plateau	100 to 20,000
Colorado Plateau and Wyoming Basin	10 to 1,000
High Plains	100 to 3,000
Nonglaciated Central	100 to 5,000
Glaciated Central	50 to 500
Piedmont and Blue Ridge	50 to 500
Northeast and Superior Uplands	20 to 200
Atlantic and Gulf Coastal Plain	100 to 5,000
Southeast Coastal Plain	1,000 to 20,000
Alluvial Valleys	100 to 5,000
Hawaiian Islands	100 to 5,000
Alaska	10 to 1,000

Areas of water table decline, 1984

Trends in water use

The Nation's freshwater needs are met by withdrawals from streams, lakes, reservoirs, and ground-water aquifers. Trends in surface-water diversions and ground-water pumpage (collectively referred to as offstream withdrawal) and instream usage provide a historical perspective on the development of water resources in the United States and serve to illustrate some of the issues related to the present and future availability of adequate water supplies.

Surface water has been and continues to be the primary source of the Nation's water supplies. Surface-water diversions have consistently exceeded ground-water pumpage by volume. Since about 1950, however, ground water has become the preferred source of additional water supply and is being used increasingly for all purposes (except thermoelectric power generation).

Currently, more water is withdrawn from offstream sources for industrial use than for any other use category. Industrial water supply services two different end users: thermoelectric power plants (or electric utility) and manufacturing industries, such as steel, chemical and allied products, paper and pulp mills, mining, and petroleum refining. Thermoelectric power plants powered by fossil fuel, geothermal, or nuclear energy use water mainly for condenser and reactor cooling. Water used for these purposes must be available in very large quantities, and 99% of it is obtained from surface-water sources. About 30% of the surface water withdrawn for thermoelectric power generation is from saline surface-water bodies.

Since 1965, thermoelectric power facilities have accounted for the largest quantity of water withdrawn for offstream use (prior to 1965, irrigation used the largest volume of offstream water). The current trend in water use by thermoelectric power shows a slowdown in the rate of increasing water use. Water conservation measures and a reduction in once-through cooling are primarily responsible for the observed trend. (The latter has been implemented to reduce thermal discharges to streams.)

Increases in recycling of power-plant cooling water through the use of cooling towers should further slow the rate of water withdrawal but probably will increase consumptive use because of evaporation from the towers.

In the other industrial sectors, conservation measures associated with pollution-control measures account for much of the long-term decline in water withdrawal, despite an increase in manufacturing activity. Many industries using large amounts of process water in their plants now recycle water to reduce the volume of water discharged into receiving waters and the associated costs of treating the wastewater discharges.

Irrigation practices developed with the settlement of the arid West because of the need for a reliable source of water for agriculture. In the wetter East, farmers supplement natural rainfall with irrigation water to increase the number of plantings per year and crop yields per acre and to reduce the risk of crop failures during drought periods. Irrigation also is used to maintain recreational lands, such as parks and golf courses.

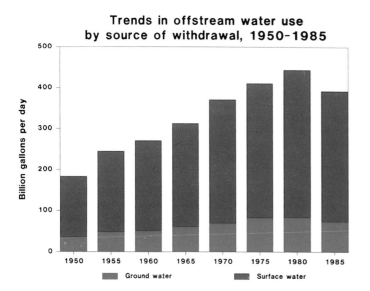

Trends in offstream water use by source of withdrawal, 1950-1985

Ground water   Surface water

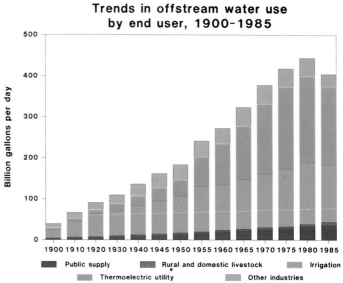

Trends in offstream water use by end user, 1900-1985

Public supply   Rural and domestic livestock   Irrigation
Thermoelectric utility   Other industries

Trend in instream water use for hydroelectric power, 1950-1985

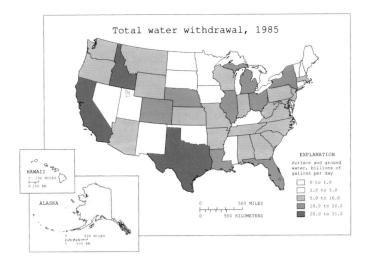

Total water withdrawal, 1985

EXPLANATION
Surface and ground
water, billions of
gallons per day

☐ 0 to 1.0
☐ 1.0 to 5.0
▨ 5.0 to 10.0
▨ 10.0 to 20.0
■ 20.0 to 51.0

HAWAII

ALASKA

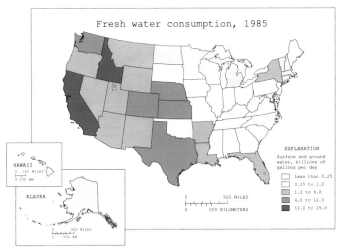

Fresh water consumption, 1985

EXPLANATION
Surface and ground
water, billions of
gallons per day

☐ Less than 0.25
☐ 0.25 to 1.2
▨ 1.2 to 4.0
▨ 4.0 to 12.0
■ 12.0 to 25.0

HAWAII

ALASKA

In 1985, irrigation withdrawals accounted for 34% of total water withdrawal and 80% of all consumptive water use in the United States. Much of the consumptive use resulted from conveyance loss between streams or reservoirs and the fields being irrigated and losses associated with inefficient water-application techniques and schedules. Improvement in irrigation methods and reduction in irrigated cropland acreages are responsible for declines in irrigation water usage between 1980 and 1985.

Public supply refers to water withdrawn by public and private water suppliers and delivered for domestic or household purposes, public use (such as fire-fighting, street washing, and swimming pools), commercial purposes (including restaurants, hotels, offices, and stores), and some industrial purposes (especially where the quantity of water required is low and the quality must be high). Rural use includes water for self-supplied domestic consumption, for livestock, dairy sanitation, fish farming, and other farm uses.

In contrast to other water uses, public and rural water use continued to increase into the 1980s. This increase mirrors population growth and reflects an

increase in per capita water use. Public and rural water use rates may stabilize or decline in the future as water costs rise, use of water-conserving appliances and fixtures increases, and public awareness of the need to conserve water improves.

Despite major droughts and chronic water shortages in some localities, the Nation is not "running out" of water. Many of the concerns about water shortage arise because of uneven distribution of water in relation to regional and seasonal distribution of water demands. Concerns also arise because of increasing demand for existing supplies and related difficulties in distribution. In some instances, changes in engineering, management, or institutional procedures and increased conservation may improve the situation.

2-7
Water quality

As water moves through the hydrologic cycle, it carries substances derived from both natural and

human sources. These substances include dissolved salts, metals, organics, and radioactive materials, as well as suspended materials, such as bacteria, viruses, and sediments. Dissolved and suspended substances can become problems, or pollutants, when they reach concentrations that impair or destroy aquatic life, threaten human health, or foul water to the extent that its ability to support shellfish harvest, fish and wildlife habitat, swimming, boating, and other intended uses is lost.

Polluting substances enter surface water and ground water either at a discrete point, such as a pipe, ditch, or well, or in a diffused manner over a large area (nonpoint source). In surface-water systems, the major point sources of pollution are municipal sewage treatment plants, industrial facilities, and combined sewer overflows. These sources discharge a variety of substances, in different quantities and combinations, including sediments and other particulates, organic materials (which create biochemical oxygen demands), nutrients, and various caustic and toxic chemicals. Treatment of effluent waters can remove substantial quantities of these conventional and hazardous pollutants.

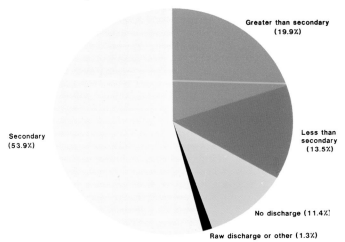

Municipal wastewater treatment, 1986

Greater than secondary (19.9%)

Secondary (53.9%)

Less than secondary (13.5%)

No discharge (11.4%)

Raw discharge or other (1.3%)

Total number of facilities = 15,587

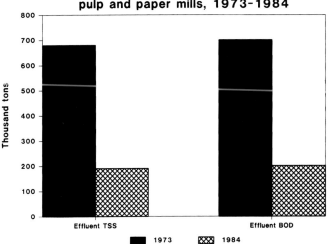

Effluent reductions associated with pulp and paper mills, 1973-1984

Thousand tons

Effluent TSS   Effluent BOD

■ 1973   ▨ 1984

Point source contributions
Biochemical oxygen demand, mid-1980s

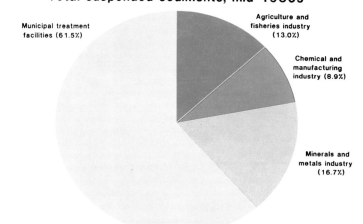

Municipal treatment facilities (72.3%)

Agriculture and fisheries industry (21.6%)

Chemical and manufacturing industry (5.8%)

Minerals and metals industry (0.3%)

Total BOD = 1.87 million tons per year

Point source contributions
Total suspended sediments, mid-1980s

Municipal treatment facilities (61.5%)

Agriculture and fisheries industry (13.0%)

Chemical and manufacturing industry (8.9%)

Minerals and metals industry (16.7%)

Total TSS = 2.13 million tons per year

Nonpoint source pollution is carried in rainwater, runoff, and snowmelt over and through soil to surface water, or in water that percolates through soils to underground aquifers. The principal nonpoint sources of pollution to surface water are runoff from cropland, pasture, forest land, and animal feedlots; runoff from construction, mining, and logging areas; drainage from waste disposal sites and landfills; runoff from urban areas and roads; and atmospheric deposition. These sources contribute both conventional and hazardous pollutants. Nonpoint source pollutants are mobilized primarily during hydrologic events (rainfall, storms) rather than as continuous discharges.

With reference to ground-water quality, the most frequently cited sources of pollution are agricultural lands, faulty septic systems, and leaky underground storage tanks and pipes. Nitrates and pesticides are common contaminants from agricultural lands, whereas microorganisms, nitrates, and synthetic organic compounds are associated with faulty septic systems. Fuels, chemicals, solvents, and other toxic

wastes are contaminants of concern from leaky underground storage tanks and pipes. Additional sources of ground-water contamination include municipal and industrial landfills, surface impoundments, abandoned mine sites, urban runoff, and ground-water mining.

Billions of gallons of wastewater are generated each day by municipalities and industries across the Nation. The types and amounts of wastewater pollutants that can be discharged are regulated according to national water quality standards.

Municipal sewage treatment facilities are the Nation's principal point source dischargers to surface water. These facilities treat and discharge wastewater from homes, public buildings, commercial establishments, storm water sewers, and some industries. Providing adequate municipal wastewater treatment to a growing population has been one of the major accomplishments of the past several decades. In addition, the level of sewage treatment has improved. Over the last 20 years, government spending on the construction and upgrading of

sewage treatment facilities has increased and, concomitantly, contaminant levels in discharges have declined, even though population and industrial activity have increased. From 1972 to 1986, the total population served by secondary treatment or better increased from 85 million to 127 million people and the population served by less than secondary treatment declined from 5 million to less than 2 million (secondary treatment involves removal of at least 85% of several key conventional pollutants). By 1986, 15,587 wastewater facilities existed nationwide and, of these, more than one-half had secondary treatment or better. Advanced (tertiary) treatment is now mandated when secondary treatment is not adequate.

Upgrading the level of sewage treatment in the Nation has produced direct benefits by reducing pollution in surface water. The most widely used measure of municipal pollution is the extent to which the treated wastewater's organic content depletes the receiving water's oxygen. Oxygen depletion reduces the amount of oxygen available to fish and

Point source contributions
Phosphorus, mid-1980s

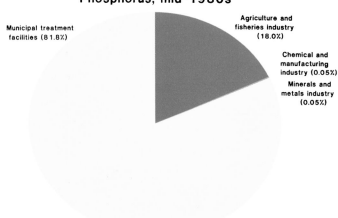

Municipal treatment facilities (81.8%)

Agriculture and fisheries industry (18.0%)

Chemical and manufacturing industry (0.05%)

Minerals and metals industry (0.05%)

Total phosphorus = 515.32 million tons per year

Point source contributions
Metals, mid-1980s

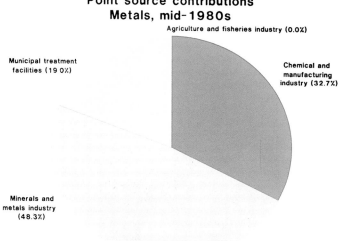

Agriculture and fisheries industry (0.0%)

Municipal treatment facilities (19.0%)

Chemical and manufacturing industry (32.7%)

Minerals and metals industry (48.3%)

Total metals = 8.95 million tons per year

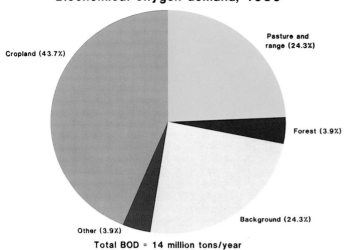

**Nonpoint source contributions
Biochemical oxygen demand, 1980**

Cropland (43.7%)

Pasture and range (24.3%)

Forest (3.9%)

Background (24.3%)

Other (3.9%)

Total BOD = 14 million tons/year

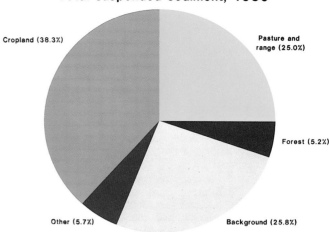

**Nonpoint source contributions
Total suspended sediment, 1980**

Cropland (38.3%)

Pasture and range (25.0%)

Forest (5.2%)

Background (25.8%)

Other (5.7%)

Total TSS = 3130 million tons/year

other aquatic life. As a result of improved waste-water treatment, municipal organic pollution has decreased dramatically and biological conditions around and downstream from treatment facilities have improved during the past decade. Components of major concern that still require attention and resolution include pretreatment of industrial wastes discharged into municipal sewage facilities, combined sanitary and storm sewers that occasionally overload treatment plant capacity, disposal of sludge produced during wastewater treatment, re-moval of excessive nutrients that enrich receiving waters, and destruction or removal of disease-related microorganisms.

Industrial pollutants include conventional pollut-ants, such as suspended solids, organics, and nutrients, as well as hazardous substances, such as synthetic organic compounds, heavy metals, and other toxic chemicals. The thrust of industrial waste-

water controls has been to require major industries to adequately treat their own wastewater rather than pipe it to municipal treatment plants. This is because most municipal facilities cannot adequately treat the more exotic contaminants found in indus-trial wastes. To comply with this requirement, indus-trial dischargers have invested heavily in best available technologies to reduce pollutant levels in wastewater discharged to surface water. One of the key measures of industries' cleanup efforts and progress is the greatly increased level of compliance with federal and state discharge limitations, espe-cially for plants with the largest wastewater flows. A challenge for the future is the development of regu-latory programs to assure pretreatment of industrial wastes before they are discharged into municipal treatment facilities.

Mineral and metal industries (for example, mines, iron and steel fabricators, metal finishers, and

petroleum refineries) are the principal direct dischargers of suspended solids and heavy metals to surface water. Textile, pulp and paper, food, and beverage industries also discharge large quantities of suspended solids and are the principal sources of industry-generated organic materials that contribute to biochemical oxygen demands. Plastics molding and forming industries along with porcelain enamel-ing and coil coating industries are the major indus-trial sources of phosphorus to surface water.

The pulp and paper industry provides an example of the progress made by industrial dischargers in controlling conventional pollutants through technol-ogy. Between 1973 and 1984, pulp and paper mills reduced biochemical oxygen demand and total suspended solids concentrations in effluent waters by approximately 500,000 tons per year and 490,000 tons per year, respectively. During this same time frame, production levels increased.

**Nonpoint source contributions
Nitrogen, 1980**

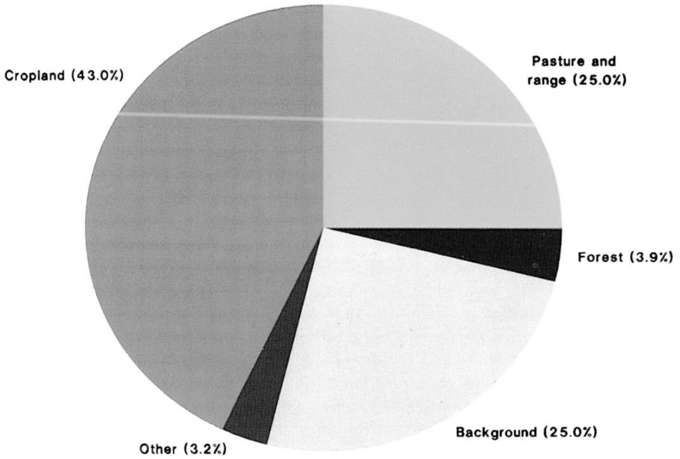

Cropland (43.0%)

Pasture and range (25.0%)

Forest (3.9%)

Background (25.0%)

Other (3.2%)

Total nitrogen = 6.8 million tons/year

**Nonpoint source contributions
Phosphorus, 1980**

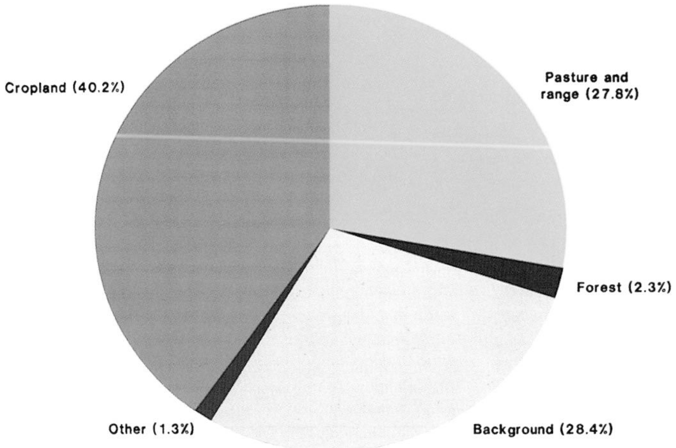

Cropland (40.2%)

Pasture and range (27.8%)

Forest (2.3%)

Background (28.4%)

Other (1.3%)

Total phosphorus = 2.66 million tons/year

A commonly recurring question is whether the quality of the Nation's surface water and ground water is improving or deteriorating. Prior to landmark water pollution legislation of the late 1960s and early 1970s, industries and municipalities discharged poorly treated or raw wastes into rivers, lakes, and estuaries. Little or no consideration was given to controlling surface runoff. In addition, hazardous materials were dumped in landfills and dump sites without regard for environmental consequences, and the use of pesticides, such as DDT, was virtually unrestricted. The result was widespread degradation of surface water, loss of aquatic habitat and recreational uses of surface water in many areas, and contamination of ground water in some localities.

In 1972, the United States made an unprecedented commitment to the restoration and enhancement of the physical, chemical, and biological integrity of the Nation's water. Much progress has been made toward achieving this goal, but it has been expensive and has required major commitments from all levels of government, industry, and the private sector. Much of this progress has been accomplished by controlling the many municipal and industrial point sources of water pollution. Other reasons for observed water quality improvements include changes in agricultural practices to reduce nonpoint source pollution (including implementation of soil conservation methods and regulation of animal feedlot runoff), improvements in mine reclamation practices, and reductions in atmospheric emissions of lead, cadmium, and oxides of sulfur and nitrogen.

In 1972 and again in 1982, water quality conditions were evaluated to determine whether surface water was supporting the uses for which it had been designated. States reached their conclusions about water quality conditions using a combination of long-term trend monitoring records, short-term intensive surveys, and professional judgments. Uses were reported as being fully supported if monitoring indicated that no chemical pollution existed, biological communities were fully supported, and/or the most sensitive designated uses were observed to be sup-

ported. Uses were partially supported if there was minor chemical pollution, aquatic community health was uncertain, or the most sensitive uses were not supported at a maximum level. Uses were not supported if there was major chemical pollution, aquatic communities were stressed or absent, or the most sensitive designated uses were severely impaired or impossible.

States found that significant accomplishments in water quality had been achieved between 1972 and 1982. Much of the Nation's streams, lakes, and estuaries had maintained water quality, which was significant in itself because the population grew by 11% and water use increased dramatically over this decade. Yet, some of the Nation's water assessed in 1982 still had water quality problems that prevented full-use support.

In many parts of the Nation, pollutant loads from nonpoint sources continue to present water quality problems and prevent attainment of designated water uses. According to a 1985 survey, virtually all states in the Nation reported water in which uses were severely or moderately impaired by nonpoint sources or in which nonpoint sources threatened to impair designated uses. This included 11% of the Nation's total river miles, 30% of total lake acres, and 17% of total estuary square miles. The impacts are not uniform nationally, however.

In 1985, agriculture was reported by states as the primary nonpoint source in 64% of impacted river miles, 57% of impacted lake acres, and 19% of impacted estuary square miles. Animal wastes from livestock and poultry production, soil erosion from cropland and overgrazing, irrigation return flows, and pesticide and fertilizer application were the main agricultural sources. Mining was responsible for nonpoint pollution in 9% of impacted river miles and 1% of lake acres in 1985. This included pollution from past practices, such as abandoned mines, improperly sealed wells, and mining waste piles, as well as some existing mining practices, particularly oil and gas drilling and mineral mining. Other major nonpoint sources in the Nation's rivers were silviculture (impacting 6% of assessed river miles), urban runoff (5%), hydromodification (4%), construction (2%), and land disposal (1%). Hydromodification,

urban runoff, land disposal, and construction-related nonpoint sources were more significant in lakes than rivers (impacting 13, 12, 5, and 4% of assessed lake acres, respectively), whereas mining and silviculture were less important (each contributing 1%).

States indicated worsening trends for some of the pollutants associated with nonpoint sources, particularly sediments, nitrate–nitrite, phosphorus, sodium, and chlorides. In 1985, sediments accounted for 47% of the nonpoint source pollutants in impacted river waters, nutrients accounted for 13%, pathogens and physical habitat alteration accounted for 9% each, and acidity, toxins, oxygen demand, pesticides, and salinity accounted for 7, 6, 4, 3, and 2%, respectively. In impacted lakes, nutrients and sediments were the major nonpoint source pollutants (accounting for 59 and 22% of the pollutants, respectively), followed by physical habitat alteration and acidity (4% each), oxygen demand, salinity, and toxins (3% each), pathogens (2%), and pesticides (less than 1%).

In a 1982 survey of the Nation's fishery biologists on the ability of perennial streams to support populations of sport fish and species of special concern, 3% of perennial streams ranked "0" (meaning they had no ability to support any fish populations). Five percent of perennial streams ranked "1" (ability to support a nonsport fish population only), and 17% ranked "2" (minimally able to support sport fish populations, species of special concern, or both). Forty percent of perennial streams were moderately able to support fish populations (ranks "3" and "4"), and only a small percentage of perennial streams (4%) were able to support sport fish, species of special concern, or both at a maximum level (rank "5"). The ability of the Nation's perennial streams to support sport fish or species of special concern did not change appreciably between 1977 and 1982.

The results of the 1982 fish survey indicate that 53% of the Nation's perennial streams have fish communities that are adversely affected by a variety of factors. The main problems were related to water quality, water quantity, usable fish habitat, and problems within the fish communities. The principal

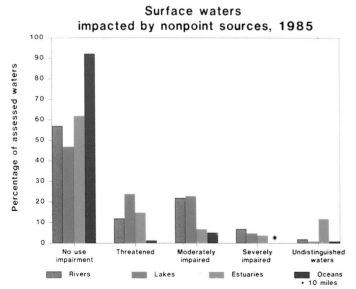

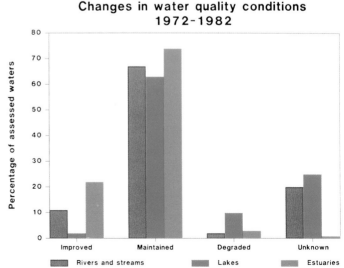

River and stream miles supporting uses 1972-1982

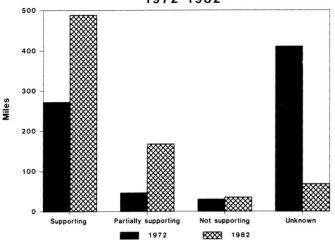

Ability of perennial streams to support fish 1977-1982

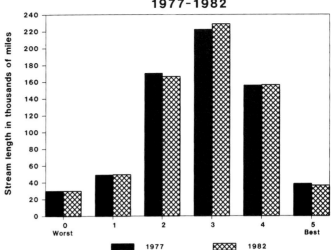

water quality factors were turbidity (affecting 29% of perennial stream miles), high water temperature (affecting 19%), excessive nutrient levels (11%), toxic substances (9%), and low concentrations of dissolved oxygen (8%). Agricultural and total non-point sources were probable contributors to water quality problems in 26 and 35% of perennial stream miles, respectively. Natural problems were probable sources in 16% of perennial stream miles and point discharges in 12%. The major water quantity factors were deficient streamflow (affecting 20% of perennial stream miles), occasional low flow (19%), and excessive flow fluctuations (12%). The major causes of habitat degradation were excessive siltation (25%), bank erosion and sloughing (16%), natural causes (13%), and channelization (10%). The primary limiting factors adversely affecting the Nation's fish communities were fish kills (in 15% of perennial stream miles), contamination (9%), overharvest and poaching (4 and 3%, respectively), and diseases or parasites (3%).

2-9
River and stream water quality

During the 1970s, several federal programs for nationally consistent water quality data collection were established as an adjunct to state and local monitoring. Only recently have sufficient data accumulated for a comprehensive analysis of long-term trends. Data for 30 regularly sampled water quality variables from more than 300 river locations for the period from 1974 to 1981, along with ancillary data on river basin characteristics and upstream pollution sources, are now available and, since 1981, continue to be collected.

Low dissolved oxygen levels were a pollution problem in streams and rivers 20 years ago but are rarely encountered today because of an overall reduction in point discharges of oxygen-demanding wastes. In the decade following 1972, municipal loads of biochemical oxygen demand decreased by an estimated 46%, and industrial loads decreased by

at least 71%, nationally. Over roughly the same period, dissolved oxygen conditions improved, most frequently in the New England, Mid-Atlantic, Ohio, and Mississippi regional basins but declined most frequently in the Southeast. Runoff from urban areas remains a leading source of materials that have biochemical oxygen demands.

Fecal coliform and fecal streptococcal bacteria are contaminants associated with municipal sewage and agricultural runoff (principally livestock feedlots). Between 1974 and 1981, decreases in fecal coliform bacteria were especially common in parts of the Gulf Coast, central Mississippi, and the Columbia River Basins. Decreases in both types of bacteria were frequent in the Arkansas–Red River Basin and along the Atlantic Coast. Improved municipal treatment and better control of livestock wastes are reasons for improved water quality conditions. (Municipal loadings, cattle population density, and feedlot activity appear to be positively associated with fecal bacteria counts.)

Fecal Streptococcus Bacteria

Suspended Sediment

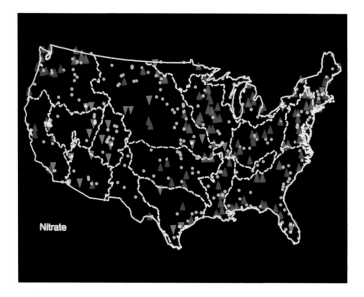

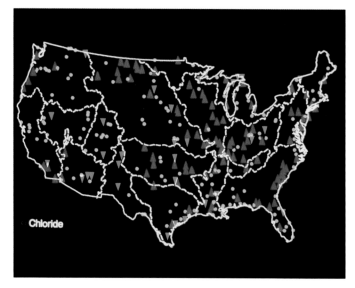

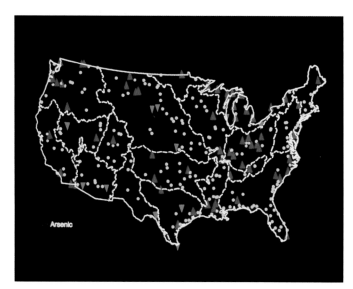

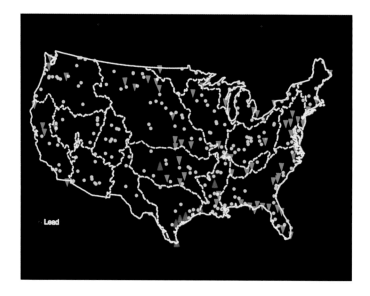

Sediments in streams and rivers come from diffuse sources—as a natural consequence of geological erosion and from accelerated erosion of cropland, timbered forest land, surface mines, and construction sites. National trends in suspended sediment concentrations were nearly equally divided between increases and decreases during the period 1974-1981. Increasing concentrations occurred in basins where land uses historically have resulted in high rates of soil erosion, such as in the Columbia River Basin where logging is a predominant land use and in the Arkansas–Red River and Mississippi River Basins, where agriculture is the predominant land use. Increased sediment loads in the Columbia River Basin in 1980 and 1981 were also associated with the volcanic eruption of Mount St. Helens. Declining concentrations of suspended sediment in the Missouri River Basin have been traced to the effects of reservoir construction during the 1950s and 1960s.

Trends in total phosphorus concentrations are similar to those for suspended sediments. Decreases in total phosphorus concentration occurred frequently in the Great Lakes and Mississippi River Basins between 1974 and 1981. Where increases occurred, evidence suggests a link to nonpoint sources, particularly agriculture. Increases in total phosphorus concentrations are often associated with increases in fertilized acreage and cattle population density.

In contrast to trends for suspended sediments and phosphorus, total nitrogen concentrations increased more frequently and affected a larger area between 1974 and 1981. Increasing trends were most frequent east of the 100th meridian and were strongly associated with increased agricultural activity (particularly fertilizer use), livestock population density, and feedlot activity. Atmospheric deposition, on the other hand, is a suspected cause of increased nitrate concentrations in surface water in the Ohio, Mid-Atlantic, Great Lakes, and Upper Mississippi River Basins during this time. Point source loads of nitrogen declined in many basins, supposedly as a result of improved wastewater treatment, but the magnitude of change nationally is poorly documented. Overall, total nitrogen trends appear to be related more to nonpoint sources than to point sources.

The differences in nitrogen and phosphorus trend patterns are also seen in recent changes in the delivery of nutrients to coastal waters. Nitrate loads to East Coast estuaries, the Great Lakes, and the Gulf of Mexico have increased significantly, whereas phosphorus loads to coastal areas have changed little or have even declined (with the exception of Gulf Coast and Pacific Northwest Basins, where phosphorus loads have increased in association with increases in sediment loads). These differences appear to result from three factors: atmospheric deposition of nitrates in the Midwest and East; moderation or delay in delivery of phosphorus by binding to sediment in stream channels; and point source pollution controls that have focused more heavily on phosphorus than nitrogen.

Trends in dissolved solids were also observed from 1974 to 1981. The major dissolved solids in streams and rivers are inorganic salts (sodium, potassium, calcium, magnesium, carbonate, bicarbonate, chloride, and sulfate ions). These salts come from a number of sources, including weathering of rocks and soil, atmospheric deposition, leaching by irrigation water (especially in semiarid basins of the West and Southwest), evaporation in reservoirs and other surface-water bodies, and runoff from highways where salt has been applied to control ice and snow (particularly in the Northeast, Mid-Atlantic, and North Central states). Between 1974 and 1981, increasing trends in chloride, sulfate, and sodium concentrations in surface water were frequent. The magnitude—an average increase of 30%—and wide distribution of these trends represent a significant increase in the salinity of the Nation's rivers during the same period.

Several factors appear responsible for the general pattern of salinity increase. First, chloride trends were moderately correlated with basin population changes, which reflects the fact that human wastes are a major source of chloride in populated basins. Second, salt use on highways, which increased nationally by a factor of more than 12 between 1950 and 1980, was positively correlated with the regional pattern of sodium and chloride increases. Finally, increases in sulfate concentrations were especially frequent in the Missouri, Arkansas, and Tennessee Basins and highly correlated with changes in surface coal production from 1974 to 1981. In contrast with much of the rest of the Nation, salinity decreased in the upper Colorado River Basin, which has had a history of salt problems. These decreases were associated, in part, with salinity control efforts in agriculture and with the temporary effects of increasing reservoir storage during the early 1970s.

Trends in toxic element concentrations in surface water have remained largely unknown, despite increasing knowledge of the potential sources and fates of toxic substances in aquatic systems. Toxic waste pollution is associated with a variety of metals and organic chemicals produced by industry. Water quality records for the period 1974–1981 frequently showed increasing trends in the dissolved forms of two potentially toxic trace elements (arsenic and cadmium). The major environmental sources of these elements are fossil-fuel combustion, primary metals manufacturing, pesticide use, and use of phosphate-bearing commodities, such as fertilizers and detergents. Increasing concentrations of arsenic and cadmium occurred with greatest frequency in river basins of the industrial Midwest, and the evidence suggests that increased atmospheric deposition of fossil-fuel combustion products was the predominant cause of the trends in both elements. This conclusion was corroborated by finding increased trace element levels in lake sediments in regions with high deposition of fossil-fuel combustion products.

In contrast to arsenic and cadmium, dissolved lead concentrations decreased along the East and West coasts and on tributaries to the Missouri and Mississippi rivers between 1974 and 1981. The few increases in dissolved lead that did occur were clustered along the Texas Gulf Coast and in the lower Mississippi River Basin. Lead enters the aquatic environment via point and nonpoint sources, including atmospheric deposition. Declining environmental lead levels have been widely attributed to the nationwide reduction in lead content of fuels and consumption of leaded fuel since the mid-1970s (for example, automobile gasoline-lead consumption decreased nationally by 67% between 1975 and 1981). Decreases in lead concentrations in streams were significantly associated with both the level and rate of decline in gasoline-lead consumption in most basins with the exception of some with large urban and suburban populations, such as the Ohio River and Great Lakes Basins.

2-10
Pesticides in rivers and streams

Pesticides, which include insecticides and herbicides, are applied extensively to agricultural land throughout the Nation and, in urban areas, they are used on lawns and gardens and for exterminating household pests. Insecticide use has gradually decreased over the past two decades, whereas herbicide use has increased, though at a declining rate over time.

The long-term adverse effects of pesticides on aquatic ecosystems or human health are not fully understood. Different pesticides have markedly different chemical properties that behave differently in the environment. Furthermore, pesticides are difficult to measure in dilute surface water, and detection limits vary among the different pesticides and their metabolites. Some broad patterns have been recognized, however, in the relationships between application rates of certain pesticides, their chemical properties, and their detection in surface water and bed sediments.

A combination of increasing regulatory restriction on and decreasing effectiveness of organochlorine insecticides, such as DDT, chlordane, and dieldrin,

has led to a dramatic decrease in their use since the mid-1960s and an erratic, but gradual, decrease in their occurrence in water and sediment samples since 1975. Most organochlorine insecticides are highly persistent in nature, have low solubility in water, and absorb strongly to sediment particles. Because of their resistance to decay, organochlorine insecticides continue to be found in sediments.

Detections of organochlorine insecticides in bed sediments are positively correlated with agricultural pesticide use. Detections are also frequent, however, in regions reporting low farm use (for example, in the highly populated and industrialized Northeast), which may indicate the importance of nonagricultural sources of these chemicals. There is no strong geographical relationship between pesticide use and detection in water, largely because of the small number of detections, which is due, in part, to the hydrophobic nature of organochlorine pesticides.

Chemicals in the organophosphate group of insecticides, such as malathion, parathion, and diazinon, are generally short lived (most persist in the soil for 1 to 12 weeks after application) and are highly soluble in water. Farm use of these chemicals declined steadily through the 1970s, although not as dramatically as for organochlorine insecticides. The geographic distribution of organophosphate insecticide use and detection are only weakly correlated, and no trends are evident in their detection on either a national or regional scale or at any individual station for either water or bed sediments. Because of their high solubility in water and their low persistence, no organophosphate chemicals were detected in bed sediments.

The use of atrazine and 2,4-D herbicides has accounted for most of the increase in herbicide use in the past 20 years, although the dominance of these chemicals had decreased somewhat by 1980. These herbicides are generally intermediate in persistence to organochlorine and organophosphate insecticides and are highly soluble in water. From 1975 to 1978, virtually no herbicides were detected in bed sediments and, except for atrazine, few were detected in water. The generally low rate of detections and the limited time span of data available make it impossible to evaluate trends in any herbicide concentrations in either bed sediments or water.

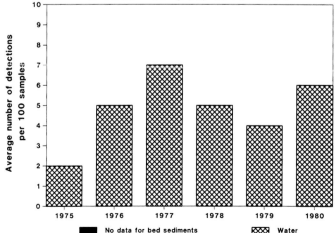

Organophosphate insecticides in stream samples, 1975-1980

Average number of detections per 100 samples

■ No data for bed sediments   ▨ Water

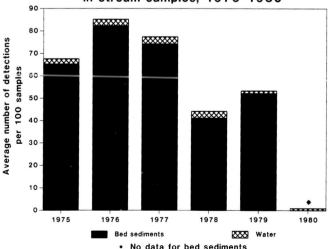

Organochlorine insecticides in stream samples, 1975-1980

Average number of detections per 100 samples

■ Bed sediments   ▨ Water
* No data for bed sediments

Water quality conditions in the Great Lakes

Over the past 10 years, water quality in the Great Lakes has generally improved. These improvements are attributed primarily to remedial action and reduced loadings of conventional pollutants from point sources (for example, nutrients, bacteria, suspended solids, oil and grease, and oxygen-consuming materials) as well as probable reduced loadings of phenols.

An encouraging trend is the overall reduction in phosphorus concentrations throughout the Great Lakes system. Phosphorus has been implicated in cultural eutrophication (the overproduction of microscopic plant life prompted by unnaturally abundant nutrient inputs) that has occurred in some areas of the lakes over the past few decades. Symptoms of cultural eutrophication have included increased turbidity, changes in algal species composition and concentrations, taste and odor problems in water supplies, oxygen depletion in lake waters, and aesthetic nuisances. Municipal and industrial dis-

charge controls and phosphorus detergent limitations have been the principal means adopted to reduce phosphorus input and reverse or prevent eutrophication.

In contrast to total phosphorus concentrations, inorganic nitrogen (nitrate plus nitrite) concentrations in the Great Lakes continue to increase. The significance of this trend to the Great Lakes ecosystem is not fully understood, and, consequently, increased attention is being paid to this emerging problem.

Persistent toxic substances are currently the principal issue confronting the Great Lakes. Chemicals, such as polychlorinated biphenyls (PCBs), mirex, hexachlorobenzene, dieldrin, DDT and its metabolites, lead, toxaphene, and mercury, are present in the Great Lakes ecosystem (some locally, some widespread). These chemicals are highly toxic, persistent, and bioaccumulate to levels that threaten human health and the aquatic ecosystem. A vast majority of these chemicals enter the system by pathways and in concentrations that are difficult to control. Major pathways include municipal and indus-

trial point sources as well as the more evasive non-point sources.

Lake Superior is classified oligotrophic (which means deficient in plant nutrients). Deteriorated water quality conditions are generally restricted to areas along the shoreline where industrial point discharges and in-place pollutants are a problem. Atmospheric deposition contributes a significant fraction of the total phosphorus loading to the lake, but the ability to measure atmospheric loadings with any degree of certainty presents problems.

Results of surveys conducted in 1968, 1983, and 1985 indicate that surface concentrations of phosphorus in Lake Superior have not changed significantly. Estimates for 1985 indicate that the target load for this lake has been met. In contrast to phosphorus loadings, concentrations of nitrate, sodium, calcium, sulfate, and magnesium ions in lake water have increased.

The open waters of Lake Michigan are classified as oligotrophic, whereas nearshore areas in Green Bay and the southern portion of the lake are mesotrophic (having moderate amounts of nutrients) as

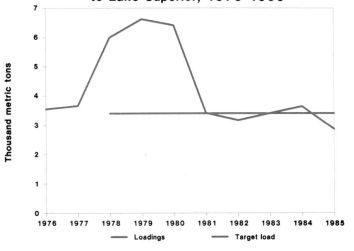

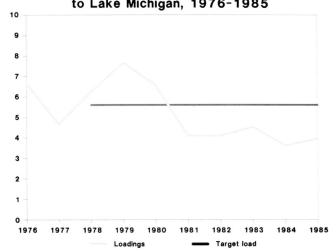

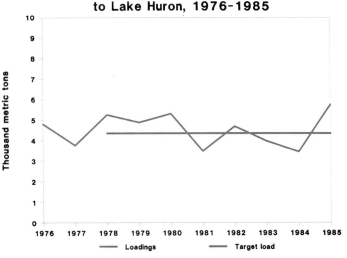

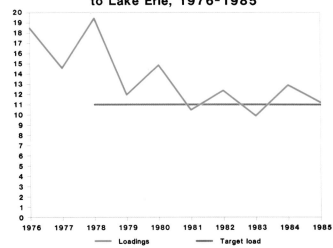

Estimated phosphorus loadings to Lake Ontario, 1976-1985

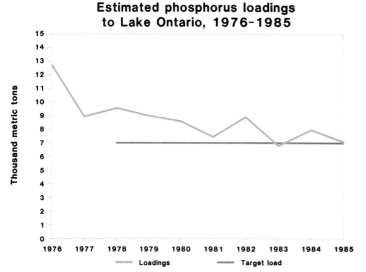

Contaminants in Lake Superior fish 1977-1983

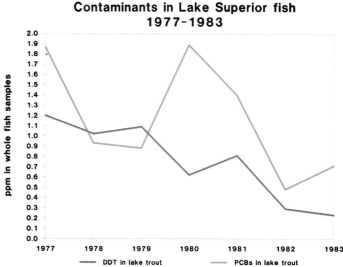

the result of nutrient inputs from industrial and urban areas.

From 1976 to 1980, phosphorus loading estimates for Lake Michigan remained fairly stable and since 1981, estimates are below the target value. As with Lake Superior, a decrease in estimated atmospheric loading accounts for the decrease in total loading to the lake and concentrations of other water quality constituents, such as nitrate, sulfate, chloride, and sodium ions, have increased.

Water quality conditions in Lake Huron have fluctuated between oligotrophic and mesotrophic since the 1970s, although conditions in Saginaw Bay and Thunder Bay have remained eutrophic. Many contaminants, such as chloride, sulfate, sodium, and potassium, remain at low levels, but nitrate and silica concentrations have increased since 1971. The estimated loadings of phosphorus to Lake Huron have been variable since 1976 with no statistically significant net change over the period.

Lake Erie has a history of chronic eutrophication although recent efforts to control eutrophication have been extremely effective. Remedial programs aimed at sewage treatment plants have resulted in a substantial decrease in total phosphorus loadings to the lake. Over the period 1968 to 1985, total phosphorus concentrations have declined, despite the release of soluble phosphorus from the central basin sediments through anoxic regeneration.

Lake Erie has suffered from seasonal anoxic conditions (oxygen depletion) for at least the past 40 years. Despite natural variability in oxygen depletion rates as the result of meteorological factors, highest depletion rates occurred during the 1960s and 1970s, at a time when Lake Erie exhibited the highest cultural eutrophication state and highest total phosphorus concentrations and algal biomass. In recent years (1980–1984), oxygen depletion rates appear to have decreased and are less variable (suggesting that phosphorus controls have had a positive effect), although the central basin still undergoes some degree of anoxia.

Eutrophication of Lake Ontario was identified as a major concern in the 1960s. Surface-water concentrations of total phosphorus peaked in 1973, but since then all measured forms of phosphorus have exhibited a marked decline. Annual surveys conducted from 1973 to 1986 have indicated that total

phosphorus has decreased significantly. Nitrogen levels, however, have risen. Nonetheless, evidence of the improving water quality conditions is seen in the shift in open lake phytoplankton from a community indicative of mesotrophic conditions to one associated with oligotrophic conditions.

Total phosphorus loadings to Lake Ontario also have decreased significantly since 1976, which reflects decreased phosphorus loadings from sewage treatment plants and from Lake Erie. Current estimates indicate that the total loading of phosphorus is approaching the target value.

With point source contributions of phosphorus under increasing control, the importance of controlling nonpoint sources is becoming more evident. Nonpoint sources may be the most significant factor in limiting achievement of target loadings in some areas. Remedial plans call for reducing nonpoint source inputs, particularly from agricultural sources.

2-12
Contaminants in Great Lakes fish

Toxic contaminant levels in Great Lakes fishes and wildlife have declined somewhat as a result of pollution controls. A major achievement, for example, has been a reduction in mercury concentrations in Great Lakes water and, subsequently, in fishes. This has been achieved through the elimination of mercury use in many industrial processes and improved housekeeping by industry. Reductions in the levels of other persistent compounds, such as DDT, PCBs, and dieldrin, in fishes have been observed also; however, health advisories for fish consumption remain in effect for certain fish species and size classes in all lakes.

DDT and mercury contamination levels in Lake Superior lake trout declined between 1977 and 1983. Despite year-to-year variability, mean annual PCB concentrations were lowest in 1982 and 1983. Dieldrin concentrations in Lake Superior lake trout have remained consistently low. Overall, contaminant levels in lake trout are relatively low in Lake Superior as compared to levels in the same species from the other lakes.

Total DDT and PCB levels have declined significantly in Lake Michigan lake trout and bloater chubs. Dieldrin concentrations in lake trout increased between 1970 and 1979 but have

decreased since then. Dieldrin in bloater chubs, however, has been increasing since 1969. Some evidence indicates that the increase in dieldrin is from residual sources in the basin since the source of most dieldrin residues (aldrin) has not been used for agricultural purposes in the United States since 1974. Mercury levels in fish from Lake Michigan have been declining since 1973, although levels in carp and brown trout and in all fish larger than 20 inches in length have remained high.

Mean levels of PCBs increased between 1979 and 1983 but declined in 1983, whereas DDT concentrations decreased in 1982 and 1983. Lake trout from northern Lake Huron have lower contaminant body burdens than the same species of fish collected in southern portions of the lake. Mercury levels in Lake Huron lake trout have been consistently below the levels set for safe human consumption. Levels of selenium and arsenic continue to be greater in top predator fish and rainbow smelt from Lake Huron than in fishes from the other lakes. This is particularly evident in fishes from sites in Georgian Bay and the northern portion of the main lake where there are natural sources of these trace metals.

In general, concentrations of PCBs and other organochlorine contaminants in walleye from Lake Erie have exhibited year-to-year variability and no obvious trends. Similarly, concentrations of PCBs and DDT in rainbow smelt have shown no significant trends. Levels of mercury, however, have decreased since 1977.

PCB concentrations in Lake Ontario lake trout declined steadily from 1977 to 1981, then increased from 1981 to 1983, then decreased from 1983 to 1985. Dieldrin, mirex, and DDT have all shown significant declines from 1977 levels; however, much of the decrease occurred between 1977 and 1978. In general, contaminant levels in rainbow smelt exhibited year-to-year variability and no obvious trends.

2-13
Contaminants in herring gull eggs from Great Lakes colonies

Data for organochlorine contaminants in herring gull eggs reveal a general decline beginning in the mid- to late-1970s and a leveling off during the 1980s.

Contaminants in Lake Michigan fish
1969-1986

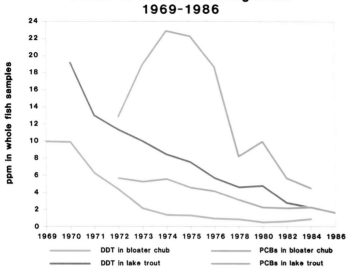

ppm in whole fish samples

— DDT in bloater chub   — PCBs in bloater chub
— DDT in lake trout   — PCBs in lake trout

Contaminants in Lake Huron fish
1978-1982

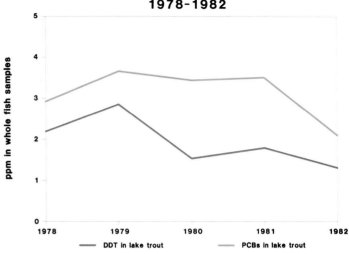

ppm in whole fish samples

— DDT in lake trout   — PCBs in lake trout

Contaminants in Lake Erie fish
1977-1983

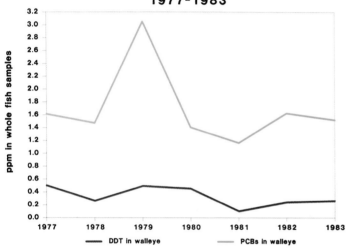

ppm in whole fish samples

— DDT in walleye   — PCBs in walleye

Contaminants in Lake Ontario fish
1977-1983

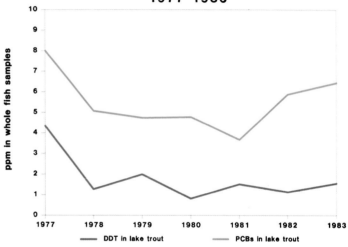

ppm in whole fish samples

— DDT in lake trout   — PCBs in lake trout

DDE in herring gull eggs
Lake Superior, Huron, and Michigan colonies, 1974-1986

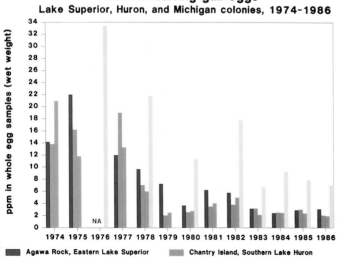

ppm in whole egg samples (wet weight)

■ Agawa Rock, Eastern Lake Superior   ■ Chantry Island, Southern Lake Huron
■ Double Island, North Channel, Lake Huron   ■ Big Sister Island, Green Bay, Lake Michigan

DDE in herring gull eggs
Lake Erie and Ontario colonies, 1974-1986

ppm in whole egg samples (wet weight)

■ Port Colborne Lighthouse 1, Eastern Lake Erie   ■ Snake Island, Eastern Lake Ontario
■ Middle Island, West Lake Erie   ■ Muggs Island, Western Lake Ontario

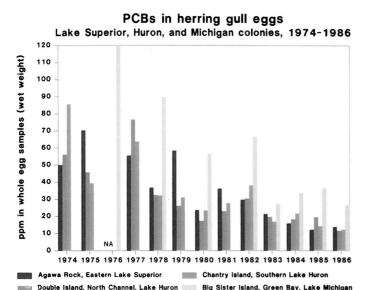

PCBs in herring gull eggs
Lake Superior, Huron, and Michigan colonies, 1974-1986

ppm in whole egg samples (wet weight)

- Agawa Rock, Eastern Lake Superior
- Double Island, North Channel, Lake Huron
- Chantry Island, Southern Lake Huron
- Big Sister Island, Green Bay, Lake Michigan

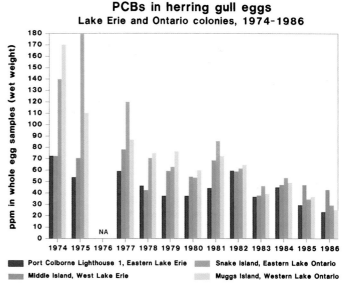

PCBs in herring gull eggs
Lake Erie and Ontario colonies, 1974-1986

ppm in whole egg samples (wet weight)

- Port Colborne Lighthouse 1, Eastern Lake Erie
- Middle Island, West Lake Erie
- Snake Island, Eastern Lake Ontario
- Muggs Island, Western Lake Ontario

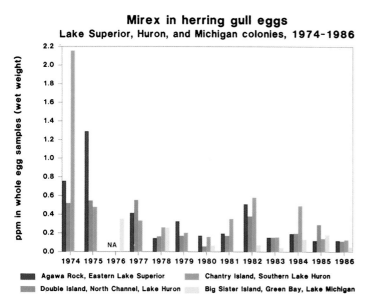

Mirex in herring gull eggs
Lake Superior, Huron, and Michigan colonies, 1974-1986

ppm in whole egg samples (wet weight)

- Agawa Rock, Eastern Lake Superior
- Double Island, North Channel, Lake Huron
- Chantry Island, Southern Lake Huron
- Big Sister Island, Green Bay, Lake Michigan

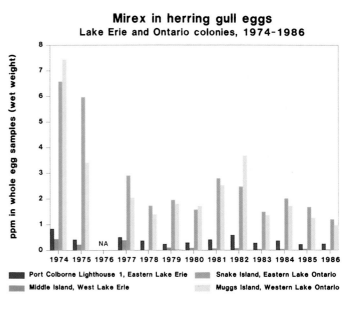

Mirex in herring gull eggs
Lake Erie and Ontario colonies, 1974-1986

ppm in whole egg samples (wet weight)

- Port Colborne Lighthouse 1, Eastern Lake Erie
- Middle Island, West Lake Erie
- Snake Island, Eastern Lake Ontario
- Muggs Island, Western Lake Ontario

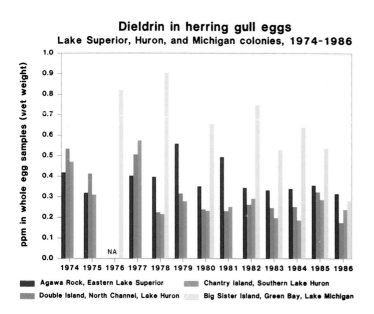

Dieldrin in herring gull eggs
Lake Superior, Huron, and Michigan colonies, 1974-1986

ppm in whole egg samples (wet weight)

- Agawa Rock, Eastern Lake Superior
- Double Island, North Channel, Lake Huron
- Chantry Island, Southern Lake Huron
- Big Sister Island, Green Bay, Lake Michigan

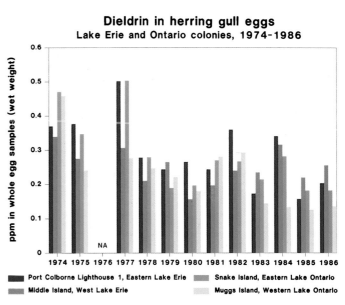

Dieldrin in herring gull eggs
Lake Erie and Ontario colonies, 1974-1986

ppm in whole egg samples (wet weight)

- Port Colborne Lighthouse 1, Eastern Lake Erie
- Middle Island, West Lake Erie
- Snake Island, Eastern Lake Ontario
- Muggs Island, Western Lake Ontario

An exception to this trend is the concentration of dieldrin, which has decreased less than other routinely measured contaminants.

Levels of organochlorine compounds in herring gull eggs from colonies on Lake Superior have decreased over the last decade. During this same time period, concentrations of dieldrin have remained fairly constant in the colonies.

Mean annual concentrations of DDE, DDT, HCB, mirex, and total PCB in herring gull eggs from colonies on Lake Michigan were lower in 1986 than they have been during any year since monitoring began in 1976. Dieldrin concentrations, on the other hand, have remained relatively high and have not decreased rapidly in response to remedial measures.

Contaminant levels in herring gull eggs from colonies on Lake Huron have also declined. It should be noted, however, that much of the decrease of contaminants in herring gull eggs from Lake Huron occurred between 1974 and 1978, and concentrations leveled off over the next 5 to 6 years.

Mean annual concentrations of contaminants in herring gull eggs from colonies on Lake Erie have declined steadily since 1977 with the exception of mirex, which increased in 1981 at Port Colborne Lighthouse 1. Much of the decrease in organochlorine contaminants occurred between 1974 and 1978, and concentrations have remained fairly stable since then. The consistently high mirex levels in Lake Erie colonies and the 1981 increase may be because of the lake's proximity to sources of mirex near Lake Ontario and herring gulls feeding there.

Although chlorinated hydrocarbon pollution is still a problem in Lake Ontario, contaminant levels in herring gull eggs from Lake Ontario colonies have decreased over the last decade. The pollution problem is attributed primarily to sources in the Niagara River. Records of contamination in Lake Ontario sediments show that chlorinated hydrocarbon levels were highest in the 1960s (during peak production and use of these chemicals) and have declined, albeit slowly, since then.

2-14
Pollutant discharges into coastal waters

The Nation's estuaries and coastal waters are critical habitat for many species of waterfowl and wildlife as well as fish, including freshwater species that migrate to salt water for a portion of their life cycles and open-ocean species that make the reverse migration. Estuaries and coastal waters are of enormous value to vast numbers of people who live near, or travel to, coastal areas to enjoy boating, swimming, and fishing. These waters are also of great economic importance to commercial fishing, shipping, industry, and tourism.

Estuaries and coastal waters have become increasingly stressed as the human population continues to grow in coastal areas. Over the years, clearing and developing land in coastal watersheds has resulted in accelerated storm-water runoff and soil erosion, sedimentation and deterioration of water quality, and loss of fish and wildlife habitat.

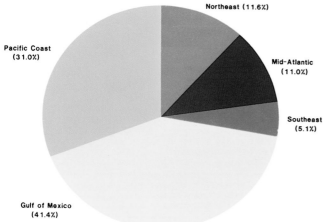

Discharges into coastal waters of biochemical oxygen demand, 1980-1985

Northeast (11.6%)
Pacific Coast (31.0%)
Mid-Atlantic (11.0%)
Southeast (5.1%)
Gulf of Mexico (41.4%)

Total BOD = 4.905 million tons/year

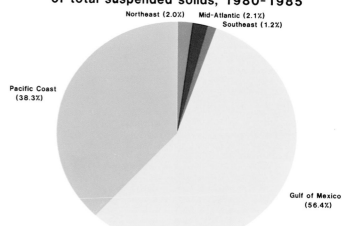

Discharges into coastal waters of total suspended solids, 1980-1985

Northeast (2.0%) Mid-Atlantic (2.1%)
Southeast (1.2%)
Pacific Coast (38.3%)
Gulf of Mexico (56.4%)

Total TSS = 264.05 million tons/year

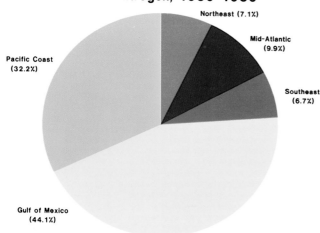

Discharges into coastal waters of total nitrogen, 1980-1985

Northeast (7.1%)
Mid-Atlantic (9.9%)
Pacific Coast (32.2%)
Southeast (6.7%)
Gulf of Mexico (44.1%)

Total nitrogen = 2.003 million tons/year

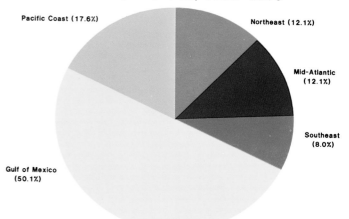

Discharges into coastal waters of total phosphorus, 1980-1985

Pacific Coast (17.6%)
Northeast (12.1%)
Mid-Atlantic (12.1%)
Southeast (8.0%)
Gulf of Mexico (50.1%)

Total phosphorus = 0.430 million tons/year

Impoundments and water diversions for agricultural, domestic, or industrial use have altered the natural timing, volume, and rate of streamflow; whereas development in flood and storm hazard areas has resulted in the loss of lives and property and the continual expenditure of public and private dollars to alleviate, prevent, or repair flood damages. Marinas, piers, bulkheads, and other induced development around urban and residential areas have contributed to the contamination of surface water and ground water, erosion of shorelines, sedimentation, and loss of wetland habitat.

Estuaries are particularly vulnerable to pollution because they serve as natural sinks for pollutants transported downstream by rivers and tributaries. They also receive runoff from coastal watershed drainage systems as well as point source discharges from municipal sewage treatment plants, industrial outfalls, and combined sewers from coastal communities.

Riverine and coastal sources deliver a variety of pollutants to estuaries and coastal waters. In 1980, about 35% of sewage effluents generated nationwide were discharged into coastal and marine waters. Offshore activities, such as oil and gas development and ocean dumping of sewage sludge and dredged material, also introduce a variety of toxicants to the near-shore environment. Accidental spills of oil and hazardous wastes occur from boats and ships, during loading and unloading operations in ports and harbors, from pipeline leakage and equipment failure, and from land vehicles and storage facilities onshore. Hazardous waste disposal sites located within the coastal drainage basins are additional sources of contaminants to the marine environment.

2-15
Harvest-limited shellfish waters

One of the most obvious results of pollution in estuaries and coastal areas of the United States is the closure, restriction, or decline of shellfish growing areas. Unlike fish and mobile invertebrates that can sometimes move out of polluted waters, shellfish, such as oysters, clams, and mussels, are sed-

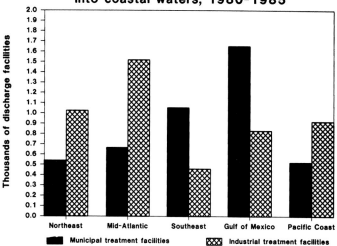

Sources of discharges into coastal waters, 1980-1985

Thousands of discharge facilities (y-axis: 0.0 to 2.0)

x-axis: Northeast, Mid-Atlantic, Southeast, Gulf of Mexico, Pacific Coast

■ Municipal treatment facilities   ▨ Industrial treatment facilities

entary, filter-feeding organisms that are affected by many environmental factors in the waters around them. They cannot escape toxic wastes, oil pollution, and other potentially lethal contaminants or changes in nutrient levels and sedimentation that can affect their food source (plankton) and, thus, their survival. Dams, canals, dredge and fill operations, and other coastal activities can alter the environment that shellfish live in and directly affect population abundance and viability.

Shellfish tend to concentrate pollutants that may have little effect on the shellfish themselves but can be harmful to the people who consume the shellfish. This risk was recognized in the late 1800s when outbreaks of various diseases were traced to the consumption of contaminated oysters. Soon thereafter, state agencies began to conduct "sanitary surveys" of their shellfish growing areas, a practice that continues today.

States classify their shellfish growing areas into four categories. Approved waters are those deter-

mined to be free of hazardous concentrations of pathogenic organisms and/or pollution. Prohibited waters are those closed as the result of hazardous levels of contamination. Conditionally approved waters are those that may or may not be suitable for shellfish harvesting, depending on predictable levels of pollution, such as increased wastewater effluent that results with seasonal population growth in coastal towns. Restricted waters produce shellfish that are unsafe for direct marketing but can be made safe by purification. Shellfish harvest-limited areas refer to the sum of prohibited, conditionally approved, and restricted waters.

Shellfish area classifications are based primarily on concentrations of fecal coliform bacteria, which indicates the presence of untreated fecal matter from humans and other warm-blooded animals. Fecal coliform bacteria are not generally harmful, but they indicate the possible presence of infectious microorganisms that cause typhoid fever, viral hepatitis, tuberculosis, and encephalitis. Pollutants, such as

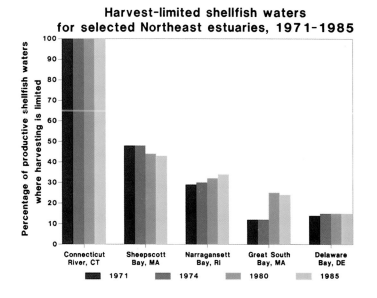

Harvest-limited shellfish waters for selected Northeast estuaries, 1971-1985

Percentage of productive shellfish waters where harvesting is limited (y-axis: 0 to 100)

x-axis: Connecticut River, CT; Sheepscott Bay, MA; Narragansett Bay, RI; Great South Bay, MA; Delaware Bay, DE

■ 1971   ■ 1974   ■ 1980   ■ 1985

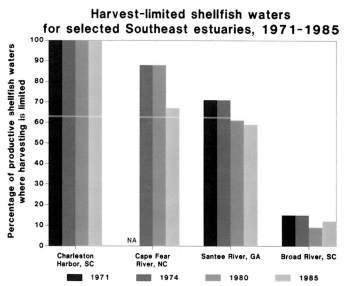

Harvest-limited shellfish waters for selected Southeast estuaries, 1971-1985

Percentage of productive shellfish waters where harvesting is limited (y-axis: 0 to 100)

x-axis: Charleston Harbor, SC; Cape Fear River, NC; Santee River, GA; Broad River, SC

■ 1971   ■ 1974   ■ 1980   ■ 1985

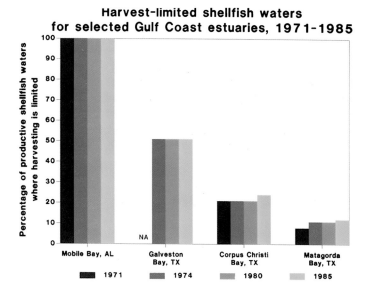

Harvest-limited shellfish waters for selected Gulf Coast estuaries, 1971-1985

Percentage of productive shellfish waters where harvesting is limited

Mobile Bay, AL | Galveston Bay, TX (NA) | Corpus Christi Bay, TX | Matagorda Bay, TX

■ 1971 ■ 1974 ■ 1980 ■ 1985

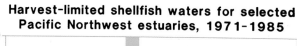

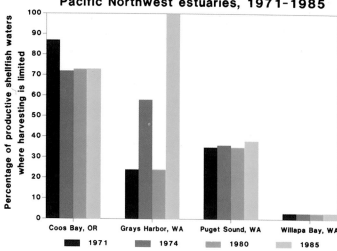

Harvest-limited shellfish waters for selected Pacific Northwest estuaries, 1971-1985

Percentage of productive shellfish waters where harvesting is limited

Coos Bay, OR | Grays Harbor, WA | Puget Sound, WA | Willapa Bay, WA

■ 1971 ■ 1974 ■ 1980 ■ 1985

viruses, toxic chemicals, oil, radioisotopes, and marine biotoxins (which are associated with paralytic and neurologic shellfish poisoning), are generally not monitored in sanitary surveys because concentrations are difficult to detect and the levels at which they pose a threat to public health are uncertain. Sources of fecal contamination include point source discharges from wastewater treatment facilities, drainage from faulty septic systems, runoff from rural and urban areas, and wastewater from boats. Shellfish waters may be closed, also, for administrative reasons, for example, to protect reproductive stocks or enhance recruitment of new or existing shellfish beds.

National patterns and trends in shellfish harvest restrictions are, unfortunately, not directly equivalent to environmental trends because the classification of shellfish growing areas is affected by factors other than changes in water quality. These include the ability of state agencies to conduct sanitary surveys, the economic importance of available shellfish resources, and the ability of state agencies to

manage the classification. Many changes in classification status are a result of changes in total area classified rather than changes between approved and restricted harvest.

In 1985, 80% of the waters in the coastal zone of the United States were classified as shellfish growing areas, yet only 58% of the total growing area was unconditionally approved for shellfish harvest. Between 1971 and 1985, the total area of approved shellfish waters declined in some estuaries but increased in others. Upgraded sewage treatment facilities and nonpoint source controls are accredited with reducing pollutant discharges into productive shellfish areas and concomitant increases in acreages approved for harvest.

2-16
Contaminants in marine sediments

Trace metals, such as cadmium, chromium, copper, lead, mercury, and silver, occur naturally in seawater in very low concentrations, generally less than

one part per billion (ppb). In contaminated marine and estuarine sediments, considerably higher concentrations, often at the parts-per-million (ppm) level, may be found. Trace metals enter aquatic environments through the geologic processes of erosion from naturally occurring ore bodies, runoff, and vulcanism. Anthropogenic activities may enhance the rates of these processes and the accumulation of certain trace elements in environmental media. Smelting and refining of primary metal sulfides and oxides contribute residual amounts of these compounds to the environment as do many other manufacturing processes. Routine input of trace metals to the aquatic environment occurs from municipal and industrial wastewater discharge, urban runoff, atmospheric deposition, vessel-related incidents, and ocean dumping.

Marine invertebrates living in sediments in areas of high metal contamination often bioaccumulate the metals above natural levels. The highest concentrations of trace metals generally occur in sediments from highly urbanized bays and estuaries of the

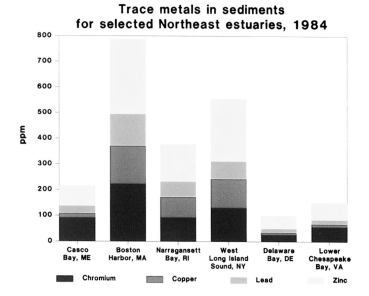

Trace metals in sediments for selected Northeast estuaries, 1984

ppm

Casco Bay, ME | Boston Harbor, MA | Narragansett Bay, RI | West Long Island Sound, NY | Delaware Bay, DE | Lower Chesapeake Bay, VA

■ Chromium ■ Copper ■ Lead ■ Zinc

Trace metals in sediments for selected Southeast estuaries, 1984

ppm

Pamlico Sound, NC | Charleston Harbor, SC | Sapelo Sound, GA | St. Johns River, FL

■ Chromium ■ Copper ■ Lead ■ Zinc

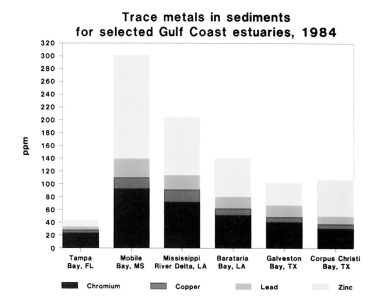

Trace metals in sediments for selected Gulf Coast estuaries, 1984

ppm

Tampa Bay, FL / Mobile Bay, MS / Mississippi River Delta, LA / Barataria Bay, LA / Galveston Bay, TX / Corpus Christi Bay, TX

■ Chromium ▨ Copper ▨ Lead □ Zinc

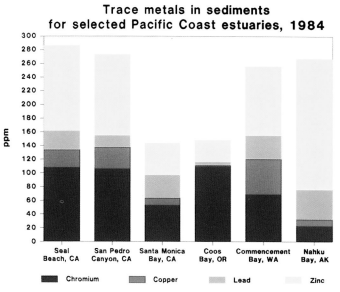

Trace metals in sediments for selected Pacific Coast estuaries, 1984

ppm

Seal Beach, CA / San Pedro Canyon, CA / Santa Monica Bay, CA / Coos Bay, OR / Commencement Bay, WA / Nahku Bay, AK

■ Chromium ▨ Copper ▨ Lead □ Zinc

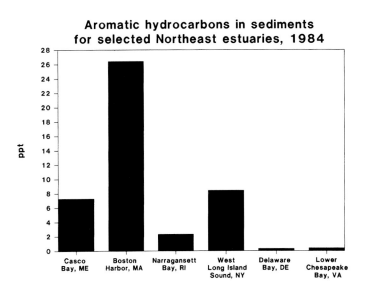

Aromatic hydrocarbons in sediments for selected Northeast estuaries, 1984

ppt

Casco Bay, ME / Boston Harbor, MA / Narragansett Bay, RI / West Long Island Sound, NY / Delaware Bay, DE / Lower Chesapeake Bay, VA

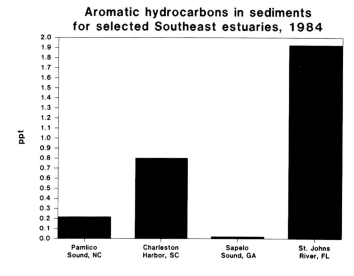

Aromatic hydrocarbons in sediments for selected Southeast estuaries, 1984

ppt

Pamlico Sound, NC / Charleston Harbor, SC / Sapelo Sound, GA / St. Johns River, FL

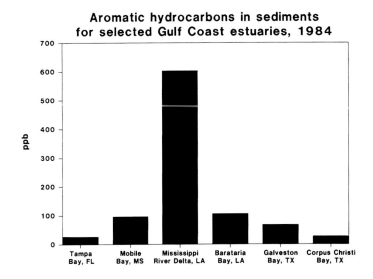

Aromatic hydrocarbons in sediments for selected Gulf Coast estuaries, 1984

ppb

Tampa Bay, FL / Mobile Bay, MS / Mississippi River Delta, LA / Barataria Bay, LA / Galveston Bay, TX / Corpus Christi Bay, TX

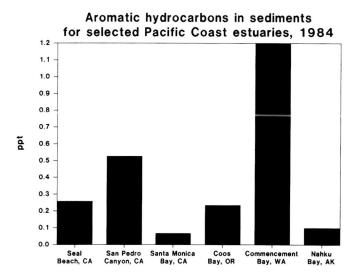

Aromatic hydrocarbons in sediments for selected Pacific Coast estuaries, 1984

ppt

Seal Beach, CA / San Pedro Canyon, CA / Santa Monica Bay, CA / Coos Bay, OR / Commencement Bay, WA / Nahku Bay, AK

45

PCBs in sediments
for selected Northeast estuaries, 1984

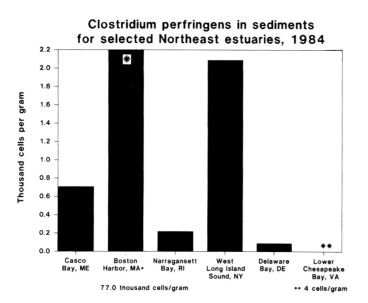

PCBs in sediments
for selected Pacific Coast estuaries, 1984

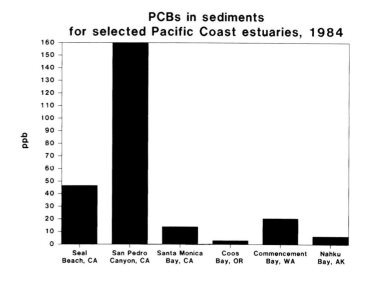

Clostridium perfringens in sediments
for selected Northeast estuaries, 1984

77.0 thousand cells/gram

•• 4 cells/gram

Clostridium perfringens in sediments
for selected Southeast estuaries, 1984

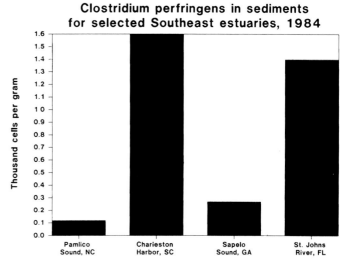

Clostridium perfringens in sediments
for selected Gulf Coast estuaries, 1984

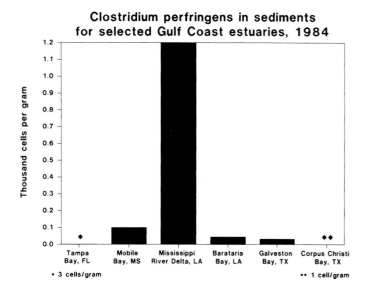

• 3 cells/gram

•• 1 cell/gram

Clostridium perfringens in sediments
for selected Pacific Coast estuaries, 1984

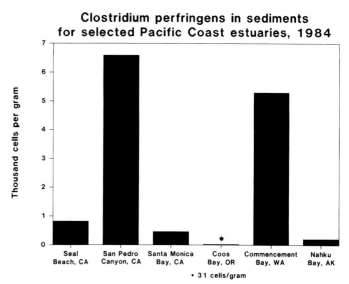

• 31 cells/gram

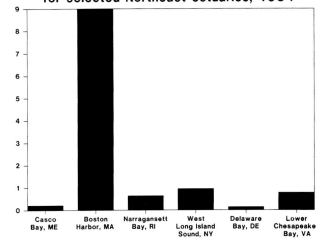

Coprostanol in sediments for selected Northeast estuaries, 1984

Thousand ng/gram

Casco Bay, ME · Boston Harbor, MA · Narragansett Bay, RI · West Long Island Sound, NY · Delaware Bay, DE · Lower Chesapeake Bay, VA

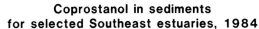
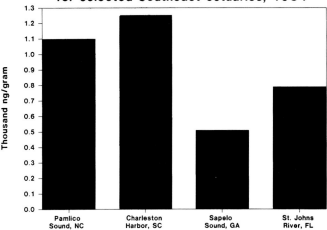

Coprostanol in sediments for selected Southeast estuaries, 1984

Thousand ng/gram

Pamlico Sound, NC · Charleston Harbor, SC · Sapelo Sound, GA · St. Johns River, FL

Northeast (Atlantic) and Pacific Coasts. On a bulk sediment basis, substantially lower concentrations are found at Southeast and Gulf Coast sites.

Polycyclic aromatic hydrocarbons (PAHs) are ubiquitous in the marine environment. PAHs are complex chemical compounds that are derived from the incomplete combustion of carbonaceous material (for example, from forest fires and fossil fuel combustion) and are found in unburned fossil fuels, such as crude oil, coal, and peat. Concentrations are usually low except in areas of high industrial activity involving petroleum production, use of petroleum-derived products, or fossil fuel combustion. High environmental levels, such as those found in Boston Harbor and Salem Harbor sediments, are linked to a variety of other sources, including municipal sewage outfalls, military waste, and dredged material. PAHs constitute about 4 to 9% of the 3.2 million tons of petroleum hydrocarbons annually deposited in the marine environment.

In relation to toxicity, a significant positive correlation has been reported between concentration of PAH metabolites and mutations in marine organisms. Studies have also shown that certain polycyclic aromatic hydrocarbons induce carcinoma formation in various marine organisms and can be acutely toxic.

Polychlorinated biphenyls (PCBs) are complex chlorinated hydrocarbons. They have been used predominantly as insulating and cooling fluids in electrical transformers since the early 1970s. Before that time, PCBs had found even wider usage in such products as lubricants, flame retardants, and plasticizers. Production of PCBs was banned in the United States in 1979, yet they continue to be produced by other countries. PCB-containing electrical products, yet to be phased out, are still in use in the United States. The major source of PCB contamination has been improper waste disposal of spent industrial equipment, and because of their extensive use in the past, PCBs have become widespread throughout the environment.

Many estuaries are sinks for PCBs bound to sediments. In the environment, PCBs are persistent and tend to bioaccumulate and biomagnify in the food chain. Body burdens have been detected in a wide range of fish and wildlife species, and the capacity of PCBs to engender toxic effects (such as reproductive failure, birth defects, tumors, liver disorders, skin lesions, and immune suppression) makes this contaminant a source of much environmental concern.

Coprostanol and *Clostridium perfringens* are indicators of sewage contamination and are used to identify marine sediments containing sewage-derived materials. Coprostanol and *C. perfringens* can be derived from sewage treatment plants, as well as from livestock feedlot runoff, aquatic mammals, illegal release from vessels, and possibly marine birds.

Coprostanol is a fecal sterol formed exclusively by digestive processes in the intestines of higher animals. Once deposited in anoxic sediments, coprostanol concentrations are not readily reduced. It is a useful indicator of sewage contamination as the result of its uniqueness and stability in the environment.

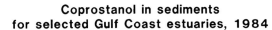

Coprostanol in sediments for selected Gulf Coast estuaries, 1984

ng/gram

Tampa Bay, FL · Mobile Bay, MS · Mississippi River Delta, LA · Barataria Bay, LA · Galveston Bay, TX · Corpus Christi Bay, TX

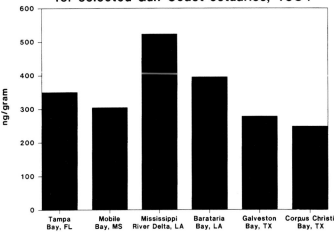
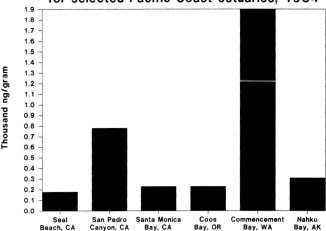

Coprostanol in sediments for selected Pacific Coast estuaries, 1984

Thousand ng/gram

Seal Beach, CA · San Pedro Canyon, CA · Santa Monica Bay, CA · Coos Bay, OR · Commencement Bay, WA · Nahku Bay, AK

Clostridium perfringens is an anaerobic spore-forming bacterium present in human feces. It is found in municipal sewage at density levels of 10,000 to 100,000 spores per milliliter of wastewater effluent. Long-term survival of the bacterium's environmentally resistant spores can provide a record of the movement and depositional history of sewage particulates.

Coprostanol and *C. perfringens* are not toxic to aquatic organisms or humans. However, their tendency to absorb on suspended particles—which resembles the behavior of pathogenic organisms, toxic metals, and toxic organic substances—makes them good indicators of the potential presence of more harmful contaminants associated with sewage waste.

Northeast (Atlantic) estuaries with high densities of coprostanol and *C. perfringens* (for example, Salem Harbor, Boston Harbor, and Raritan Bay) appear to be highly contaminated from sewage outfalls. Estuaries that appear to be moderately contaminated are on the Charleston Harbor and St. John's River in the Southeast, the Mississippi River

Delta in the Gulf of Mexico, and Elliott Bay and Commencement Bay on the Pacific Coast.

Marine fish that live and feed on the bottom are exposed to contaminated sediments in polluted areas. For these fish, the primary route of contaminant bioaccumulation is through food intake. Predator species accumulate contaminants through the consumption of their prey, and thus biomagnify contaminant levels in the food chain. Although not always acutely toxic to aquatic organisms, the contaminants pose a threat to birds and humans who consume these fish.

The accumulation of chlorinated hydrocarbons, such as PCBs and DDT, in body tissues of marine fish, shellfish, and seabirds has been observed in areas with highly contaminated sediments. The Hudson River in New York, for example, has received much attention because of PCB contamination and its effect on the striped bass fishery. Since 1976, sections of the Hudson River have been closed to fishing as the result of excessive PCB contamination, and in 1986, a total ban was imposed.

2-17
Oil spills in and around U.S. waters

The number of oil spills has decreased since 1977. In 1984, 10,360 oil spills were reported to the United States Coast Guard as compared to 15,330 spills reported in 1977. The size of oil spills, however, varies widely, and a few polluting incidents can account for most of the volume of oil spilled in a given year. For example, the quantity of oil spilled in 1983 was nearly double that spilled the previous year, yet the number of polluting incidents in 1983 was lower than in 1982.

Oil substances reported in spills include crude oil, fuel oil, diesel fuel, gasoline, liquid petroleum gas, waste oils, petroleum distillate, and other petroleum products. The potential for oil spills is greatest in the transportation of these products. The most common means of transporting petroleum products are by ships (generally called oil tankers), pipelines, trucks, and trains. Nearly all of the over-the-sea transportation of petroleum is done by tankers and ships; whereas on land, almost 50% of the oil

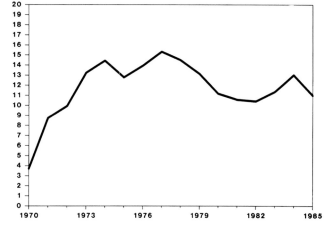

Number of oil pollution incidents reported 1970-1985

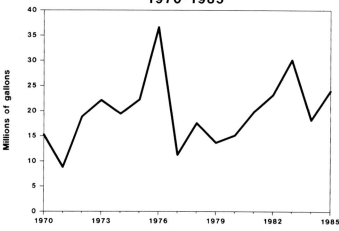

Volume of oil spilled 1970-1985

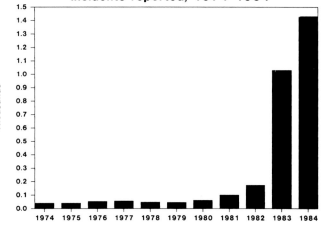

Number of hazardous waste pollution incidents reported, 1974-1984

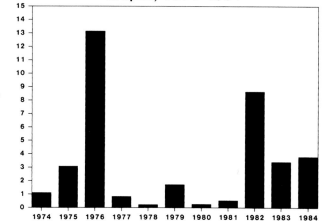

Quanity of hazardous waste released in spills, 1974-1984

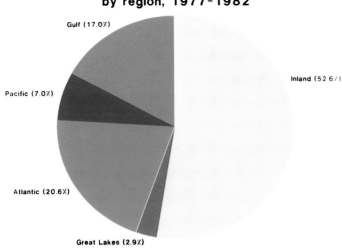

**Mean volume of oil spilled
by region, 1977-1982**

Gulf (17.0%)

Pacific (7.0%)

Atlantic (20.6%)

Great Lakes (2.9%)

Inland (52.6%)

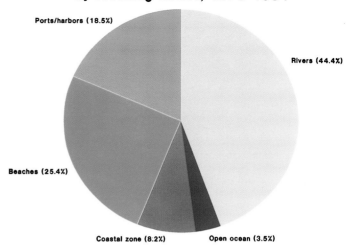

**Mean volume of oil spilled
by receiving waters, 1976-1984**

Ports/harbors (18.5%)

Beaches (25.4%)

Coastal zone (8.2%)

Open ocean (3.5%)

Rivers (44.4%)

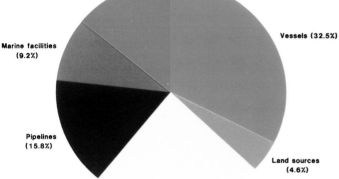

**Mean volume of oil spilled
by source, 1973-1982**

Nonpoint (14.1%)

Marine facilities
(9.2%)

Pipelines
(15.8%)

Storage (23.8%)

Vessels (32.5%)

Land sources
(4.6%)

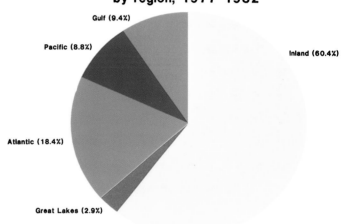

**Mean volume of hazardous waste spilled
by region, 1977-1982**

Gulf (9.4%)

Pacific (8.8%)

Atlantic (18.4%)

Great Lakes (2.9%)

Inland (60.4%)

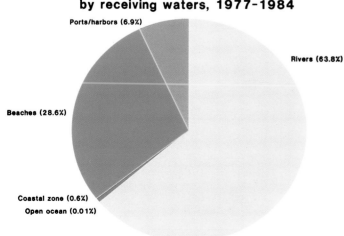

**Mean volume of hazardous waste spilled
by receiving waters, 1977-1984**

Ports/harbors (6.9%)

Beaches (28.6%)

Coastal zone (0.6%)

Open ocean (0.01%)

Rivers (63.8%)

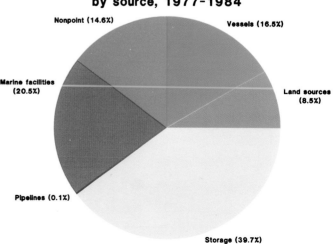

**Mean volume of hazardous waste spilled
by source, 1977-1984**

Nonpoint (14.6%)

Marine facilities
(20.5%)

Pipelines (0.1%)

Storage (39.7%)

Vessels (16.5%)

Land sources
(8.5%)

transported in the continental United States is by pipeline, about 30% by tank trucks, about 22% by barges, and less than 2% by rail. All modes of petroleum transportation have to comply with certain safety standards set by the industry and the relevant regulatory bodies. In spite of safety precautions and improved technologies, however, accidents occur because of human error, unforeseen circumstances, and equipment failure. Intentional discharges also occur.

The major sources of oil pollution in and around United States waters are discharges of sludge from oil tankers, disposal of oil-containing wastewater from ships, and accidental rupture of oil tankers. Oil spills as the result of pipeline accidents do occur, but the frequency is very low. Oil spills also occur at production wells, refineries, and storage facilities. Nonpoint sources, such as municipal and industrial runoff and atmospheric "rainout," also contribute to oil in the environment.

Comparatively small amounts (about 2%) of the oil that is accidentally spilled into the marine environment occurs at domestic offshore oil wells. With over 22,000 wells drilled in marine waters, there have been only four oil spills greater than 1,000 barrels from offshore platforms in high seas waters since 1970, and these involved stored oil rather than loss from wells.

More oil spills in the United States occur in inland waters of the United States (rivers, canals, lakes) than in any particular coastal zone. Prior to 1983, most spills occurred in rivers; since then the number of reported spills has been nearly equally distributed among rivers, ports, and beaches. The fewest spills occur in coastal waters in the nearshore zone that extends from the shoreline out to 12 nautical miles and in the open ocean.

Much effort has been expended over the past two decades to develop measures to lessen the impact

of oil spills in and around U.S. waters. The key to pollution control when oil spills occur is prompt and planned action in preventing the spread of the oil, removing the oil, and cleaning up the polluted area. Contingency plans to combat and control possible oil pollution problems have helped to avert catastrophes in many areas.

Damage to the aquatic environment from spilled oil depends upon the type of oil, volume spilled, and the length of contact. The effects of spilled oil include: direct lethal toxicity to organisms; sublethal disruption of physiological or behavioral activities (which may reduce many species' resistance to infection or stress); direct coating (which impedes vital processes of respiration and feeding in animals, prevents light penetration to plants, and increases temperature by absorbing solar radiation); incorporation of hydrocarbons into the food chain (which may act as a carbon source to hydrocarbon-degrading organisms); changes in biological habitats (through the alteration of substrate characteristics); changes in species diversity and density patterns; and coating the air–water interface with oil (which may act as a physical barrier interfering with gas exchange). Many of these effects can be acute, however, it is generally agreed that catastrophic and long-lasting damage to the environment only rarely occurs, and within a few years, oiled environments appear to recover to support communities similar to those that existed before the spill.

After an oil spill, many of the more toxic petroleum components evaporate, oxidize, and/or biodegrade relatively rapidly, at least in warm climates. However, this may not be the case in arctic and subarctic areas where lower temperatures and burial under fine-grain, low-oxygen sediments delay the degradation processes of petroleum and allow relatively undegraded hydrocarbons to be released gradually from under the ice. Under these kinds of

conditions, the continuous leaching of undegraded oil into surrounding waters could possibly evoke long-term effects in marine benthic populations.

2-18
Ground-water quality

Ground-water contamination has historically received little attention at the national level. One major reason has been the widespread, albeit erroneous, belief that potential contaminants percolating through subsurface layers would adhere to soils or be degraded by natural processes and, therefore, would not enter ground-water aquifers or greatly affect ground-water quality. Unlike surface-water pollution, ground-water contamination occurs out of sight and without early warning signals. For a long time, land surface and subsurface disposal of wastes and nonwaste byproducts generated by society was considered safe and convenient. Only recently has it become known that natural soil processes have only limited capacity to change contaminants into harmless substances before they reach ground water.

Today, there is a growing concern that ground-water quality is in decline. Incidents of ground-water contamination—by organic chemicals, inorganic chemicals, radionuclides, or microorganisms—are being reported with increasing frequency and have now occurred in some aspect in every state in the Nation. Although the activities that cause contamination are varied and have been in practice for many years, ground-water contamination has only recently come to the attention of the public, primarily in the context of threats to human health. Most of this attention has focused on sources associated with hazardous pollutants discarded or generated in landfills, surface impoundments, waste piles, and illegal dumps because of the severity of their impacts on

Sources of ground-water contamination

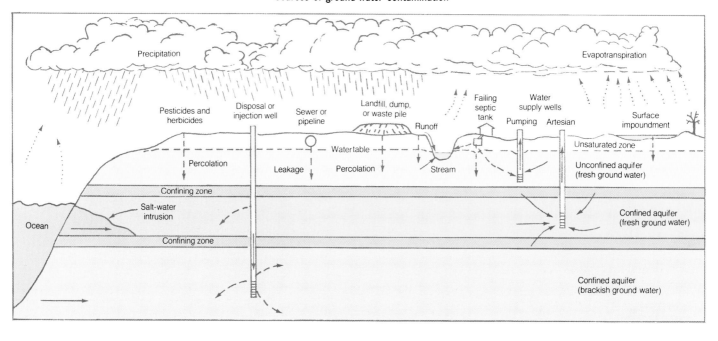

· · · · · · · ▷ Evaporation   – – – ▷ Movement of ground water contamination   ───▷ Ground water flow

surrounding populations and the environment. However, nonhazardous wastes and nonwastes also may contribute to the contamination of ground water.

Only a small portion of the Nation's ground-water supply—from 1 to 2%—is considered to be contaminated. This portion is small, yet individual incidences of contamination may be significant when they occur in heavily populated areas. Another reason is because ground water is relied upon more and more for a variety of uses. Ground water is the source of about 40% of the Nation's streamflow (through discharge), and over 50% of the population depends upon it for drinking water. It is an alternative to surface-water supplies (particularly during drought) and a source of water for future demands. It is also particularly vulnerable to contamination and exceededly difficult to treat in the aquifer once contaminated.

Contaminants found in ground water are associated with adverse health, social, environmental, and economic impacts. Public health concerns arise because some contaminants are linked to cancers, liver and kidney diseases, and damage to the central nervous system. There are many uncertainties about human health impacts because empirical data on the nature and extent of ground-water contamination are limited and because the impacts are often difficult to study (impacts may not be observable until after long exposure).

Social impacts include anxiety and fear about exposure to contaminants and expenditures on ground-water purification systems. Exposure can occur unknowingly because most contaminated ground water is odorless, colorless, and tasteless. Exposure can also occur over many years and in many ways—by drinking contaminated water, eating foods that have been in contact with contaminated ground water, bathing in contaminated water, and breathing contaminants when they volatilize in shower water.

Vegetation, fish, and wildlife also can be adversely affected by contaminated ground water. Because ground water provides a significant portion of base flow to streams, the potential for adverse impacts on surface-water quality may be large, especially during periods of low rainfall when dilution is minimal. Changes in the quantity of ground water can also affect its quality. If ground water pumpage exceeds the natural flow to the sea, salt water will move inland until it reaches the pumping center and a saltwater intrusion problem will exist. Other environmental impacts include volatilization of chemicals in ground water to the atmosphere in the vicinity of certain sources, such as landfills.

Sources and technical notes

2-1
Hydrologic cycle

2-1a
Hydrologic cycle

U.S. Department of the Interior, Geological Survey. 1984. *National water summary 1983—Hydrologic events and issues.* Water-Supply Paper 2250 (Reston, Va.), figure 1, Hydrologic cycle showing the gross water budget of the conterminous United States, p. 9.

U.S. Department of the Interior, Geological Survey. 1985. *National water summary 1984–Hydrologic events, selected water-quality trends, and ground-water resources.* Water-Supply Paper 2275 (Reston, Va.), pp. 2-13.

U.S. Department of the Interior, Geological Survey. 1986. *National water summary 1985—Hydrologic events and surface-water resources.* Water-Supply Paper 2300 (Reston, Va.), pp. 2-27.

2-1b
Average annual precipitation

U.S. Department of the Interior, Geological Survey. 1986. *National water summary 1985—Hydrologic events and surface-water resources.* Water-Supply Paper 2300 (Reston, Va.), figure 27, Average annual precipitation in the United States and Puerto Rico, 1951–1980, p. 52.

2-1c
Average annual runoff

U.S. Department of the Interior, Geological Survey. 1986. *National water summary 1985—Hydrologic events and surface-water resources.* Water-Supply Paper 2300 (Reston, Va.), figure 28, Average annual runoff in the United States and Puerto Rico, 1951–1980, p. 52.

2-1d
Average annual pan and surface evaporation

Farnsworth, R. K., and E. L. Peck. 1982. *Evaporation atlas for the contiguous 48 United States.* U.S. Department of Commerce, National Oceanic and Atmospheric Administration, National Weather Service Technical Report NWS 33 (Washington, D.C.).

2-2
Flow of selected rivers

2-2a
Flow of selected rivers

U.S. Department of the Interior, Geological Survey. 1986. *National water summary 1985—Hydrologic events and surface-water resources.* Water-Supply Paper 2300 (Reston, Va.), figure 31, Flow of major rivers in the conterminous United States and Alaska, p. 54.

2-2b
Mean monthly discharge, Boise River near Twin Springs, Idaho, 1951–1980

U.S. Department of the Interior, Geological Survey. 1986. *National water summary 1985—Hydologic events and surface-water resources.* Water-Supply Paper 2300 (Reston, Va.), figure 32, Average monthly distribution of runoff as a percentage of annual runoff at diverse locations in the United States and Puerto Rico, p. 56.

2-2c
Mean monthly discharge, Middle Concho River in Texas, 1931–1968

Sauer, S. P., 1972. "Factors contributing to unusually low runoff during the period 1962-1968 in the Concho River basin, Texas," in *National water summary 1985—Hydrologic events and surface-water resources.* U.S. Geological Survey. Water-Supply Paper 2300 (Reston, Va.), figure 33, Annual mean discharge of the Middle Concho River in Texas, 1931–1968, p. 58.

The large range, from practically no flow in 1962 and 1963 to more than 140 cubic feet per second in 1936 and 1957, illustrates the highly variable runoff in a semiarid region. The principal cause of the unusually low runoff during the 1962–1963 period was the lack of long-duration, high-intensity rainfall.

2-2d
Mean annual discharge, Red River of the North at Grand Forks, North Dakota, 1885–1986

U.S. Department of the Interior, Geological Survey. 1986. *National water summary 1985—Hydrologic events and surface-water resources.* Water-Supply Paper 2300 (Reston, Va.), figure 36, Annual mean discharges of the Red River

of the North at Grand Forks, N. Dak., for the period 1885-1984, indicating major multiyear droughts, p. 59 (updated).

2-2e
Peak annual discharge, North Platte River at North Platte, Nebraska, 1895–1986

U.S. Department of the Interior, Geological Survey. 1986. *National water summary 1985—Hydrologic events and surface-water resources.* Water-Supply Paper 2300 (Reston, Va.), figure 67, Peak annual discharge at North Platte River at North Platte, Nebr., 1895–1980, p. 91 (updated).

2-2f
Annual suspended-sediment discharge, Missouri River at Omaha, Nebraska, 1939–1982

U.S. Department of the Interior, Geological Survey. 1985. *National water summary 1984—Hydrologic events, selected water-quality trends, and ground-water resources.* Water-Supply Paper 2275 (Reston, Va.), figure 27, Annual discharge of suspended sediment at six stations on the Missouri River and two stations on the Mississippi River showing the effects of reservoirs on downstream sediment loads, 1939–1982, p. 52.

2-2g
Annual suspended-sediment discharge, Juniata River at Newport, Pennsylvania, 1952–1983

U.S. Department of the Interior, Geological Survey. 1985. *National water summary 1984—Hydrologic events, selected water-quality trends, and ground-water resources.* Water-Supply Paper 2275 (Reston, Va.), figure 33, Annual suspended-sediment discharge of three rivers showing the frequencies of suspended-sediment discharges within individual years and the importance of infrequent heavy storms in producing large sediment loads, p. 59.

2-3
Water levels in lakes

2-3a
Water levels in Great Salt Lake, Utah

Arnow, T. 1985. "Rise of Great Salt Lake, Utah," pp. 31-33, in *National water summary 1984–Hydrologic events, selected water-quality trends, and ground-water resources.* U.S. Geological Survey. Water-Supply Paper 2275 (Reston, Va.), figure 11, Changes in water level and dissolved-mineral concentrations of Great Salt Lake, Utah, 1847 to 1984, p. 33.

Data are arthimetic means of readings over a calendar year. Since 1959, the northern and southern parts of the lake have differed in water level and mineralization.

2-3b
Water levels in the Great Lakes, Lake Superior, 1950-1985

2-3c
Water levels in the Great Lakes, Lakes Michigan and Erie, 1950–1985

2-3d
Water levels in the Great Lakes, Lake Ontario, 1950–1985

Hitt, K. J., and J. B. Miller. 1986. "Great Lakes set record high water levels," pp. 35-40. in *National water summary 1985–Hydrologic events and surface-water resources.* U.S. Geological Survey. Water-Supply Paper 2300 (Reston, Va.), figure 15, Long-term fluctuations in the water levels of the Great Lakes, 1950–1985, p. 39.

Levels are to International Great Lakes Datum 1955.

2-4
Surface-water development

2-4a
Intensity of reservoir development, 1982

U.S. Department of the Interior, Geological Survey. 1984. *National water summary 1983—Hydrologic events and issues,* Water-Supply Paper 2250 (Reston, Va.), figure 14, Intensity of reservoir development, in acre-feet of reservoir capacity per square mile, by water-resources region, p. 32.

Williams, G. P., and M. G. Wolman. 1986. "Effects of dams and reservoirs on surface-water hydrology—changes in rivers downstream from dams," pp. 83-88. in *National water summary 1985—Hydrologic events and surface-water resources.* U.S. Geological Survey. Water-Supply Paper 2300 (Reston, Va.).

2-4b
Number of dams, 1836–1986

U.S. Department of Defense, Army Corps of Engineers. 1988. *The inventory of dams* (Washington, D.C.), unpublished data.

Data include dams owned and operated by the U.S. Army Corps of Engineers, dams owned and operated by others with federally owned flood control storage controlled by the Corps of Engineers, and dams constructed by the Corps and turned over to others for operation and maintenance. Dams are 25 feet in structural height and/or 50 acre-feet capacity or greater.

2-4c
Active reservoir storage volume, U.S. Army Corps of Engineers dams, 1920–1986

Langbein, W. B. 1982. *Dams, reservoirs and withdrawals for water supply—historical trends.* U.S. Geological Survey, Open File Report 82-256 (Reston, Va.), p. 3.

U.S. Department of Defense, Army Corps of Engineers. 1988. *The inventory of dams* (Washington, D.C.), unpublished data.

An acre-foot is the volume of water that would cover one acre to a depth of one foot.

2-4d
Average volume of reservoir completed for 10-year period, 1920–1986

U.S. Department of Defense, Army Corps of Engineers. 1988. *The inventory of dams* (Washington, D.C.), unpublished data.

2-5
Ground-water development

2-5a
Ground-water regions

Heath, R. 1984. *Ground-water regions of the United States.* U.S. Geological Survey, Water-Supply Paper 2242 (Reston, Va.), figure 12, Ground-water regions used in this report, p. 17.

2-5b
Characteristics of ground-water regions

Heath, R. 1984. *Ground-water regions of the United States.* U.S. Geological Survey, Water Supply Paper 2242 (Reston, Va.), table 6, Common ranges on the hydraulic characteristics of ground-water regions of the United States, p. 19.

All values rounded to one significant figure.

2-5c
Areas of water table decline, 1984

U.S. Department of the Interior, Geological Survey. 1985. *National water summary 1984—Hydrologic events and surface-water resources.* Water-Supply Paper 2275 (Reston, Va.), figure 58, Areas of the United States where water-table decline or artesian water-level decline in excess of 40 feet in at least one aquifer has occurred since development began, p. 17.

Mann, L. J. 1985. "Ground water level changes in five areas of the United States," pp. 106-113, in *National water summary 1984—Hydrologic events and surface-water resources.* U.S. Department of the Interior, Geological Survey. Water-Supply Paper 2275 (Reston, Va.).

2-6
Trends in water use

2-6a
Trends in offstream use by source of withdrawal, 1950–1985

2-6b
Trends in offstream water use by end user, 1900–1985

2-6c
Trends in instream use for hydroelectric power, 1950–1985

2-6d
Total water withdrawal, 1985

2-6e
Freshwater consumption, 1985

Solley, W. B., C. F. Merk, and R. R. Pierce. 1988. *Estimated use of water in the United States in 1985.* U.S. Geological Survey Circular Report 1004 (Reston, Va.), p. 69.

U.S. Department of Commerce, Bureau of the Census. 1976. *Historical statistics of the United States,* part 1, series J, 92-103. (Washington, D.C.).

2-7
Water quality

2-7a
Municipal wastewater treatment facilities data by level of treatment, 1986

U.S. Environmental Protection Agency, *Municipal Pollution Control.* 1987. 1986 needs survey to Congress—assessment of needed publicly owned wastewater treatment facilities in the United States (Washington, D.C.).

2-7b
Effluent reductions from pulp and paper mills, 1973-1984

U.S. Environmental Protection Agency, Economics Studies Branch. 1988. *Costs and reductions and production associated with direct dischargers* (Washington, D.C.), unpublished data.

U.S. General Accounting Office. 1987. *Water pollution: Application of national cleanup standards to the pulp and paper industry.* GAO/RCED-87-52 (Washington, D.C.).

TSS = total suspended solids. BOD = biochemical oxygen demand. The data show what the Clean Water Act accomplished. Without the Clean Water Act pollution controls, the 1984 water effluents would have been 1,090 thousand tons of TSS and 1,100 thousand tons of BOD (assuming 1973 effluent limitations in pounds per tons as applied to 1984 production).

2-7c
Point source loadings, biochemical oxygen demand, mid-1980s

2-7d
Point source loadings, total suspended sediments, mid-1980s

2-7e
Point source loadings, phosphorus, mid-1980s

2-7f
Point source loadings, metals, mid-1980s

U.S. Environmental Protection Agency, Office of Water Regulations and Standards, Monitoring and Data Support Division. 1988. *Summary of effluent characteristics and guidelines for selected industrial point source categories: Industry status sheets* (Washington, D.C.).

U.S. Environmental Protection Agency, Municipal Pollution Control. 1987. *1986 needs survey report to Congress—assessment of needed publicly owned wastewater treatment facilities in the United States* (Washington, D.C.).

U.S. Environmental Protection Agency, Office of Water Regulations and Standards. 1985. *Report to Congress on the discharge of hazardous wastes to publicly owned treatment works* (Washington, D.C.).

Mineral and metals includes aluminum forming, coal mining, copper forming, foundries, iron and steel, metal finishing, nonferrous metals mining and forming, ore mining and petroleum refining industries. Chemical and manufacturing includes battery manufacturing, coil coating, electrical and electronic components, organic and inorganic chemicals, plastics, synthetic fibers, pesticide manufacturing, pharmaceuticals manufacturing, plastics molding and forming, porcelain enameling, leather tanning, pulp and paper, and textile industries. Agriculture and fisheries includes animal feedlots, fish hatcheries, food and beverages, fruits and vegetables, meat packing, and seafood industries. POTWs = publicly owned treatment works. TSS = total suspended solids. BOD = biochemical oxygen demand. Metals = cadmium, copper, lead, mercury and zinc. Industrial loadings are direct discharges based on long-term average concentrations and total industry flows at Best Available Technology (BAT) presented in U.S. EPA (1983) except as follows: loadings for electrical and electronic components reflect current level of treatment (U.S. EPA, 1983); conventional loadings for agriculture and fisheries industries represent post-BAT treatment levels: and conventional and toxic pollutant loadings for POTWs include indirect industrial [at Pretreatment Standards for Existing Systems (PSES) discharge levels] and residential/commercial loadings not removed by the POTWs. Phosphorus loadings for POTWs represent effluent levels of 5 mg/l. POTW removal efficiencies of 82 and 78 percent are assumed for copper and zinc, respectively.

2-7g
Nonpoint source contributions, biochemical oxygen demand, 1980

2-7h
Nonpoint source contributions, total suspended sediments, 1980

2-7i
Nonpoint source contributions, nitrogen, 1980

2-7j
Nonpoint source contributions, phosphorus, 1980

Adopted from Bailey, G. W., and T. E. Waddell. 1979. "Best management practices from agriculture and silviculture: An integrated review," p. 37, in *Best management practices for agriculture and silvaculture.* Ann Arbor Science (Ann Arbor, Mich.).

TSS = total suspended solids. BOD = biochemical oxygen demand. Excluded from the survey area are 207 million acres of public lands (14% of the contiguous United States), mostly in the Rocky Mountains, because of inadequacy of information. Urban runoff includes separate storm sewers only.

2-8
Trends in water quality

2-8a
Surface waters impacted by
nonpoint sources, 1985

The Association of State and Interstate Water Pollution
Control Administrators, in cooperation with the U.S.
Environmental Protection Agency. 1985. *America's clean
water: The states' nonpoint source assessment, 1985*
(Washington, D.C.).

Does not include data for Alaska. Data cover 1.48 million
river miles, 26.6 million lake acres, 32,000 estuary square
miles, and 23,000 ocean coastline miles.

2-8b
Changes in water quality, 1972–1982

The Association of State and Interstate Water Pollution
Control Administrators, in cooperation with the U.S.
Environmental Protection Agency. 1984. *America's clean
water: The states' evaluation of progress, 1972–1982*
(Washington, D.C.).

Does not include data for Alaska.

2-8c
River and stream miles
supporting uses, 1972–1982

The Association of State and Interstate Water Pollution
Control Administrators, in cooperation with the U.S.
Environmental Protection Agency. 1984. *America's clean
water: The states' evaluation of progress, 1972–1982*
(Washington, D.C.).

Data cover 758,000 river and stream miles and 16.3 million lake acres. Forty-nine (49) states reported on water
quality conditions between 1972 and 1982. Some proportion of the 1972 data unknown or not reported fell into
each of the levels of use support for 1982.

2-8d
Ability of perennial streams to
support fish, 1972–1982

U.S. Department of the Interior, Fish and Wildlife Service.
1984. *1982 national fisheries survey.* FWS/OBS-84/06
(Washington, D.C.), volume 1, Initial findings.

2-9
River and stream water quality

2-9a
Fecal streptococcus bacteria

2-9b
Suspended sediments

2-9c
Nitrate

2-9d
Chlorine

2-9e
Arsenic

2-9f
Lead

Smith, R. A., R. A. Alexander, and M. G. Wolman. 1987.
*Analysis and interpretation of water-quality trends in major
U.S. rivers, 1974–81.* U.S. Geological Survey Water-Supply
Paper 2307 (Reston, Va.).

Trends in flow-adjusted concentrations of six common
water quality constituents at NASQAN and NWQSS stations,
1974–1981. Up arrow indicates increase; down arrow indicates decrease; and closed circle indicates no trend.

2-10
Pesticides in rivers and streams

2-10a
Organophosphate insecticides in
stream samples, 1975–1980

Gillom, R. J., R. B. Alexander, and R. A. Smith. 1985.
*Pesticides in the Nation's rivers, 1975–1980, and implica-
tions for future monitoring.* U.S. Geological Survey Water-
Supply Paper 2271 (Reston, Va.), figure 3, Frequency of
detection of organochlorine insecticides in Pesticide Monitoring Network samples, p. 12.

2-10b
Organochlorine insecticides in
stream samples, 1975–1980

Gillom, R. J., R. B. Alexander, and R. A. Smith. 1985.
*Pesticides in the Nation's rivers, 1975–1980, and implica-
tions for future monitoring.* U.S. Geological Survey Water-
Supply Paper 2271 (Reston, Va.), figure 6, Frequency of
detection of organophosphate insecticides in Pesticide Monitoring Network samples, p. 19.

2-11
Water quality conditions in the
Great Lakes

2-11a
Estimated phosphorus loadings to
Lake Superior, 1976–1985

2-11b
Estimated phosphorus loadings to
Lake Michigan, 1976–1985

2-11c
Estimated phosphorus loadings to
Lake Huron, 1976–1985

2-11d
Estimated phosphorus loadings to
Lake Erie, 1976–1985

2-11e
Estimated phosphorus loadings to
Lake Ontario, 1976–1985

Great Lakes Water Quality Board. *Great Lakes water quality, 1976; 1977; 1981; 1983; 1985.* Appendix B. Surveillance Subcommittee Report to the International Joint Commission, Canada and United States (Windsor, Ont.).

The 1978 Great Lakes Water Quality Agreement set target
loadings for each lake (in metric tons per year): Lake
Superior, 3400; Lake Michigan, 5600; Lake Huron, 4360;
Lake Erie, 11000; and Lake Ontario, 7000.

2-12
Contaminants in Great Lakes fish

2-12a
Contaminants in Lake Superior fish,
1977–1983

2-12b
Contaminants in Lake Michigan fish,
1969–1986

2-12c
Contaminants in Lake Huron fish,
1978–1983

2-12d
Contaminants in Lake Erie fish,
1977–1983

2-12e
Contaminants in Lake Ontario fish,
1977–1983

Devault, D. S., W. A. Willford, R. J. Hesselberg, D. A. Nor-
trupt, E. G. S. Rundberg, A. K. Alwan, and C. Bautista.
1986. "Contaminant trends in lake trout *(Salvelinus
namaycush)* from the Upper Great Lakes." *Arch. Environ.
Contam. Toxicol.,* 15: 349-356.

U.S. Department of the Interior, Fish and Wildlife Service,
Great Lakes Fishery Laboratory (Ann Arbor, Mich.), unpublished data.

Great Lakes Water Quality Board. 1985. *1985 report on
Great Lakes water quality to the International Joint Commission, Canada and United States* (Windsor, Ont.).

Devault, D. S., J. M. Clark, G. Lahvis, and J. Weishaar.
1988. "Contaminants and trends in fall run coho salmon."
J. Great Lakes Res. 14(1): 23-33.

2-13
Contaminants in herring gull
eggs from Great Lakes colonies

2-13a
DDE in herring gull eggs,
Lake Superior, Huron, and
Michigan colonies, 1974–1986

2-13b
DDE in herring gull eggs,
Lake Erie and Ontario colonies,
1974–1986

2-13c
PCBs in herring gull eggs,
Lake Superior, Huron, and
Michigan colonies, 1974–1986

2-13d
PCBs in herring gull eggs,
Lake Erie and Ontario colonies,
1974–1986

2-13e
Mirex in herring gull eggs,
Lake Superior, Huron, and
Michigan colonies, 1974–1986

2-13f
Mirex in herring gull eggs,
Lake Erie and Ontario colonies,
1974–1986

2-13g
Dieldrin in herring gull eggs,
Lake Superior, Huron, and
Michigan colonies, 1974–1986

2-13h
Dieldrin in herring gull eggs,
Lake Erie and Ontario colonies,
1974–1986

Environment Canada, Canadian Wildlife Service, Canada
Centre for Inland Waters. 1986. *Organochlorine contaminant concentrations in herring gull eggs from Great Lakes
colonies* (Burlington, Ont.).

Mineau, P., G. A. Fox, R. J. Norstrom, D. U. Weseloh, and
D. J. Hallet. 1984. "Using the herring gull to monitor levels and effects of organochlorine contamination in the
Canadian Great Lakes," pp. 425-452, in *Toxic Contaminants in the Great Lakes.* J. O. Nriagu and M. S. Simmons
(eds.), John Wiley and Sons, Inc.

Struger, J., D. U., Weseloh, D. J. Hallet, and P. Mineau.
1985. "Organochlorine contaminants in herring gull eggs
from the Detroit and Niagara Rivers and Saginaw Bay
(1978-1982): Contaminant discriminants." *J. Great Lakes
Res.,* 11(3): 223-230.

Weseloh, D. U., P. Mineau, J. Struger, S. Teeple, D. Hallett,
R. Norstrom, A. Gilman, and L. Reynolds. 1987. *An
11-year monitoring study of organochlorine contaminants*

levels in herring gull eggs from the Great Lakes 1974–1984. Canadian Wildlife Service, unpublished manuscript.

Data are parts per million in whole egg samples, wet weight. No data available for all sites except Big Sister Island for 1976; for Big Sister Island for 1974, 1975, 1977, 1979, and 1981; and for Granite Island for 1983. N/A = Not available. DDE = Metabolite of dichloro-diphenyl-trichloro ethane (DDT). PCBs = Polychlorinated biphenyls.

2-14
Pollutant discharges into coastal waters

2-14a
Discharges into coastal waters of biochemical oxygen demand, 1980–1985

2-14b
Discharges into coastal waters of total suspended sediments, 1980–1985

2-14c
Discharges into coastal waters of total nitrogen, 1980–1985

2-14d
Discharges into coastal waters of total phosphorus, 1980–1985

U.S. Department of Commerce, National Oceanic and Atmospheric Administration, National Ocean Survey, Ocean Assessments Division, Strategic Assessment Branch. 1986. *Pollutant discharges from East Coast and Gulf of Mexico coastal counties, circa 1980–1985* and unpublished data compiled from the National Coastal Pollutant Discharge Inventory database (Rockville, Md.).

U.S. Environmental Protection Agency, Municipal Pollution Control. 1987. *1986 needs survey to Congress—assessment of needed publicly owned wastewater treatment facilities in the United States* (Washington, D.C.).

BOD = biochemical oxygen demand. TSS = total suspended solids. TN = total nitrogen. TP = total phosphorus.

2-14e
Sources of discharges into coastal waters, 1980–1985

U.S. Department of Commerce, National Oceanic and Atmospheric Administration, National Ocean Survey, Ocean Assessments Division, Strategic Assessment Branch. 1986. *Pollutant discharges from East Coast and Gulf of Mexico coastal counties, circa 1980–1985* and unpublished data compiled from the National Coastal Pollutant Discharge Inventory database (Rockville, Md.).

U.S. Environmental Protection Agency, Municipal Pollution Control. 1987. *1986 needs survey to Congress—assessment of needed publicly owned wastewater treatment facilities in the United States* (Washington, D.C.).

2-15
Harvest-limited shellfish waters

2-15a
Harvest-limited shellfish waters for selected Northeast estuaries, 1971–1985

2-15b
Harvest-limited shellfish waters for selected Southeast estuaries, 1971–1985

2-15c
Harvest-limited shellfish waters for selected Gulf Coast estuaries, 1971–1985

2-15d
Harvest-limited shellfish waters for selected Pacific Northwest estuaries, 1971–1985

U.S. Department of Commerce, National Oceanic and Atmospheric Administration, National Ocean Survey, Ocean Assessments Division, Strategic Assessment Branch. 1986. *Trends in harvest limited shellfish areas by estuary.* Data compiled from the National Estuarine Inventory database (Rockville, Md).

2-16
Contaminants in marine sediments

2-16a
Trace metals in sediments for selected Northeast estuaries, 1984

2-16b
Trace metals in sediments for selected Southeast estuaries, 1984

2-16c
Trace metals in sediments for selected Gulf Coast estuaries, 1984

2-16d
Trace metals in sediments for selected Pacific Coast estuaries, 1984

Young, D., and J. Means. 1987. "Trace metals in sediments." pp. 11-25, in *Preliminary assessment of findings of the Benthic Surveillance Project—1984.* National Oceanic and Atmospheric Administration, National Ocean Service, Ocean Assessments Division. Progress report prepared by the National Status and Trends Program for Marine Environmental Quality (Rockville, Md.).

2-16e
Aromatic hydrocarbons in sediments for selected Northeast estuaries, 1984

2-16f
Aromatic hydrocarbons in sediments for selected Southeast estuaries, 1984

2-16g
Aromatic hydrocarbons in sediments for selected Gulf Coast estuaries, 1984

2-16h
Aromatic hydrocarbons in sediments for selected Pacific Coast estuaries, 1984

Holm, S. E. 1987. "Aromatic hydrocarbons in sediments," pp. 26-32, in U.S. Department of Commerce, National Oceanic and Atmospheric Administration, National Ocean Service, Ocean Assessments Division. *Preliminary assessment of findings of the Benthic Surveillance Project—1984.* Progress report prepared by the National Status and Trends Program for Marine Environmental Quality (Rockville, Md.).

PAH data for Casco Bay, Maine, come from a single sample, whereas all other data for other sites are averages of at least two samples.

2-16i
PCBs in sediments for selected Northeast estuaries, 1984

2-16j
PCBs in sediments for selected Pacific Coast estuaries, 1984

Ernst, M. C. 1987. "PCBs in sediments and fish liver," pp. 46-57, in U.S. Department of Commerce, National

Oceanic and Atmospheric Administration, National Ocean Service, Ocean Assessments Division. *Preliminary assessment of findings of the Benthic Surveillance Project—1984.* Progress report prepared by the National Status and Trends Program for Marine Environmental Quality (Rockville, Md.).

2-16k
***Clostridium perfringens* in sediments for selected Northeast estuaries, 1984**

2-16l
***Clostridium perfringens* in sediments for selected Southeast estuaries, 1984**

2-16m
***Clostridium perfringens* in sediments for selected Gulf Coast estuaries, 1984**

2-16n
***Clostridium perfringens* in sediments for selected Pacific Coast estuaries, 1984**

2-16o
Coprostanol in sediments for selected Northeast estuaries, 1984

2-16p
Coprostanol in sediments for selected Southeast estuaries, 1984

2-16q
Coprostanol in sediments for selected Gulf Coast estuaries, 1984

2-16r
Coprostanol in sediments for selected Pacific Coast estuaries, 1984

Holm, S. E. 1987. "Sewage indicators in sediments," pp. 58-64, in U.S. Department of Commerce, National Oceanic and Atmospheric Administration, National Ocean Service, Ocean Assessments Division. *Preliminary assessment of findings of the Benthic Surveillance Project—1984.* Progress report prepared by the National Status and Trends Program for Marine Environmental Quality (Rockville, Md.).

ND = Not detected.

2-17
Oil spills in and around U.S. waters

2-17a
Number of oil pollution incidents reported, 1970–1985

2-17b
Volume of oil spilled, 1970–1985

2-17c
Number of hazardous waste incidents reported, 1970–1985

2-17d
Quantity of hazardous waste released in spills, 1970–1985

2-17e
Mean volume of oil spilled by region, 1977–1982

2-17f
Mean volume of oil spilled
by receiving waters, 1976–1984

2-17g
Mean volume of oil spilled
by source, 1973–1982

2-17h
Mean volume of hazardous waste
spilled by region, 1977–1982

2-17i
Mean volume of hazardous waste
spilled by receiving waters,
1977–1984

2-17j
Mean volume of hazardous waste
spilled by source, 1977–1984

U.S. Department of Transportation, United States Coast Guard. *Polluting incidents in and around U.S. waters, annual.* COMDTINST M16450A-F (old CG-487, Washington, D.C.).

Adewumi, M. A., and T. Ertekin. 1987. "Oil and natural gas drilling and transportation: environmental problems and controls," in *Environmental Consequences of Energy Production: Problems and Prospects.* S. K. Majumdar, F. J. Brenner, and E. W. Miller (eds.). The Pennsylvania Academy of Science (Easton, Pa.).

U.S. Department of Commerce, National Oceanic and Atmospheric Administration, National Marine Pollution Program Office. 1985. *Marine Pollution Problems and Needs* (Rockville, Md.).

2-18
Ground-water quality

2-18
Sources of ground-water
contamination

Office of Technology Assessment, Congress of the United States. 1984. *Protecting the Nation's groundwater from contamination.* OTA-O-233 (Washington, D.C.).

U.S. Department of the Interior, Geological Survey. 1984. *National water summary 1983—Hydrologic events and issues.* Water-Supply Paper 2250 (Reston, Va.), pp. 57-61.

U.S. Environmental Protection Agency, Municipal Pollution Control. 1987. *1986 needs survey to Congress—assessment of needed publicly owned wastewater treatment facilities in the United States* (Washington, D.C.).

Ward, C. H., W. Giger, and P. L. McCarthy (eds.). 1985. *Groundwater quality.* National Center for Groundwater Research. John Wiley and Sons, Inc. (New York).

Chapter 3
Climate and Air Quality

3-1
Climatic zones

Climate is the average weather in an area over a long period of time. Climate is usually described in terms of the temperature, precipitation, humidity, sunshine, atmospheric pressure, and wind conditions that prevail at different times of the day or year, as well as the extremes in range, variability, and frequency of variation. The factors that determine climate are: (1) the balance of incoming and outgoing radiation at any place; (2) the temperatures of land and water surfaces and of the atmosphere that result partly from the radiation balance and partly from the heat transported into and out of the area by winds and ocean currents; (3) the horizontal and vertical motion of the air from wind circulation; and (4) the moisture cycle involving evaporation, transport, and precipitation. Differences in latitude affect these factors the most; however, the climate of any place is also modified by topography, the presence of water bodies or vegetation, and the nature of soil. These factors affect the local heat budget, flow of wind, and supply of moisture. Climate is not static but subject to fluctuation, with changes occurring over the diurnal cycle, from day-to-day, season-to-season, and over periods of years.

Climate is often described in terms of average yearly temperature and precipitation and the seasonal variations in both. Different types of climate may be recognized and defined in accordance with how they are generated and what effects they have on living organisms. The climatic zones of the United States are representative of all of the major climatic regions of the world, except ice cap. Climagraphs for cities in each of the climatic zones illustrate the differences in climate from one zone to another.

Tropical rainforest

Tropical rainforest climates are found in a latitude belt near the Equator where the sun shines almost directly overhead throughout the entire year and the climate is warm or hot. The tropical rainforest zone roughly covers the zone of convergence of the trade winds of the Northern and Southern Hemispheres and is characterized by intense uplift of air and by cloud and rain development. The greatest amount of moisture is absorbed from the warm oceanic waters near the equator, and much of it falls as rain, making areas in this climatic zone some of the wettest in the world. Normally no month in this zone is dry and all are warm and moist, although wetter and drier seasons occur. A typical example is Hilo, Hawaii, where mean temperature of every month is near 79°F and average monthly rainfall ranges from 6 to 14 inches. Rainfall is fairly evenly distributed over the year, although least in summer.

Tropical savanna

Tropical grassland or savanna climates occur in a transition zone from the rainforest climates of the

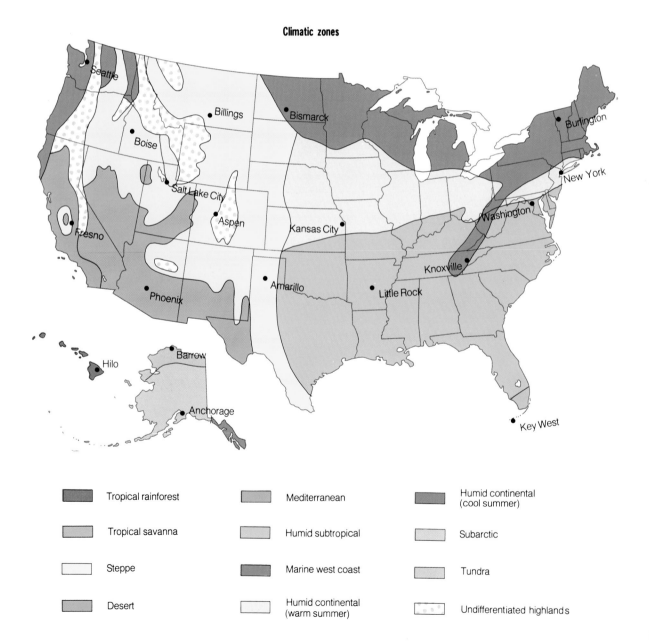

Climatic zones

Tropical rainforest

Tropical savanna

Steppe

Desert

Mediterranean

Humid subtropical

Marine west coast

Humid continental
(warm summer)

Humid continental
(cool summer)

Subarctic

Tundra

Undifferentiated highlands

Mean monthly temperature and precipitation
Hilo, Hawaii

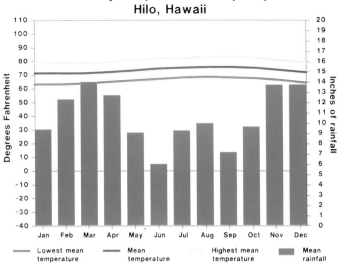

- Lowest mean temperature
- Mean temperature
- Highest mean temperature
- Mean rainfall

Mean monthly temperature and precipitation
Key West, Florida

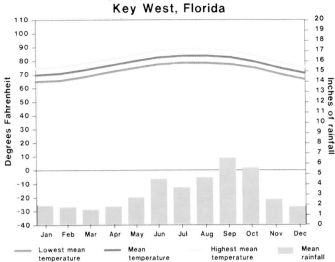

- Lowest mean temperature
- Mean temperature
- Highest mean temperature
- Mean rainfall

equatorial zone to the desert. Areas in this climatic zone are always hot, with alternate dry and wet seasons. The climagraph for Key West, Florida, illustrates the differences between the dry and wet seasons. The period from December through April receives abundant sunshine but less than 25% of annual rainfall. June through October is normally the wet season, receiving approximately 53% of the yearly total in numerous showers and thunderstorms. Humidity remains relatively high throughout the year.

Desert

Desert climates are hot and dry. Temperatures in Phoenix, Arizona, for example, range from very hot in summer to mild in winter. Many winter temperatures reach over 70°F and typical high temperatures in the middle of winter are in the 60s. The climate becomes less attractive in the summer when the normal high temperature is over 90°F from early May through early October and over 100°F from early June through early September. Temperatures for many summer days will exceed 110°F in the afternoon and remain above 85°F all night. Annual precipitation is only around 7 inches. Rain comes

mostly in two seasons. From late November to early April, there are periodic rains from Pacific storms, and in July and August moisture from the south and southeast results in thunderstorms. The transition from extreme dryness in June to the onset of thunderstorms in early July is very abrupt. High winds associated with thunderstorms occur periodically in summer and occasionally create dust storms, which move large distances across the desert.

Mediterranean

The warm temperate climate of Fresno, California, is an example of the Mediterranean climatic zone. Fresno has dry summers and wet and sometimes stormy winters. Desert winds affect the summertime climate, and cyclonic disturbances of the middle latitudes affect the wintertime climate. The months of June to August are usually rainless, and occasionally the rainless season lasts six months. More than 80% of Fresno's rainfall comes from November through February. Reduction of sunshine during these months is caused by fog, at times lasting nearly two weeks, and short periods of stormy weather. In the summer, skies are clear, and the San Joaquin Valley protects Fresno from marine effects. Daily maximum

temperatures can reach the high 90s during the latter part of the summer.

Humid subtropical

The humid subtropical continental climate of Little Rock, Arkansas, is characterized by warm to hot summers and cool winters, with moderate precipitation in all seasons. Little Rock's proximity to the Gulf of Mexico causes the summer season to be marked by prolonged periods of warm and humid weather. Rainfall is less in the summer, however, and the driest period usually occurs in the late summer and early fall. Winters are mild, although polar and Arctic outbreaks are not uncommon.

Steppe

Steppe climate prevails over much of the Great Plains, northern Basin and Range, and southern Columbia Plateau. In these continental interiors, which are screened by mountains from moisture brought by the prevailing winds from the west, summers are hot, winters are cold or very cold, and precipitation is little. Precipitation comes largely in the form of thunderstorms, sometimes with damaging hail, in summertime; in winter, it comes mainly

Mean monthly temperature and precipitation
Phoenix, Arizona

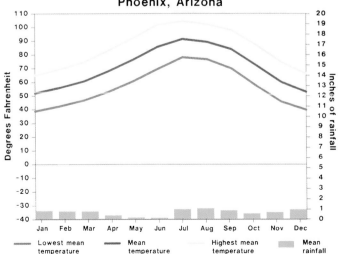

- Lowest mean temperature
- Mean temperature
- Highest mean temperature
- Mean rainfall

Mean monthly temperature and precipitation
Fresno, California

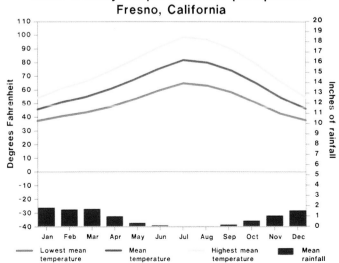

- Lowest mean temperature
- Mean temperature
- Highest mean temperature
- Mean rainfall

Mean monthly temperature and precipitation
Little Rock, Arkansas

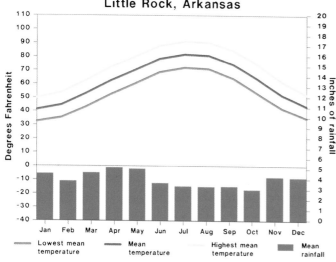

Mean monthly temperature and precipitation
Billings, Montana

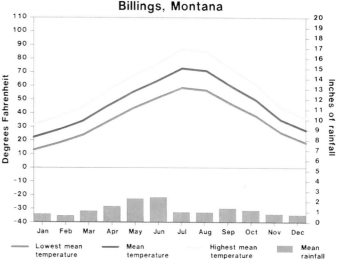

as snow. Deficiency in either season can cause drought. The climate of Billings, Montana, is characteristic of the steppe climatic zone. About one-third of the annual precipitation falls during May and June, and the period of least precipitation extends from November to February. The heaviest snows occur during the spring and fall months. The winter cold is usually ushered in by moderately strong north and northeast winds and snow, and the coldest temperatures occur after the snow has ended and the sky clears. Blizzard conditions may develop in the surrounding area several times during the winter. Cold weather moderates with the onset of moderate to strong southwest winds. Spring brings a period of frequent and rapid fluctuations in weather, with cloudy and cool conditions and periods of rain or snow. The summer season is characterized by warm days with abundant sunshine and low humidity. Seldom is there a protracted rainy spell during summer. Frequent thunderstorms bring afternoon cloudiness but usually only small amounts of rain.

Humid continental

Continental climates are characterized by heavy rainfall in summer (frequently in the form of thunder-

storms), great extremes of temperature, and few strong winds (except for gusts, squalls, and occasional tornadoes that accompany thunderstorms). The most extreme continental conditions are observed toward the eastern limits of continents. On the eastern seaboard of the United States, for example, the climates are more continental than maritime, and in winter much more severe than the western limits of continents. There are two types of continental climate: humid continental with warm summers (Kansas City, Missouri) and humid continental with cool summers (Burlington, Vermont).

The terrain surrounding Kansas City is gently rolling, and there are no topographic obstructions to prevent the free sweep of air from all directions. The influx of moist air from the Gulf of Mexico or the dry air from the semiarid regions to the southwest determine whether wet or dry conditions will prevail. There is often conflict between the warm moist air and the cold polar continental air from the north. Frequent and rapid fluctuations in weather occur in early spring. The summer season is characterized by warm days and mild nights, with moderate humidity. The fall season is usually mild and winters are not extremely cold. Nearly 60% of

the annual precipitation occurs during six months (from April through September).

Burlington is located on the eastern shore of Lake Champlain, which modifies the many rapid and marked weather changes of a true New England climate. As the result of its location in the St. Lawrence Valley storm track and the lake effects, however, it is one of the cloudiest areas in the United States. High pressure systems moving down from central Canada or Hudson Bay produce cold temperatures during the winter. Burlington's northerly latitude assures that summers are cool, with few days reaching 90°F or more. Precipitation is plentiful and well distributed throughout the year. The heaviest rainfall usually occurs during the summer thunderstorms.

Maritime

Seattle, Washington, has a typical maritime climate. The most obvious features are the windiness, relatively small temperature variations, pronounced although not sharply defined rainy season with fall and winter rainfall maxima, and considerable cloudiness, particularly during the winter months. The Cascade Mountains are effective in shielding Seattle

Mean monthly temperature and precipitation
Kansas City, Missouri

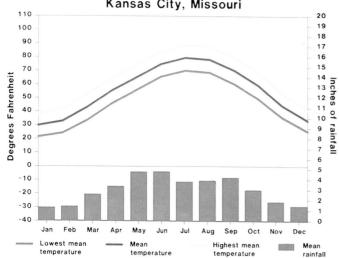

Mean monthly temperature and precipitation
Burlington, Vermont

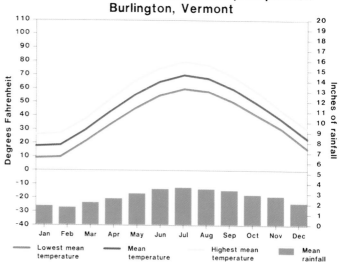

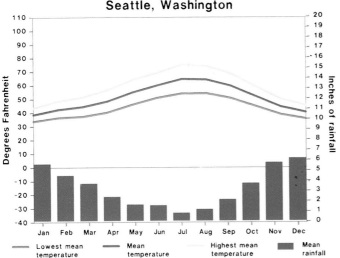

Mean monthly temperature and precipitation
Seattle, Washington

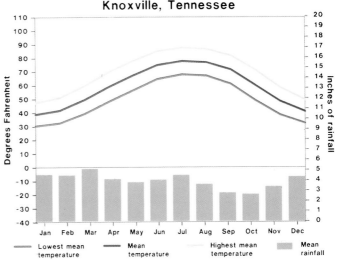

Mean monthly temperature and precipitation
Knoxville, Tennessee

from cold, dry continental air during winter and hot, dry continental air during summer. The average daytime temperature in winter is in the 40s and the nighttime readings are in the 30s. During summer, daytime temperatures are in the 70s with nighttime lows in the 50s. Extremes of temperatures during either season are usually short in duration.

Knoxville, Tennessee, although not located on the coast, exhibits many features of a maritime climate. Knoxville is located in a broad valley between the Cumberland Mountains and the Great Smoky Mountains, which exert a marked influence upon the climate of the valley. The Cumberland Mountains retard and weaken the force of cold winter air that frequently penetrates far south to the west of the mountains. The mountains also modify the hot summer winds that are common on the plains to the west. In addition, they serve as a fixed incline plane that lifts the warm, moist air flowing northward from the Gulf of Mexico and thereby increases the frequency of thunderstorms that, in turn, reduce the number of extremely warm days in the valley. Sudden great temperature changes occur infrequently. Rainfall is ample and favorably distributed, with precipitation greatest in winter and again during the

late spring and summer months. The period of lowest rainfall occurs during the fall.

Undifferentiated highlands

Mountain or highland climates are generally cooler than the surrounding lowlands, except in the quiet of winter when temperature inversions can develop. They are also windier, with high wind velocities on summits and ridges and where valleys channel the general windstream off the slope. Diurnal upslope and nocturnal downslope breezes are characteristic and tend to promote, and intensify, cloud development over ridges and peaks by day. Rainfall generally increases with height and steepness of the slopes facing the prevailing wind, partly because of the forced uplift and partly because of the frequency of clouds. Aspen, Colorado, exhibits these climatic conditions.

Subarctic

The subarctic climatic zone, in which Anchorage, Alaska, is located, is characterized by short, cool summers, long, cold winters, and light to moderate

precipitation, mostly in summer. In summer, the high temperature in Anchorage averages about 60°F. Rain increases after mid-June, and about two-thirds of the days in July and August are cloudy and one-third have rain. Autumn is brief, beginning in early September and ending by mid-October. Temperatures begin to fall in September with snow becoming more frequent in October. Winter lasts from mid-October to early April. The coldest weather is usually in January, with high temperatures around 20°F and lows near 5°F. Annual snowfall is between 70 and 90 inches, although most snow is light or dry (low in water content). Spring occurs in late April and May. Spring days are warm and sunny, nights are cool, and precipitation is exceedingly small.

Boreal

North of the timberline, where the sun never rises far above the horizon and the land and water surfaces become free of snow and ice only during a brief, chilly summer, a special climate occurs; this is the tundra. The climatic profile of Barrow, Alaska, provides a good example of tundra climate. Temperatures at this northernmost U.S. weather station

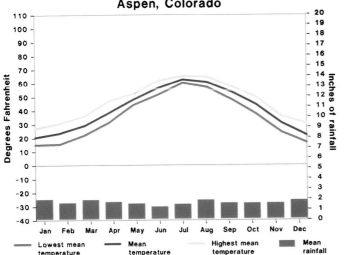

Mean monthly temperature and precipitation
Aspen, Colorado

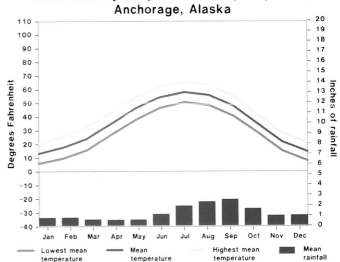

Mean monthly temperature and precipitation
Anchorage, Alaska

remain below the freezing point for most of the year and precipitation is slight in all seasons. February is generally the coldest month. In April, temperatures begin a general upward trend, with May becoming the transitional period from winter to summer. July is the warmest month of the year, with an average temperature of 45°F. During this month or in early August, the Arctic Ocean becomes ice free. The end of the short summer is reached in September, and by November, Barrow returns to the clutches of winter cold. In mid-November, the sun sets and is not seen again until late-January. Afterwards, the amount of possible sunshine increases each day until mid-May when it has increased to 24 hours per day. The sun remains visible from that time to the first days of August, after which time hours of possible sunshine begin to decrease. The amount of sunshine appears to have a direct relationship to the occurrence of clouds, precipitation, and heavy fog. All three build up to a maximum along with the hours of possible sunshine.

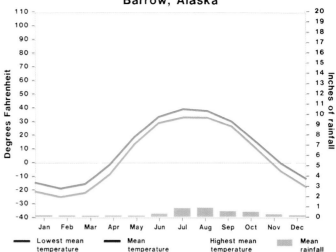

Mean monthly temperature and precipitation
Barrow, Alaska

Lowest mean temperature — Mean temperature — Highest mean temperature — Mean rainfall

3-2
Urban climates

The climates of most urban areas differ from that of their rural surroundings. Differences in air temperature, atmospheric humidity, precipitation, and visibility as well as in concentrations of pollutants, such as sulfur dioxides, nitrogen oxides, hydrocarbons, particulate matter, carbon monoxide, and oxidants, distinguish urban and rural areas.

Urban areas tend to create "heat islands" as a result of seasonal causes and effects of increased pollutants in the atmosphere above them. In summer, the buildings, pavement, and concrete of the city absorb and store larger amounts of solar radiation than the vegetation and soil typical of rural areas. In addition, less of this energy is used for evaporation in the city because of the large amount of precipitation runoff from streets and buildings. During the night, both the city and countryside cool by radiative losses, but the urban construction material generally gives off the additional heat accumulated during the day and thus makes urban air warmer than that of the outlying areas. In winter, the heat generated by combustion for energy production is largely responsible for warmer urban temperatures. Pollutants, which blanket many major

cities, absorb a portion of the upward-directed thermal radiation emitted by the surfaces of buildings and pavement. Part of this radiation is re-emitted by the pollutants and part warms the surrounding air. The latter process tends to increase low-level atmospheric stability over the city and thus enhances the probability of higher pollutant concentrations.

As a general rule, the larger the city, the greater the average difference between its temperature and that of the surrounding countryside. The greatest extreme city–country temperature difference occurs in winter, and the heat island of a city is detected more readily during the evening.

Trends in other meteorological parameters are also evident. The average absolute humidity is lower in cities than in surrounding areas, primarily because the presence of buildings, paved streets, and parking lots lowers evaporation rates. Wind speeds over cities are 20 to 30% lower than over the nearby countryside, but the excess heat and frictional drag of tall buildings in cities produce more turbulence. The blanket of particulates in the atmosphere over most large cities causes solar energy reaching urban areas to be significantly less than that reaching rural areas. Increased concentrations of particulates also cause visibilities to be lower in cities. More-

over, some pollution particles are hygroscopic; that is, water vapor readily condenses on them to form small water droplets, the ingredients of fog. A city also influences the occurrence and amount of precipitation in its vicinity, although the significance of this has not been completely established.

Of increasing concern is the extent to which the urban atmosphere influences both life within it and the larger scale climate surrounding it. Warmer city temperatures cause greater death rates for urban residents during summer heat waves; air pollution frequently causes eye irritation and respiratory illness; and certain plants and building materials are damaged by air pollutants. A more subtle aspect of air pollution may be the long-term modification of climate, particularly on a global scale, brought about by the worldwide buildup of pollutants from urban and industrial areas.

3-3
Climatic change

Beyond short-term oscillations in climatic variables, such as diurnal and seasonal changes in temperature and precipitation or year-to-year differences in weather conditions, are fluctuations that move in

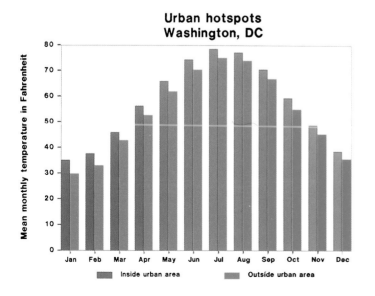

Urban hotspots
Washington, DC

Inside urban area — Outside urban area

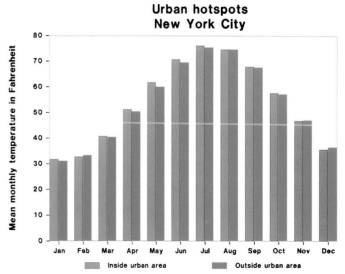

Urban hotspots
New York City

Inside urban area — Outside urban area

one direction sufficiently long and are effective enough to modify other environmental parameters. These trends constitute climatic change.

Climatic changes vary in length and periodicity. Several orders of climatic change are recognized through geological time. First-order variations in climate include fluctuations within the instrument record (10 years) that operate over regular intervals (30 to 100 years) and can be observed within a lifetime. Second-order climatic variations can be detected within the historical record (100 years) and include variations that last over intervals of 300 to 1000 years. Third-order variations, called glacial, occur on the order of tens of thousands of years and coincide with the phases of an ice age (for example, the length of the Wisconsin glacial episode during the last ice age was on the order of 65,000 years). Fifth-order variations are on the order of a minor geological climatic event, such as an entire ice age, and are measured in 1 million-year intervals (for example, the last ice age lasted around 3 million years). Sixth-order climatic variations are measured on the order of 100 million years and coincide with major geological events, such as the onset of

ice ages which have occurred at intervals of approximately 280 million years.

During the past 100 years, a worldwide first-order climatic fluctuation in global atmospheric temperature has been discernible. Between 1870 and 1940, there was a general warming trend that raised the temperature of the lower atmosphere by at least 1°F (0.6°C). This trend reversed between the early 1940s and late 1960s as temperatures fell in each latitude. Since then, the world appears to be warming again. To a large extent, these trends can be explained in terms of changes in the general atmospheric circulation, shifts in the position and intensity of pressure cells and wind belts, and frequency of large-scale pressure systems. However, there is evidence that the general warming is also a result of human influences. The estimated increase in global mean temperature in the past 100 years is consistent with the observed increase in concentrations of atmospheric carbon dioxide and other trace gases, such as methane, chlorofluorocarbons (CFCs), and nitrous oxide. These gases are transparent to incoming short-wave radiation from the sun but absorb outgoing long-wave radiation.

Increases in atmospheric concentrations can lead to a warming of the lower atmosphere and the earth's surface, a phenomenon that is known as "the greenhouse effect."

Changes in concentrations of these trace gases also contribute to changes in concentration of ozone at different altitudes. Ozone in the lower stratosphere absorbs heat radiated from the earth, and changes in its concentration can affect surface temperatures as a result of the greenhouse effect. Ozone also screens the earth from harmful ultraviolet radiation, and its reduction allows more ultraviolet radiation to reach the earth's surface and increases exposure doses for living organisms. The effects of increased ultraviolet radiation on living organisms are poorly understood, except for its association with human skin cancer and apparent damage to the human immune system. Models show that carbon dioxide and methane increase stratospheric ozone, whereas CFCs and nitrous oxide are implicated in ozone reductions. The forecast in ozone loss over the next 30 years ranges from 1 to 4%.

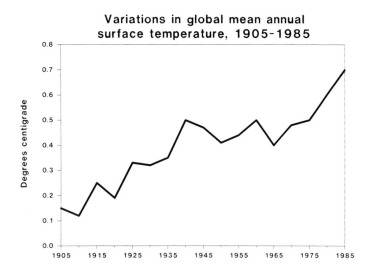

Variations in global mean annual surface temperature, 1905-1985

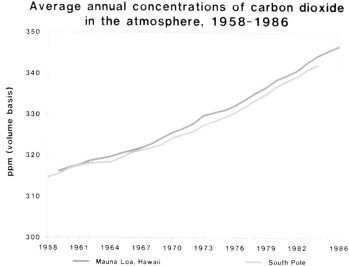

Average annual concentrations of carbon dioxide in the atmosphere, 1958-1986

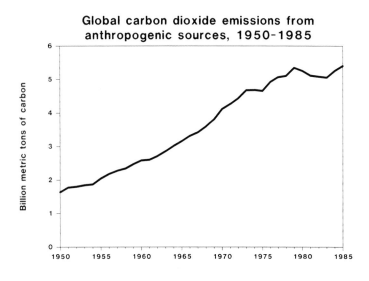

Global carbon dioxide emissions from anthropogenic sources, 1950-1985

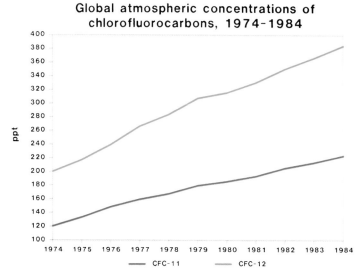

Global atmospheric concentrations of chlorofluorocarbons, 1974-1984

Carbon dioxide is naturally released to the atmosphere during respiration and decomposition. It is also released by the combustion of fossil fuels and biomass. Largely because of increased burning of fossil fuels, carbon dioxide concentrations in the atmosphere have been increasing. Since the beginning of the industrial era, atmospheric concentrations of carbon dioxide have increased by 25%, yet over the last three decades, this trend has accelerated. Carbon dioxide concentrations at Mauna Loa, Hawaii, for example, have increased at an average annual rate of 1.4%. Additional increases in carbon dioxide concentrations are expected to cause further warming.

Methane gas is a natural by-product of the breakdown of organic compounds under anaerobic conditions which occurs in wetland sediments, rice paddies, and the intestines of ruminants. It is also emitted to the atmosphere when biomass is burned and during the production of coal and natural gas. Methane concentrations began to increase about 300 years ago; however, over the past 20 years, atmospheric methane concentrations have been increasing at a rapid rate. Global atmospheric methane concentrations were 1.71 parts per million

volume at the end of 1985, increasing at an average annual rate of 1%.

Atmospheric concentrations of CFCs are increasing more rapidly than those of carbon dioxide and methane. CFCs are highly stable chemical compounds used in aerosol propellants, refrigeration, foam-blowing, and solvents. Average global atmospheric concentrations of CFC-11 and CFC-12 are increasing annually at rates of about 5% each, whereas concentrations of CFC-113 and CFC-22 are increasing even more rapidly, at annual rates of 10% and 11%, respectively. Not only do CFCs contribute to the greenhouse effect but they also destroy ozone in the stratosphere. As a result of global concern over the implications of increased CFC concentrations, thirty-one nations have agreed to stabilize CFC emissions and reduce them to one-half of their 1986 levels. Even with sharp reductions in emissions, however, CFC levels in the atmosphere would not stabilize for years because CFCs take 7 to 10 years to reach the stratosphere, which is 6 to 15 miles above the earth, and once there, these chemicals can persist for 75 to 130 years.

Concentrations of nitrous oxide in the lower atmosphere have shown a steady increase, primarily

because of increasing emissions from fertilizer application and fossil fuel combustion. Like CFCs, nitrous oxide has a long atmospheric residence time (about 170 years), and even if release rates are stabilized or reduced, elevated concentrations would persist for several decades.

Air quality

Air pollutants range from completely odorless and colorless gases, such as carbon monoxide, to highly visible dense smoke and soot composed of suspended particulates emitted from smokestacks.

Some pollutants are highly toxic in minute concentrations—lead, asbestos, and beryllium. Lead accumulates in body organs and is associated with anemia, kidney damage, and damage to the central nervous system. Other pollutants, such as carbon monoxide, can cause headaches, angina attacks, and at very high concentrations, death.

High concentrations of sulfur dioxide, nitrogen oxides, suspended particulates, and photochemical oxidants can affect human health by aggravation of respiratory and cardiovascular diseases, irritation of eyes and respiratory tract, and increased mortality. These pollutants also deteriorate building materials and other surfaces and reduce visibility. Sulfur and nitrogen oxides are considered primary precursors of acidic precipitation and deposition, and anthropogenic emissions of these pollutants are the primary sources of "acid rain."

National ambient air quality standards have been set for certain pollutants that have been determined to adversely affect human health and welfare. These pollutants include oxides of sulfur and nitrogen, volatile organic compounds, suspended particulates, carbon monoxide, and lead.

3-4
Sulfur dioxide

Sulfur dioxide is a colorless gas with a pungent odor. It is readily oxidized in the atmosphere to sulfur trioxide, which forms sulfuric acid with water.

Ambient sulfur dioxide concentrations result primarily from combustion of sulfur-bearing fuels, (chiefly coal and residential fuel oil), smelting of sulfur-bearing metal ores, industrial processes, and volcanic eruptions. Sulfur dioxide emissions in the

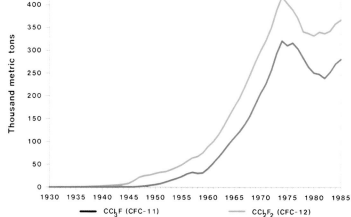

Annual emissions of chlorofluorocarbons 1930-1985

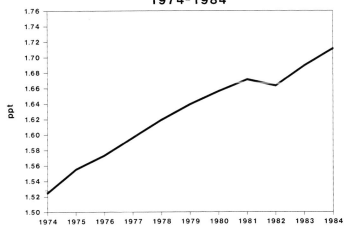

Global atmospheric concentrations of methane 1974-1984

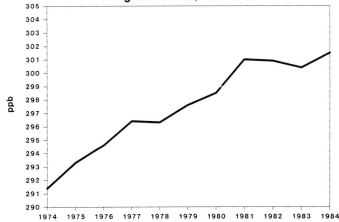

Global atmospheric concentrations of nitrogen dioxide, 1974-1984

United States increased from about 10 million tons per year in 1900 to over 20 million tons per year in 1925. After peaks in 1944 and the early 1970s and troughs in 1933 and 1954, sulfur dioxide emissions in 1986 were about the same as they were in 1930.

From 1900 to 1970, major increases in sulfur dioxide emissions occurred as the result of increased combustion of fossil fuels. The long-term trend in sulfur dioxide emissions follows the general trend for coal consumption in the United States. Between 1970 and 1986, use of coal continued to increase, but emissions decreased primarily because of a general decrease in sulfur content of fuels combusted and reductions resulting from pollution control, such as gas flue desulfurization. Sulfur content in combusted coal has decreased to a large extent as a result of coal cleaning and mixing eastern coal with cleaner western coal. Sulfur oxide emissions have also decreased as a result of the replacement of coal-fired railroad locomotives with diesel-powered ones and a decrease in coal refuse burning.

National sulfur dioxide emissions decreased 21% from 1977 to 1986. Emissions from electric utilities, which have accounted for more than one-half of the total emissions after 1970, decreased at a median rate of approximately 4% per year, for an overall

change of about 37%. Emission reductions from industrial processes have occurred also, mostly from nonferrous smelters and sulfuric acid plants. Sulfur oxide emissions that previously would have been released by smelters are now recovered as sulfuric acid. In addition, since 1972, new sulfuric acid plants must meet more stringent emission limitations than old facilities.

Ambient concentrations of sulfur dioxide decreased by 37% between 1977 and 1986. The disparity between sulfur dioxide air quality improvement and sulfur dioxide emission reductions is attributed to several factors. Ambient sulfur dioxide monitors with sufficient historical data for establishing trends are located mostly in urban areas and as such do not monitor many of the major industrial emissions, which tend to occur in more rural areas. In residential and commercial areas, sulfur oxide emission decreases are comparable to ambient sulfur dioxide improvement. Another factor that may account for differences in sulfur dioxide emissions and ambient air quality is stack height. The utilization of tall stacks to reduce the local impacts of emissions became prevalent in the 1960s and early 1970s. Taller stacks carry emissions higher and to greater distances and can permit ground level con-

centrations of sulfur dioxide concentrations to decrease at a faster rate than emissions. Under these circumstances, ambient concentrations can, in fact, decrease even if emissions increase.

3-5
Nitrogen oxides

Among the oxides of nitrogen, nitric oxide and nitrogen dioxide occur most frequently. Nitric oxide is commonly formed during high temperature combustion. Nitrogen oxide is formed both by combustion and within the atmosphere when nitric oxide combines with oxygen. At low nitric oxide concentrations this atmospheric reaction proceeds slowly, but in the presence of sunlight and hydrocarbons, nitrogen dioxide is formed rapidly. In urban areas, nitrogen dioxide gives the atmosphere a yellow-brown cast, and concentrations greater than one part per million can affect human health and sensitive plants. The oxides of nitrogen also play an important role in the formation of photochemical smog, acid precipitation, and ozone.

Nitrogen oxide emissions result almost entirely from fuel combustion by industry, energy producers,

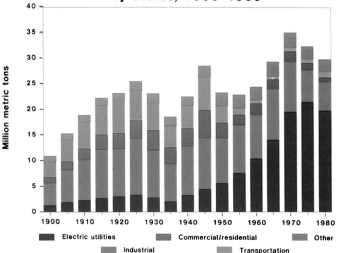

Long-term trends in sulfur dioxide emissions by source, 1900-1980

■ Electric utilities　　■ Commercial/residential　　■ Other
　　　　■ Industrial　　　　■ Transportation

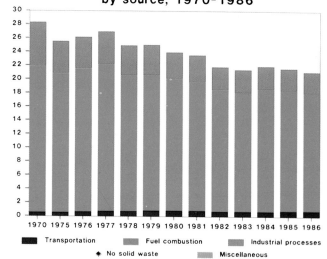

Recent trends in sulfur dioxide emissions by source, 1970-1986

■ Transportation　　■ Fuel combustion　　■ Industrial processes
　✦ No solid waste　　　　■ Miscellaneous

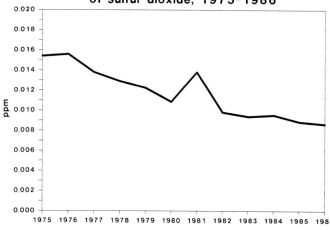

National ambient concentrations of sulfur dioxide, 1975-1986

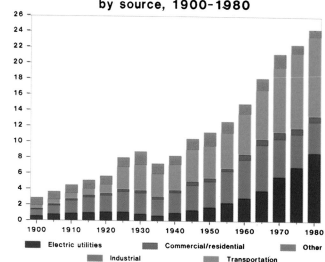

Long-term trends in nitrogen oxides emissions by source, 1900-1980

■ Electric utilities　　■ Commercial/residential　　■ Other
　　■ Industrial　　　　■ Transportation

Recent trends in nitrogen oxides emissions by source, 1970-1986

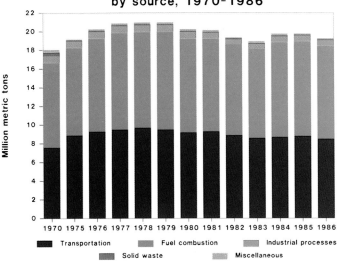

National ambient concentrations of nitrogen dioxide, 1975-1986

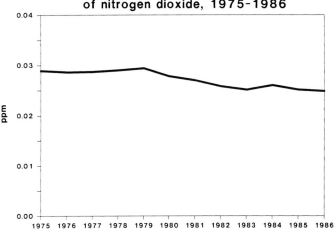

and motor vehicles. Since 1900, nitrogen oxide emissions have increased steadily as a result of increased fuel consumption.

Long-term trends in estimated national emissions show nitrogen oxides increasing until 1979 and then decreasing slightly through 1986. Pollution controls applied to sources of nitrogen oxides have had some effect in reducing emissions through 1986; however, emissions from stationary fuel combustion sources largely reflect an actual growth in fuel consumption. Nitrogen oxide emissions from electric utilities increased 50% from 1970 to 1986, even though control requirements reduced the growth of the emissions somewhat. Between 1970 and 1986, highway vehicle emissions, the source impacting the majority of nitrogen oxide air quality in urban areas, increased by 10%. Light duty gasoline vehicles accounted for about one-half of the nitrogen oxide emissions from the transportation sector and heavy duty diesel vehicles accounted for one-third.

The national trend in annual average ambient levels of nitrogen dioxide is similar to the nitrogen oxide emissions trend in that average concentrations increased from 1975 to 1979 and then decreased through 1986, except for a slight increase in 1984.

Composite average concentrations for large metropolitan areas, however, were higher than those for all other sites. Year-to-year differences in the ambient and emissions changes are probably insignificant given the relatively low ambient nitrogen dioxide levels.

3-6
Volatile organic compounds and ozone

Ozone is a photochemical oxidant and the major component of smog. Ozone is not emitted directly into the air but is formed through chemical reactions between precursor emissions of volatile organic compounds and nitrogen oxides in the presence of sunlight. Because sunlight is necessary for these reactions, maximum oxidant concentrations usually occur around noon, whereas nighttime concentrations are quite low. The reactions are also stimulated by temperature so that peak ozone levels typically occur during the warmer times of the year. Whereas ozone in the upper atmosphere is beneficial to life by shielding the earth from harmful ultraviolet radiation given off by the sun, high concentrations of ozone at ground level are a major health and environmental concern.

Ozone precursors—volatile organic compounds (VOCs)—are emitted from sources as diverse as automobiles, chemical manufacturers, dry cleaners, paint shops, and other sources using solvents. From 1940 through 1970, VOC emissions increased about 50%. Major increases in highway vehicle travel and industrial production were chiefly responsible for the increase. Emissions from these two source categories were about two and one-half times higher in 1970 than in 1940. Emissions from residential fuel combustion and forest fires, which accounted for 42% of total national emissions of VOCs in 1940, declined substantially through 1970. By 1970, their contribution to the total national emissions of this oxidant was reduced to 6%.

Since 1970, emissions of VOCs have decreased primarily as a result of motor vehicle emission controls and less burning of solid waste. As a result of pollution controls, VOC emissions from highway vehicles decreased 52% between 1970 and 1986. Emissions also decreased as a result of the substitution of water-based emulsified asphalts used in road paving for asphalts liquefied with petroleum distillates. This substitution is primarily responsible for the decreased emissions reported for organic solvent use.

Trends in volatile organic compound emissions by source, 1940-1986

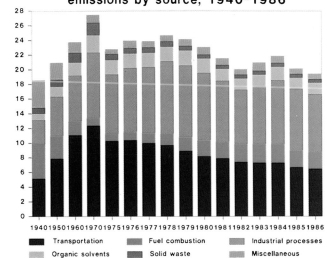

National ambient concentrations of ozone, 1975-1986

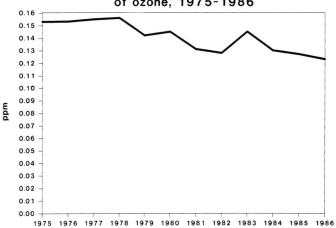

Trends in total suspended particulate emissions by source, 1940-1986

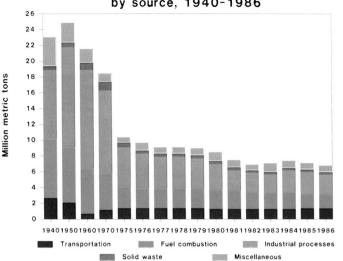

- Transportation
- Fuel combustion
- Industrial processes
- Solid waste
- Miscellaneous

National ambient concentrations of total suspended particulates, 1975-1986

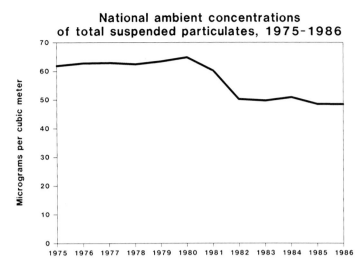

Through 1978, VOC decreases were offset by increases in industrial process emissions, particularly in petroleum refining, organic chemical production, and industrial uses of organic solvents. Since then, pollution controls have been effective in limiting the growth of emissions from industrial processes and, consequently, VOC emissions have declined. Emissions from petroleum product storage and marketing operations have decreased since 1978 also, primarily as a result of declining product demand.

In 1970, emissions of VOCs from residential fuel combustion were insignificant. However, in the late 1970s emissions began to increase as a result of the popularity of wood stoves and fireplaces for residential space heating. In 1986, residential fuel combustion accounted for about 11% of total VOC emissions.

The overall trend in VOC emissions from 1970 through 1986 showed a reduction of about 11%. The trend in ozone air quality showed a similar improvement, with a 13% reduction in ambient ozone levels between 1979 and 1986. Year-to-year fluctuations in ambient levels are mainly attributable to changes in the meteorological conditions conducive to ozone formation.

3-7
Total suspended particulates

Air pollutants, called suspended particulate matter, include dust, dirt, soot, smoke, and liquid droplets directly emitted into the air by such sources as factories, power plants, refuse incineration, cars, construction activity, fires, and natural windblown dust and volcanic ejecta. They also include particles formed in the atmosphere by transformation of emitted gases, such as sulfur dioxide, oxides of nitrogen, and volatile organic compounds. The particulates resulting from anthropogenic sources are of particular concern because they have the potential of carrying toxic (including carcinogenic) trace substances, and the particles themselves may be toxic. Total suspended particulate is one indicator of suspended particles in the ambient air.

Estimated particulate emissions for 1940, 1950, and 1960 were 10 to 30% higher than for 1970. Even though industrial production levels and quantities of fuels consumed were lower than the post-1970 period, the general lack of air pollution controls before 1970 resulted in relatively large particulate emissions. Also, for the years 1940 and

1950, particulate emissions from coal combustion by railroads and from forest wildfires were significant. Since 1970, particulate emissions have decreased by about 64% as the result of air pollution control efforts. The 1986 actual particulate emissions were about one-third of what they might have been without additional control efforts since 1970.

A large portion of the particulate emissions from stationary source fuel combustion results from the combustion of coal. In 1940, coal was consumed largely in the industrial and residential sectors. Residential coal use has declined substantially since 1940; this has resulted in a corresponding reduction in emissions. Industrial coal use also has declined, but not to the same extent. The degree of control employed by industrial coal consumers has increased, however, so that overall industrial coal combustion emissions decreased by 1970 to about 40% of the estimated 1940 level. By 1986, industrial coal emissions had decreased to 13% of the estimated 1970 level. On the other hand, annual coal combustion by electric utilities has increased greatly, from an estimated 51 million tons in 1940 to 321 million tons in 1970 to 685 million tons in 1986. Increased consumption resulted in increased

Trends in carbon monoxide emissions by source, 1940-1986

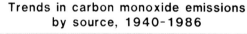
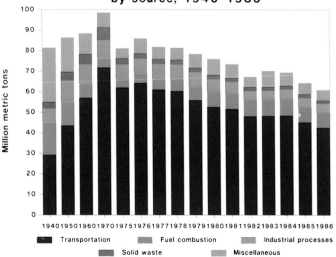

- Transportation
- Fuel combustion
- Industrial processes
- Solid waste
- Miscellaneous

National ambient concentrations of carbon monoxide, 1975-1986

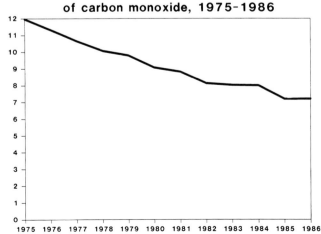

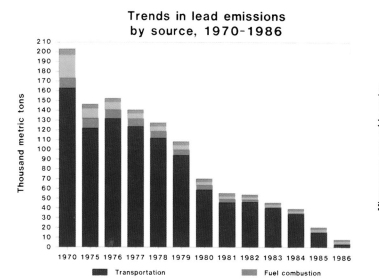

Trends in lead emissions by source, 1970-1986

Thousand metric tons

1970 1975 1976 1977 1978 1979 1980 1981 1982 1983 1984 1985 1986

Transportation   Fuel combustion
Industrial processes   Solid waste

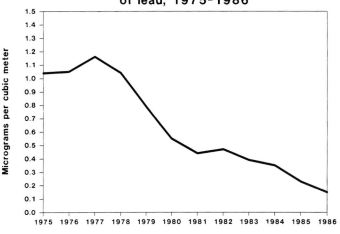

National ambient concentrations of lead, 1975-1986

Micrograms per cubic meter

1975 1976 1977 1978 1979 1980 1981 1982 1983 1984 1985 1986

emissions from 1940 to 1950. Since 1950, particulate emissions from electric utilities have decreased, despite continued increases in coal consumption, primarily because of the installation of improved emission control equipment.

Particulate emissions from industrial processes increased from 1940 to 1950, reflecting increased industrial production. From 1950 to 1986, industrial output continued to grow, but installation of emission control equipment helped offset the potential for emissions to increase. Industrial process emissions stayed about the same from 1950 to 1960 and decreased slightly from 1960 to 1970. Since 1970, actual emissions from industrial processes declined by 83%.

Particulate emissions from the transportation sector have remained relatively stable since 1970 despite use of emission control devices. The potential for emission reductions has been offset by an increase in motor vehicle use.

Average annual ambient levels of total suspended particulates decreased 23% between 1977 and 1986. Particulate air quality levels generally do not improve in direct proportion to estimated emission reductions, however, because air quality levels are influenced by such factors as natural dust, reentrained street dust, and construction activity, which are not included in the emission estimates.

3-8
Carbon monoxide

Carbon monoxide is a colorless, odorless, and poisonous gas that is produced by incomplete burning of carbon in fuels. Over two-thirds of the total national carbon monoxide emissions come from transportation sources, principally from highway motor vehicles. In many cities, the mass of carbon monoxide annually emitted exceeds that of any other pollutant. The highest urban concentrations are usually found where automobile traffic is heaviest, and variation in daily concentrations over most cities shows a bimodal distribution, reflecting usual weekday commuter traffic patterns. Carbon monoxide has a notably detrimental effect on human health; large doses can cause death.

From 1940 through 1970, the relative contribution by the various sources of total carbon monoxide emissions changed considerably. In 1940, high-

way vehicles contributed only 27% of these emissions. Residential fuel combustion (primarily of wood and coal), forest fires, and burning of agricultural crop residues and coal refuse contributed 50% of total carbon monoxide emissions. From 1940 to 1970, highway vehicle emissions nearly tripled, whereas emissions from residential fuel combustion and miscellaneous burning sources decreased significantly. As a result, in 1970, vehicle emissions accounted for 40% of total carbon monoxide emissions. Emissions from industrial processes also increased between 1940 and 1970 by about 35%. The largest increase occurred in the petroleum refining sector, primarily as the result of expansion of catalytic cracking to meet increasing demands for gasoline and other middle distillates.

Since 1970, highway motor vehicles have become the largest contributing source of carbon monoxide emissions, even though emission levels for this category have declined. Recent emission trends reflect both the effect of emission control devices on motor vehicles and the vehicle miles of travel. From 1970 through 1978, motor vehicle miles of travel increased 38%, but because of controls on new vehicles, emissions of carbon monoxide from highway vehicles decreased 16%. From 1978 to 1980, travel miles declined 1.7% and together with stricter emission standards for new vehicles and the gradual disappearance of older uncontrolled vehicles from the vehicle fleet resulted in an estimated 14% reduction in highway vehicle emissions. From 1980 to 1985, vehicle travel increased by 21%; however, as the result of emission controls, carbon monoxide emissions from highway vehicles actually decreased 28% during the period.

Emissions from other sources also have decreased. In 1970, emissions from the burning of agricultural residues were greater than in more recent years. Solid waste disposal emissions have decreased as the result of regulations limiting or prohibiting solid waste burning in many areas. Emissions of carbon monoxide from stationary source fuel combustion occur mainly from the residential sector. These emissions were reduced somewhat through the mid-1970s as residential consumers converted to natural gas, oil, or electric heating equipment. Recent growth in the use of residential wood stoves has reversed this trend, however, and in 1986 residential wood combustion accounted for

about 10% of the national carbon monoxide emissions, more than any source category except highway vehicles. Carbon monoxide emissions from industrial processes have declined since 1970 as the result of the obsolescence of high-polluting processes, such as manufacture of carbon black by the channel process and the installation of controls on other processes.

Although there have been some year-to-year fluctuations in ambient carbon monoxide concentrations, a general long-term improvement in carbon monoxide air quality is evident. There is general agreement between air quality and emission changes over the monitoring period. It is noted, however, that the emission changes reflect estimated national totals, whereas carbon monoxide air quality may reflect local conditions where monitors are frequently located to identify problems.

3-9
Lead

The most significant contributors to atmospheric lead emissions are lead gasoline additives, nonferrous smelters, and battery plants. Emissions of lead have decreased principally as part of an overall automobile emission control program involving the reduction in gasoline lead content; the use of catalytic converters to reduce emissions of nitrogen oxides, volatile organic compounds, and carbon monoxide; and the use of unleaded gasoline in vehicles with converters. Regulations issued in the early 1970s required the lead content of all gasoline to be gradually decreased over a period of many years, and by the early 1980s the lead content was to be reduced to an average of 1.0 gram per gallon. From 1970 through 1975, highway use of gasoline increased 16%, but because of a decrease in lead content in leaded gasoline, lead emissions from highway vehicles decreased 24%. Unleaded gasoline was introduced in 1970 and, from 1975 to 1986, the percent of unleaded gasoline sales increased from 13 to 69%. During this same period, lead emissions decreased 94%. Major reductions in lead emissions occurred between 1984 and 1986 because of further reductions in the lead content of leaded gasoline, to 0.5 gram per gallon in 1985 and to 0.1 gram per gallon in 1986. From 1970 to 1986, off-highway consumption of gasoline decreased 34% and lead emissions decreased 98%.

Lead emissions from stationary sources have declined substantially as a result of pollution control programs oriented toward attainment of lead and total suspended particulate ambient standards. The overall effect of these programs has been major reductions in lead emissions and levels of lead in ambient air. A 95% decrease in lead emissions from stationary source fuel combustion has occurred as a result of the decrease in lead concentration in waste oil utilized in industrial boilers. Lead emissions decreased 92% for industrial processes from 1970 through 1986, partly because of the installation of air pollution control equipment. Lead emissions from solid waste disposal decreased 60% from 1970 through 1986, principally as a result of a reduction in solid waste incineration.

There has been a dramatic improvement in ambient lead concentrations for the entire distribution of trend sites. There was an overall (1977-1986) decrease for urban monitoring sites. These trends compare with the overall reduction in lead emissions.

3-10
Acid deposition

Man-induced acid deposition has been present in the United States since the beginning of the 20th century, but over the past decade or so, the phenomenon has evolved into an issue of considerable public concern. "Acid rain" is the popular term for the deposition of acidic substances in rain, snow, fog, and dew, yet acidic substances also fall as dry particles and gases. Acid deposition is the end product of a series of complex processes involving emissions of precursor chemicals, transformations of these chemicals in the atmosphere, transport of these pollutants through the atmosphere, and subsequent wet or dry deposition.

The primary pollutants—sulfur dioxide, oxides of nitrogen, and volatile organic compounds—contribute to acid formation. Since the early 1970s, man-made emissions of acidic deposition and oxidant precursors as well as levels of acidic deposition and oxidants have decreased or remained relatively constant.

Natural sources of acid deposition precursors include soils, tidal areas, ocean waters, dust storms, and lightning. At present, natural sources of sulfur dioxide and nitrogen oxides, which are estimated to be about 2 million tons per year and 3 million tons per year, respectively, contribute only a small percentage of the total emissions. The contribution of natural sources of volatile organic compounds, on the other hand, which is estimated to be about 35 million tons per year, approaches or exceeds man-made emissions on a continental basis for the United States. Whereas man-made emissions can be and have been reduced, primarily through pollution control and energy conservation, natural background levels constitute an irreducible limit that legislation, regulations, and emission controls cannot influence.

The highest levels of acid deposition are in the regions with the highest levels of man-made sulfur and nitrogen emissions. Beginning in the 1960s, however, as a result of using tall stacks to carry utility emissions of sulfur and nitrogen away from the source, both rain acidity and dry deposition may have decreased locally, but increased regionally. Dry

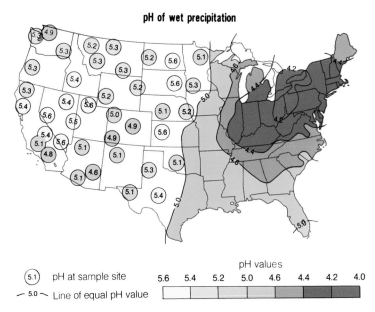

pH of wet precipitation

(5.1) pH at sample site
~ 5.0 ~ Line of equal pH value

pH values
5.6 5.4 5.2 5.0 4.6 4.4 4.2 4.0

deposition is relatively more important closer to the source.

Meteorological and climatic conditions also influence conditions conducive for acid formation and deposition. Weather conditions that prevail at the time the pollutants are emitted determine the direction and the rate of both horizontal and vertical dispersal, and subsequent changes in these conditions determine whether precipitation will occur and to what extent the atmosphere will be cleansed of its pollutant load. Some seasonal trends in pollutant concentrations and geographic distribution also are evident. In the summer, most of the daily nitrogen oxide emissions are converted to nitric acid in one day, and most of the nitric acid produced is expected to be deposited nearer its source than in winter. The rate of ozone formation is greater in summer as is the concentration of hydrogen peroxide; ozone and hydrogen peroxide are the primary agents for the production of sulfuric acid in clouds. In the winter (in the northeastern United States), the formation of sulfuric acid from sulfur dioxide is limited by oxidant availability, and the ratio of nitric acid to sulfuric acid in wet deposition is higher in winter compared to summer, even though ratios of emissions are about the same. This is explained in part by the more efficient uptake of nitric acid by absorption on snowflakes.

Precipitation is naturally acidic, with a pH of between 5.6 and 6.8, as a result of carbon dioxide, natural sulfur and nitrogen compounds, and organic acids in the atmosphere. The pattern for annual average pH of wet deposition for the United States shows that large areas in and downwind of major emission zones have deposition with pH of 4.1 to 4.5. Individual rainfall events can produce deposition as acidic as pH 3 or below.

Terrestrial and aquatic ecosystems in the United States have been subjected to elevated levels of atmospheric pollutants on a regional scale for several decades. Research over recent decades has attempted to address the effects of acid deposition on agricultural crops, forests, surface waterbodies, and shallow ground water.

High concentrations of sulfur dioxide and nitrogen oxides are known to damage crop plants in the United States through leaf injury and reduced plant growth. An evaluation of scientific research on the response of crop plants to acidic deposition, how-

ever, indicates that there are no measurable and consistent effects on crop yield from the direct effects of simulated acidic rain at ambient levels of acidity. In addition, an evaluation of the input of sulfur and nitrogen from acidic deposition indicated that crops may benefit indirectly by nutritional enrichment of agricultural soils. Average ambient concentrations of sulfur dioxide and nitrogen dioxide gases that occur over most agricultural areas in the United States are not high enough or elevated frequently enough to affect crop production on a regional scale, yet negative impacts may occur in local situations close to sources. In contrast to sulfur and nitrogen deposition, controlled studies indicate that ambient levels of ozone in the United States are sufficient to reduce the yield of many agricultural crops. The economic effects of annual crop loss associated with current levels of ozone have been estimated to be on the order of a billion dollars.

Increased concern about the health of forests in the United States has developed recently because of observed declines in many regional forest types. Several ongoing declines affecting managed or low-elevation natural forests are suspected of having an air pollution component to their stress. Damages to mixed forests of the San Bernardino National Forest in California and foliar symptoms in some varieties of white pine throughout the eastern United States are known to be caused by increased ozone levels. Cases with suspected air pollution causes are: Northeastern spruce-fir (where growth reductions are reported for red spruce at lower elevations); New Jersey Pine Barrens (where natural stands of pitch pine and shortleaf pine showed abnormally narrow growth rings over seventeen years of observation, regardless of species or age); Northeastern sugar maple (in which crown dieback symptoms and reduced maple syrup yields have been observed in northeastern United States in recent years and in southeast Canada since the late 1970s, although localized and episodic declines in sugar maple have been observed historically in both countries); and yellow pine in several southeastern Atlantic coast states (where annual basal area growth rates for natural pine stands at coastal plain, piedmont, and mountain sites were 25 to 50% lower in the intervals 1961-1972 and 1972-1982 than 1956-1961). Forests that occur above the cloud

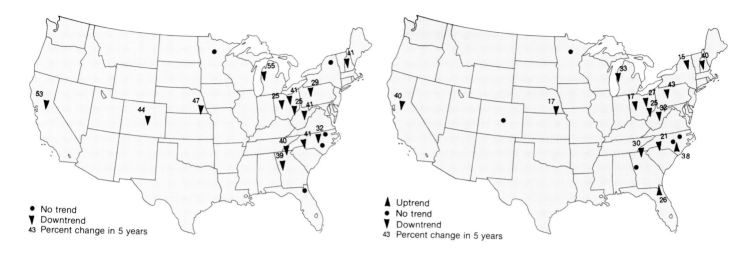

Sulfate ion concentration in precipitation

• No trend
▼ Downtrend
43 Percent change in 5 years

Nitrate ion concentration in precipitation

▲ Uptrend
• No trend
▼ Downtrend
43 Percent change in 5 years

base, represented in the eastern United States primarily by the high-elevation spruce–fir forests of the southern and northern Appalachians, are exposed to severe natural stresses as well as frequent immersion in clouds containing pollutants in concentrations greater than those observed in rain. Foliar damage, reductions in growth rate, and mortality in these forests are common symptoms that strongly suggest adverse impacts caused by air pollutants. Ozone is the leading suspected pollutant that may stress regional forests and cause direct effects, such as growth reduction. Indirect effects of air pollutants and acid deposition are less well understood but appear to be more subtle, complex, and long-term. These indirect effects may increase nutrient leaching, aluminum concentrations (to toxic levels for roots), acidity (to the detriment of soil microbiology), and accumulation of trace metals in soils.

Acidifying compounds also are deposited on watersheds by wet and dry deposition. The acidifying influence of the compounds can be reduced by buffering interactions with vegetation, mineral weathering, absorption of the acidifying agents onto soil surfaces, or buffering processes active within the stream or lake. Surveys of lakes larger than 4 hectares (9.89 acres) in the East and 1 hectare (2.471 acres) in the West show that there are no lakes or reservoirs in the mountainous West, northeastern Minnesota, and the southern Blue Ridge province of the Southeast with pH less than 5.0 (at a pH less than 5.0, most clear lakes do not support fish) and very few with pH less than 5.5. Most other subregions show less than 0.5% of lake area and less than 1% of the number of lakes with pH less than 5.0. The highest percentage of acidic lakes (pH less than 5.0) occur in the Adirondacks and the Upper Peninsula of Michigan, where up to 2% of the lake area and 10% of the lakes are acidic, and in Florida, where 12% of lakes and lake area are acidic. Acidic lakes in Florida are found predominantly in the Okefenokee Swamp, which is naturally acidic, and in the Panhandle subregion where the cause of acidity is uncertain but may reflect acidic deposition as well as other factors. A stream survey conducted in the southern Blue Ridge province found no acidic streams.

Episodic pulses of acidic water in streams and lakes occur during snowmelt and during rainstorms. Both anthropogenic and natural sources of acidity contribute to these pulses. Surface sulfate concentrations from 1965 to 1981 roughly track trends in sulfur emissions. In the Northeast, sulfur dioxide emissions have decreased in recent years; over the same period, surface-water sulfate concentrations have decreased. In the Southeast, sulfur emissions have continued to increase and sulfate concentrations in streams have continued to increase also.

There is a strong positive correlation between lake pH and the probability of fish presence. At a pH below 5.0, serious deterioration in fish distribution occurs unless calcium or organic materials are abundant to increase the pH. Lake acidity can be neutralized for a period of months to years by the application of limestone to the lake or watershed, and fish populations usually benefit from this treatment. Economic damage associated with an estimated reduction in freshwater recreational fishing assumed to be the result of acidification of lakes in the Adirondacks of New York State (circa 1976–1984) was estimated at 1 to 13 million dollars per year (approximately 2 to 26% of the annual value of freshwater recreational fishing for New York State).

Sources and technical notes

3-1
Climatic zones

3-1a
Climatic zones

Executive Office of the President, Council on Environmental Quality. 1981. *Environmental trends* (Washington, D.C.), figure 1, Climatic zones of the United States, p. 3.

Encyclopedia Britannica, Inc. 1981. *The New Encyclopedia Britannica*, Macropaidia Volume 4 (Chicago, Ill.), "Climate," pp. 714-730.

3-1b
Mean monthly temperature and precipitation—Hilo, Hawaii

U.S. Department of Commerce, National Oceanic and Atmospheric Administration, National Climatic Data Center. 1987. *Local climatological data: Annual summary with comparative data, Hilo, Hawaii* (Asheville, N.C.), pp. 4A, 4B, and 7.

3-1c
Mean monthly temperature and precipitation—Key West, Florida

U.S. Department of Commerce, National Oceanic and Atmospheric Administration, National Climatic Data Center. 1987. *Local climatological data: Annual summary with comparative data, Key West, Florida* (Asheville, N.C.), pp. 4A, 4B, and 7.

3-1d
Mean monthly temperature and precipitation—Phoenix, Arizona

U.S. Department of Commerce, National Oceanic and Atmospheric Administration, National Climatic Data Center. 1987. *Local climatological data: Annual summary with comparative data, Phoenix, Arizona* (Asheville, N.C.), pp. 4A, 4B, and 7.

3-1e
Mean monthly temperature and precipitation—Fresno, California

U.S. Department of Commerce, National Oceanic and Atmospheric Administration, National Climatic Data Center. 1987. *Local climatological data: Annual summary with comparative data, Fresno, California* (Asheville, N.C.), pp. 4A, 4B, and 7.

3-1f
Mean monthly temperature and precipitation—Little Rock, Arkansas

U.S. Department of Commerce, National Oceanic and Atmospheric Administration, National Climatic Data Center. 1987. *Local climatological data: Annual summary with comparative data, Little Rock, Arkansas* (Asheville, N.C.), pp. 4A, 4B, and 7.

3-1g
Mean monthly temperature and precipitation—Billings, Montana

U.S. Department of Commerce, National Oceanic and Atmospheric Administration, National Climatic Data Center. 1987. *Local climatological data: Annual summary with comparative data, Billings, Montana* (Asheville, N.C.), pp. 4A, 4B, and 7.

3-1h
Mean monthly temperature and precipitation—Kansas City, Missouri

U.S. Department of Commerce, National Oceanic and Atmospheric Administration, National Climatic Data Center.

1987. *Local climatological data: Annual summary with comparative data, Kansas City, Missouri* (Asheville, N.C.), pp. 4A, 4B, and 7.

3-1i
Mean monthly temperature and precipitation—Burlington, Vermont

U.S. Department of Commerce, National Oceanic and Atmospheric Administration, National Climatic Data Center. 1987. *Local climatological data: Annual summary with comparative data, Burlington, Vermont* (Asheville, N.C.), pp. 4A, 4B, and 7.

3-1j
Mean monthly temperature and precipitation—Seattle, Washington

U.S. Department of Commerce, National Oceanic and Atmospheric Administration, National Climatic Data Center. 1987. *Local climatological data: Annual summary with comparative data, Seattle, Washington* (Asheville, N.C.), pp. 4A, 4B, and 7.

3-1k
Mean monthly temperature and precipitation—Knoxville, Tennessee

U.S. Department of Commerce, National Oceanic and Atmospheric Administration, National Climatic Data Center. 1987. *Local climatological data: Annual summary with comparative data, Knoxville, Tennessee* (Asheville, N.C.), pp. 4A, 4B, and 7.

3-1l
Mean monthly temperature and precipitation—Aspen, Colorado

U.S. Department of Commerce, National Oceanic and Atmospheric Administration, National Climatic Data Center. 1987. *Local climatological data: Annual summary with comparative data, Aspen, Colorado* (Asheville, N.C.), pp. 4A, 4B, and 7.

3-1m
Mean monthly temperature and precipitation—Anchorage, Alaska

U.S. Department of Commerce, National Oceanic and Atmospheric Administration, National Climatic Data Center. 1987. *Local climatological data: Annual summary with comparative data, Anchorage, Alaska* (Asheville, N.C.), pp. 4A, 4B, and 7.

3-1n
Mean monthly temperature and precipitation—Barrow, Alaska

U.S. Department of Commerce, National Oceanic and Atmospheric Administration, National Climatic Data Center. 1987. *Local climatological data: Annual summary with comparative data, Barrow, Alaska* (Asheville, N.C.), pp. 4A, 4B, and 7.

3-2
Urban climates

Encyclopedia Britannica, Inc. 1981. *The New Encyclopedia Britannica*, Macropaidia Volume 4 (Chicago, Ill.), "Urban climates," pp. 1045-1053.

3-2a
Urban hotspots—Washington, D.C.

U.S. Department of Commerce, National Oceanic and Atmospheric Administration, National Climatic Data Center. 1987. *Local climatological data: Annual summary with comparative data, Washington, D.C. National Airport* (Asheville, N.C.), pp. 4B and 7.

U.S. Department of Commerce, National Oceanic and Atmospheric Administration, National Climatic Data Center.

1987. *Local climatological data: Annual summary with comparative data, Washington, D.C. Dulles International Airport* (Asheville, N.C.), pp. 4B and 7.

Data for inside Washington, D.C., are record means (1872-1987) for Washington, D.C. National Airport. Data for outside Washington, D.C., are record means (1963-1987) for Dulles International Airport.

3-2b
Urban hotspots—New York City

U.S. Department of Commerce, National Oceanic and Atmospheric Administration, National Climatic Data Center. 1987. *Local climatological data: Annual summary with comparative data, New York, Central Park, New York* (Asheville, N.C.), pp. 4B and 7.

U.S. Department of Commerce, National Oceanic and Atmospheric Administration, National Climatic Data Center. 1987. *Local climatological data: Annual summary with comparative data, New York, J.F.K. International Airport, New York* (Asheville, N.C.), pp. 4B and 7.

Data for inside New York City are record means (1919-1987) for Central Park. Data for outside New York City are record means (1951-1987) for J.F.K. International Airport.

3-3
Climatic change

Encyclopedia Britannica, Inc. 1981. *The New Encyclopedia Britannica*, Macropaidia Volume 4 (Chicago, Ill.), "Climatic change," pp. 730-747.

World Resources Institute. 1987. *World Resources 1987: An assessment of the resource base that supports the global economy with data tables for 146 countries* (Washington, D.C.), "Atmosphere and climate," pp. 143-161.

3-3a
Variations in global mean annual surface temperature, 1905–1985

Bolin, B., et al. 1986. "The greenhouse effect: Climatic change and ecosystems: A synthesis of present knowledge." Scientific Committee on Problems of the Environment (SCOPE) Ser. No. 29, in *World Resources 1986: An assessment of the resource base that supports the global economy with data tables for 146 countries*, World Resources Institute (Washington, D.C.), figure 10.9, Variation with time of the global mean annual surface temperature, 1900–1985, p. 174.

Data have been obtained from land and marine temperature records. The filtered curve has been obtained by suppressing variations on time scales of less than 10 years.

3-3b
Average annual concentrations of carbon dioxide in the atmosphere, 1950–1986

Keeling, C. D. 1986. Scripps Institution of Oceanography (La Jolla, Calif.), unpublished data.

3-3c
Global carbon dioxide emissions from anthropogenic sources, 1950–1985

Rotty, R. M. 1986. University of New Orleans (New Orleans, La.), unpublished data.

3-3d
Global annual concentrations of chlorofluorocarbons, 1974–1984

Rasmussen, R. A., and M. A. K. Khalil. 1986. "Atmospheric trace gases: Trends and distributions over the last decade." *Science*, 232: 1623-1624.

3-3e
Global annual emissions of chlorofluorocarbons, 1930–1985

Chemical Manufacturers Association. 1986. *Production, sales, and calculated release of CFC-11 and CFC-12 through 1985* (Washington, D.C.).

3-3f
Global atmospheric concentrations of methane, 1974–1984

Rasmussen, R. A., and M. A. K. Khalil. 1986. "Atmospheric trace gases: trends and distributions over the last decade." *Science*, 232: 1623-1624.

3-3g
Global atmospheric concentrations of nitrogen dioxide, 1974–1984

Rasmussen, R. A., and M. A. K. Khalil. 1986. "Atmospheric trace gases: trends and distributions over the last decade." *Science*, 232: 1623-1624.

3-4
Sulfur dioxide

3-4a
Long-term trends in sulfur dioxide emissions by source, 1900–1980

Gschwandtner, G., K. Gschwandtner, K. Eldridge, C. Mann, and D. Mobley. 1986. "Historic emissions of sulfur and nitrogen oxides in the United States from 1900 to 1980." *J. Air Pollut. Control Assoc.*, 36(2): 139-149.

Knudson, D. A., 1986. *Estimated monthly emissions of sulfur dioxide and oxides of nitrogen for the 48 contiguous states, 1975–1984.* ANL/EES-TM-318, vol. 1. Argonne National Laboratory (Argonne, Ill.).

Kohout, E. J., D. A. Knudson, C. L. Saricks, and D. J. Miller. 1987. *Estimated monthly emissions of sulfur dioxide, oxides of nitrogen, and volatile organic compounds for the 48 contiguous states, 1985–1986.* ANL/EES-TM-335, vol. 1. Argonne National Laboratory (Argonne, Ill.).

3-4b
Recent trends in sulfur dioxide emissions by source, 1977–1986

U.S. Environmental Protection Agency, Office of Air Quality Planning and Standards. 1988. *National air quality and emissions trends report, 1986.* EPA-450/4-88-001 (Research Triangle Park, N.C.), table 3-2, National sulfur oxide emission estimates, 1977–1986, p. 3-16.

U.S. Environmental Protection Agency, Office of Air Quality Planning and Standards, National Air Data Branch. 1988. *National air pollutant emission estimates, 1940–1986.* EPA-450/4-87-024 (Research Triangle Park, N.C.), table 1, Summary of national emission estimates, p. 2.

3-4c
National ambient concentrations of sulfur dioxide, 1975–1986

U.S. Environmental Protection Agency, Office of Air Quality Planning and Standards. 1988. *National air quality and emissions trends report, 1986.* EPA-450/4-88-001 (Research Triangle Park, N.C.), trend statistics used to generate figure 3-8, National trend in composite average of the annual average sulfur dioxide concentration at both NAMS and all sites with 95% confidence intervals, 1977–1986, p. 3-12.

3-5a
Long-term trends in nitrogen oxide emissions by source, 1900–1980

Gschwandtner, G., K. Gschwandtner, K. Eldridge, C. Mann, and D. Mobley. 1986. "Historic emissions of sulfur and nitrogen oxides in the United States from 1900 to 1980." *J. Air Pollut. Control Assoc.*, 36(2): 139-149.

Knudson, D. A. 1986. *Estimated monthly emissions of sulfur dioxide and oxides of nitrogen for the 48 contiguous states, 1975–1984.* ANL/EES-TM-318, vol. 1. Argonne National Laboratory (Argonne, Ill.).

Kohout, E. J., D. A. Knudson, C. L. Saricks, and D. J. Miller. 1987. *Estimated monthly emissions of sulfur dioxide, oxides of nitrogen, and volatile organic compounds for the 48 contiguous states, 1985–1986.* ANL/EES-TM-335, vol. 1. Argonne National Laboratory (Argonne, Ill.).

3-5b
Recent trends in nitrogen oxide emissions, 1970–1986

U.S. Environmental Protection Agency, Office of Air Quality Planning and Standards. 1988. *National air quality and emissions trends report, 1986.* EPA-450/4-88-001 (Research Triangle Park, N.C.), table 3-4, National nitrogen oxides emission estimates, 1977–1986, p. 3-29.

U.S. Environmental Protection Agency, Office of Air Quality Planning and Standards, National Air Data Branch. 1988. *National air pollutant emission estimates, 1940–1986.* EPA-450/4-87-024 (Research Triangle Park, N.C.), table 1, Summary of national emission estimates, p. 2.

3-5c
National ambient concentrations of nitrogen dioxide, 1975–1986

U.S. Environmental Protection Agency, Office of Air Quality Planning and Standards. 1988. *National air quality and emissions trends report, 1986.* EPA-450/4-88-001 (Research Triangle Park, N.C.), trend statistics used to generate figure 3-23, National trend in the composite average of nitrogen dioxide concentrations at both NAMS and all sites with 95% confidence intervals, 1977–1986, p. 3-27.

3-6
Volatile organic compounds and ozone

3-6a
Trends in volatile organic compound emissions by source, 1940–1986

U.S. Environmental Protection Agency, Office of Air Quality Planning and Standards. 1988. *National air quality and emissions trends report, 1986.* EPA-450/4-88-001 (Research Triangle Park, N.C.), table 3-5, National volatile organic compound emission estimates, 1977–1986, p. 3-35.

U.S. Environmental Protection Agency, Office of Air Quality Planning and Standards, National Air Data Branch. 1988. *National air pollutant emission estimates, 1940–1986.* EPA-450/4-87-024 (Research Triangle Park, N.C.), table 1, Summary of national emission estimates, p. 2.

3-6b
National ambient concentrations of ozone, 1975–1986

U.S. Environmental Protection Agency, Office of Air Quality Planning and Standards. 1988. *National air quality and emissions trends report, 1986.* EPA-450/4-88-001 (Research Triangle Park, N.C.), trend statistics used to generate figure 3-28, National trend in the composite average of the second highest maximum 1-hour ozone concentration at both NAMS and all sites with 95% confidence intervals, 1977–1986, p. 3-32.

3-7
Total suspended particulates

3-7a
Trends in total suspended particulate emissions by source, 1940–1986

U.S. Environmental Protection Agency, Office of Air Quality Planning and Standards. 1988. *National air quality and emissions trends report, 1986.* EPA-450/4-88-001 (Research Triangle Park, N.C.), table 3-1, National particulate emission estimates, 1977–1986, p. 3-8.

U.S. Environmental Protection Agency, Office of Air Quality Planning and Standards, National Air Data Branch. 1988. *National air pollutant emission estimates, 1940–1986.* EPA-450/4-87-024 (Research Triangle Park, N.C.), table 1, Summary of national emission estimates, p. 2.

3-7b
National ambient concentrations of total suspended particulates, 1975–1986

U.S. Environmental Protection Agency, Office of Air Quality Planning and Standards. 1988. *National air quality and emissions trends report, 1986.* EPA-450/4-88-001 (Research Triangle Park, N.C.), trend statistics used to generate figure 3-3, National trend in the composite average of the geometric mean total suspended particulate at both NAMS and all sites with 95% confidence intervals, 1977–1986, p. 3-6.

3-8
Carbon monoxide

3-8a
Trends in carbon monoxide emissions by source, 1940–1986

U.S. Environmental Protection Agency, Office of Air Quality Planning and Standards. 1988. *National air quality and emissions trends report, 1986.* EPA-450/4-88-001 (Research Triangle Park, N.C.), table 3-3, National carbon monoxide emission estimates, 1977–1986, p. 3-23.

U.S. Environmental Protection Agency, Office of Air Quality Planning and Standards, National Air Data Branch. 1988. *National air pollutant emission estimates, 1940–1986.* EPA-450/4-87-024 (Research Triangle Park, N.C.), table 1, Summary of national emission estimates, p. 2.

3-8b
National ambient concentrations of carbon monoxide, 1975–1986

U.S. Environmental Protection Agency, Office of Air Quality Planning and Standards. 1988. *National air quality and emissions trends report, 1986.* EPA-450/4-88-001 (Research Triangle Park, N.C.), trend statistics used to generate figure 3-17, National trend in the composite average of the second highest nonoverlapping 8-hour average carbon monoxide concentration at both NAMS and all sites with 95% confidence intervals, 1977–1986, p. 3-21.

3-9
Lead

3-9a
Trends in lead emissions by source, 1970–1986

U.S. Environmental Protection Agency, Office of Air Quality Planning and Standards. 1988. *National air quality and emissions trends report, 1986.* EPA-450/4-88-001 (Research Triangle Park, N.C.), table 3-6, National lead emission estimates, 1977–1986, p. 3-41.

U.S. Environmental Protection Agency, Office of Air Quality Planning and Standards, National Air Data Branch. 1988. *National air pollutant emission estimates, 1940–1986.* EPA-450/4-87-024 (Research Triangle Park, N.C.), table 1, Summary of national emission estimates, p. 2.

3-9b
National ambient concentrations of lead, 1975–1986

U.S. Environmental Protection Agency, Office of Air Quality Planning and Standards. 1988. *National air quality and emissions trends report, 1986.* EPA-450/4-88-001 (Research Triangle Park, N.C.), trend statistics used to generate figure 3-34, National trend in the composite average of the maximum quarterly average lead concentration at 82 sites and 7 NAMS sites with 95% confidence intervals, 1977–1986, p. 3-39.

3-10
Acid deposition

3-10a
pH of wet precipitation

3-10b
Sulfate ion concentration in precipitation

3-10c
Nitrate ion concentration in precipitation

National Acid Precipitation Assessment Program, Office of the Director of Research. 1986. *Annual Report, 1986* (Washington, D.C.).

Irving, P. M. 1986. Chapter 6. "Effects on agricultural crops," pp. 6-i-6-50, in *NAPAP interim assessment. Volume IV: Effects of acid deposition.* National Acid Precipitation Assessment Program, Office of the Director of Research (Washington, D.C.).

Kulp, J. L. 1986. Chapter 7. "Effects on forests," pp. 7-i-7-59, in *NAPAP interim assessment. Volume IV: Effects of acid deposition.* National Acid Precipitation Assessment Program, Office of the Director of Research (Washington, D.C.).

Malanchuk, J. L., and R. S. Turner. 1986. Chapter 8. "Effects on aquatic systems," pp. 8-i-8-81, in *NAPAP interim assessment. Volume IV: Effects of acid deposition.* National Acid Precipitation Assessment Program, Office of the Director of Research (Washington, D.C.).

Chapter 4
Land Resources

4-1
Land cover and land use

The United States encompasses wide variations in environment, from forest to desert to tundra. Management of such a heterogeneous area requires an understanding of the overall structure and functioning of natural ecosystems, their relationships and influences on each other, and their capability and availability to support various uses and produce different goods and services.

The land is recognized as falling into spatial patterns of broad physical and biological similarities and can be systematically classified. Within the ecoregion classification, abiotic and biotic classifications are reconciled into a single geographical classification. Each ecoregion covers a contiguous geographical area and is characterized by the occurrence of one or more important ecological associations that differ, at least in proportional area covered, from the associations of adjacent regions. In general, ecoregions are characterized by distinctive flora, fauna, climate, landform, soil, vegetation, and ecological climax. Within such a region, ecological relationships between plant species, soil, and climate are essentially similar, and similar management treatments give compatible results.

The boundaries between adjacent ecoregions are usually difficult to locate precisely. Frequently one region merges gradually into another. The area covered by a particular ecoregion also varies from time to time, not only because of production of new habitats through ecologic succession, but also because of slow but more or less permanent climatic changes. Consequently, regional boundaries are not stationary.

The United States has a land area of 2.3 billion acres. In 1982, about 18% of the land area was in cropland; 26% was in grassland, pasture, and range; and 29% was in forest land. About 12% of the land was not classified in 1982 (but included wetlands, tundra, desert, and urban areas), and the remaining 12% was used for special purposes, including transportation routes, surface-water reservoirs, parks and wildlife refuges, and national defense.

In 1959, the total land area of the United States increased with the addition of Alaska and Hawaii as

Ecoregions

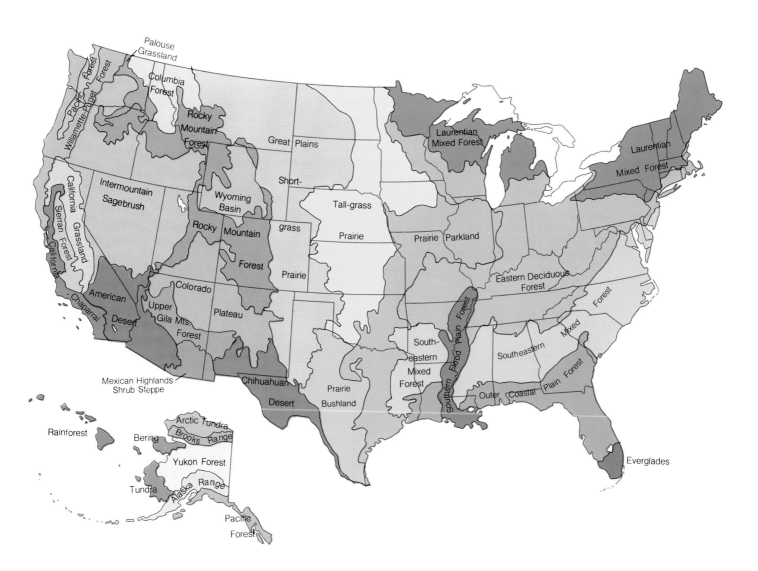

Major uses of land, 1910-1982

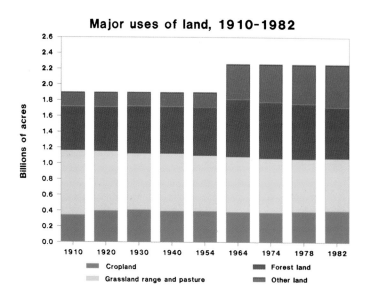

Land in special use areas, 1982

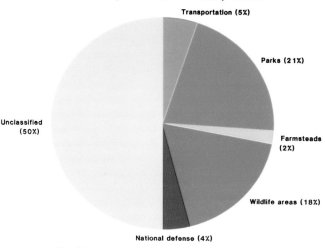

Total land area in special use = 544 million acres

states. Other changes in total land area since 1910 are a result of remeasurement and changes in methods used to measure land area. Changes within use categories correspond to changes in the way land is used.

The total acreage of land actively used for crops, cropland pasture, and idle cropland has remained relatively stable over the past decades. Declines in cropland acreage used for crops are associated with factors such as cropland abandonment and conversion, cropland acreage controls to curb surplus production, and conservation programs that encourage the idling of highly erodable cropland. Since 1985, retirement of erosion-prone cropland has resulted in further reductions in cropland acreage.

Acreages in range, native pasture, and cropland pasture have declined steadily since the turn of the century. These grazing lands have been economically less competitive than other lands; some acreages have been converted to cropland, and others have been abandoned and have reverted to forest land. Additional acreages have been withdrawn from the grassland category for recreational, wildlife, and urban use.

Total forest land, exclusive of forest areas in parks, wildlife refuges, and other special areas, declined from colonial times until about 1920 as forests were cleared for agricultural and residential use. From 1920 to 1960, total forest acreage increased, mainly as a result of reforestation of abandoned cropland and pastureland and additions to the forest-land base when Alaska and Hawaii became states. After 1960, the trend reversed during a period of accelerated forest-land clearing for crops and pasture, highways, reservoirs, and urban and residential development. Part of the reduction also resulted from the reclassification of marginal forest land to rangeland. Beginning in 1985, some diverted cropland has been direct seeded with trees, primarily pines. A national goal is to have at least 5 million acres of highly erodable cropland planted with trees by 1990.

Land in the special-use category increased from 87 million acres in 1950 to 270 million acres in 1982. The large increase in special-use lands since 1950 is attributable primarily to the reclassification of forest and unclassified land with the establishment of national parks, wilderness areas, and

wildlife refuges. Some cropland used for crops and rangeland also was incorporated into these special-use areas. Much of the land involved, however, was remote, rugged, and/or mountainous.

Other changes in the special-use category occurred between 1950 and 1982. Land used for transportation increased by about 2 million acres, whereas land used for national defense purposes decreased by about the same amount. Land in transportation use actually increased somewhat more than this, but some of the acreage was assigned to urban land use and hence is included in the unclassified category.

Two hundred seventy-four (274) million acres of the Nation's land area were not inventoried in 1982 and were placed in the unclassified category. Of unclassified land, 135 million acres (about 49%) were located in Alaska and about 47 million acres (about 6%) were built-up or urbanized (this includes settlements with 2500 or more inhabitants). Between 1970 and 1980, total land area in the urban category increased at a rate of 1.3 million acres per year.

Land ownership 1982

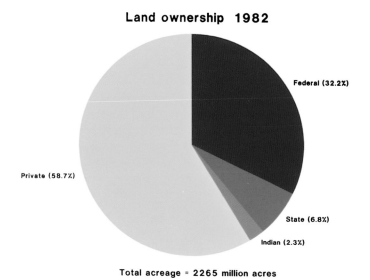

Total acreage = 2265 million acres

Land use by ownership, 1982

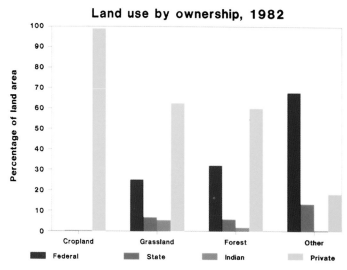

In 1982, more than one-half of the land area of the United States was privately owned, whereas nearly one-third was federally owned and the remainder was owned by states, local governments, and Indian nations. Included in the private ownership category was 99% of the Nation's cropland, 63% of the grassland, and 60% of the forest land.

Land use patterns vary on a regional scale. Proportions of land used for crops, for example, are particularly large in the Corn Belt and Northern Plains, whereas grazing of pasture and range is the predominant use of land in the Southern Plains, Mountain States, Pacific States, Alaska, and Hawaii. Forest-land acreages are particularly large, both in total acreage and as proportion of land area, in the Northeast, Appalachian, and Southeast regions. Forest lands are large in the Mountain region and in Alaska but are less dominant proportions of the total land area. Land for special purposes is also distributed unevenly. In 1982, 66% of special-use lands used for recreation and wildlife purposes was in Alaska, 22% was in the Mountain and Pacific regions, and 10% was in a few Eastern States, including New York, Pennsylvania, Tennessee, and Florida.

4-2
Farmland

The pattern of farm distribution seen in 1982 has not changed markedly since the 1920s. The distribu-tion of farms relates to settlement patterns and geo-graphic differences in climate, water resources, and land use.

When Europeans first colonized what is now known as the conterminous United States, they found an endless expanse of forest broken only by marshes and swamps, cliffs and bluffs too steep for forest, small grassy openings, and prairies and bar-rens of the interior. As settlement increased, first in the Southeast in the early 1500s and later in the East, forests were cleared for cropland and pasture-land to provide food for the people and forage for livestock. By the time of the American Revolution, nearly three-quarters of a 100-mile-wide strip of land from Georgia to southern Maine had been converted to farmland. Some of this land was only marginally suited for farmland and farming practices of the day. Continuous tilling and increased erosion left soils depleted and damaged, causing crop yields to decline. But land was abundant and cheap, and abandonment of poor or worn-out land became a common practice in the settlement of the United States.

In the early 1800s, farmers began moving west to New York, then to Ohio, Indiana, Illinois and Michi-gan, and south to Tennessee and Alabama, abandon-ing the poor farmlands in the East to be reclaimed by forests. The prairies of the Midwest were later opened for settlement, and settlers began farming the fertile Corn Belt. After a lull during the Civil War, the West continued to attract settlers. Better transportation, new and improved farm machinery, end of the Indian wars, rapidly growing markets back East and overseas, and favorable public land policies and costs were among the factors that attracted homesteaders and farmers west of the Mississippi River.

Homesteading and farming in western areas were not without obstacles, however. Woodlands and prairies of the Midwest, when cleared and tilled, were less able to absorb heavy rains of spring and summer, and frequent flooding destroyed fields. Drainage was needed for cultivation of seasonally flooded prairie soils, especially in the Great Lakes region. In semiarid regions, rainfall was lower and less dependable, and irrigation became necessary.

In the 1920s, the remaining public lands were withdrawn from homesteading, and the era of farm-land expansion soon ended. Land clearing for new farmland and abandonment of worn-out farmland continued to occur, but the overall pattern of farm-land distribution has changed very little since then.

Number of farms and land in farms

The number of farms and land in farms in the United States grew rapidly during the 1800s as the Nation's population grew and its territory expanded with the settlement of the West.

In the early 1900s, after western expansion slowed and industrialization began, the number of

Land use by region, 1982

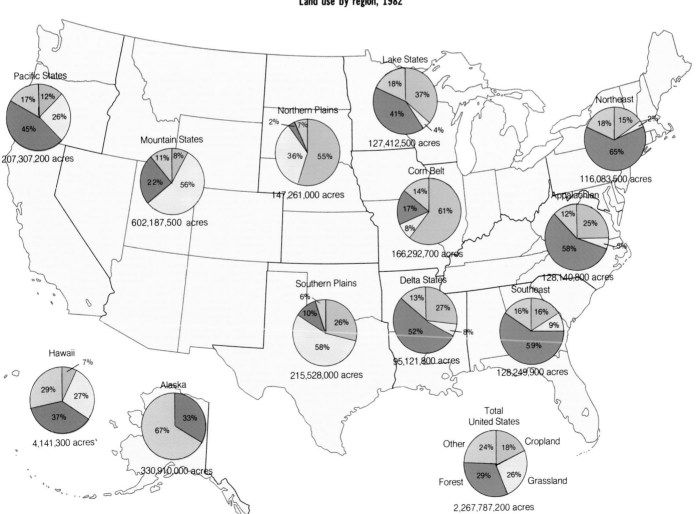

Distribution of farms, 1982

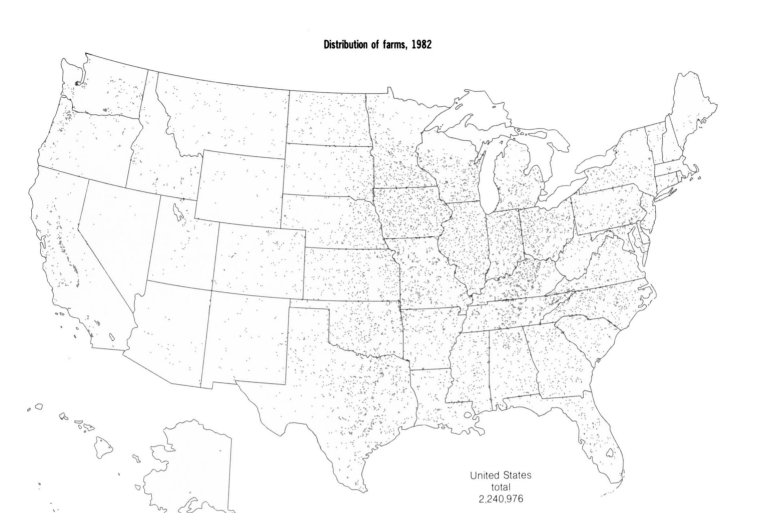

United States
total
2,240,976

farms in the United States began to decline. A second wave of farm abandonment began. The movement was not so much from poor farms to better farms, but from farms to nonfarm areas or jobs. Except for an increase in the number of farms during the depression years when more than one-half million families returned to the land, farm numbers have continued to decline since 1935. In 1986, approximately the same number of farms existed in the United States as there was in 1860.

Even though the number of farms started to decline after the turn of the 20th century, the amount of land in farmland in the United States continued to grow until the 1950s. Between 1950 and 1982, loss of farmland has averaged about 5.4 million acres per year.

Reductions in the number of farms and total farmland area are attributable to a combination of factors, including a chronically depressed farm economy, farm production technologies that have reduced labor requirements, consolidation of small farms into larger operating units, government-sponsored land retirement programs, and conversion of farmland to nonfarm use.

Changes in farm numbers and area have not occurred evenly across the Nation. In the East, the abandonment of some of the poorer farmland in mountain and hill regions and the growth of metro-politan areas along the coasts have resulted in a sig-nificant reduction in farm numbers. Most of the

reductions in the South have resulted from share-tenant and sharecropper farms being absorbed into larger operations. In other parts of the country, however, increases in farm numbers have occurred as a result of new technology and policies affecting land for farms. In the arid West, for example, huge public works involving water storage and irrigation have reclaimed desert lands for agriculture, and in the Corn Belt, vast areas of waterlogged lands have been converted to agriculture by draining.

Farm tenure

Tenure arrangements under which farms are operated include full owners who own all the land they operate, part owners who own part and rent part, tenants who rent all the land they farm, and farm managers who operate someone else's land under a management contract.

A significant trend in farm numbers and tenure in the United States is the increasing importance of part owners. The number of farms operated by full owners and tenants has decreased steadily since the depression years, while at the same time, the number of farms operated by part owners has increased. From 1950 to 1982, part owners con-trolled more farmland than any other tenure group, accounting for nearly 55% of all farmland in 1982. The part owner form of tenure has been a major

factor in adjusting the Nation's agriculture into larger farm units.

Part owners tend to rent only the best agricul-tural land. Farm tracts may be far apart, and it takes additional management skills to operate one's own land as well as that owned by another. The percentage of part owner tenancy is higher on crop farms than on livestock or fruit-and-nut farms.

Farm size

The number of farms and the distribution of land in farms by farm size illustrate trends toward fewer, larger farms. The number of farms of less than 500 acres represented nearly 85% of all farms in 1982 but has been declining since 1935. By contrast, the number of farms of 500 acres or more represented about 6% of the total number of farms in 1982 but has increased steadily since 1900. Farms of 1000 acres or more have grown more rapidly in number than farms of 500 to 1000 acres. The number of farms of less than 50 acres also increased between 1978 and 1982.

The amount of land in farms of 1000 acres or more has increased significantly over the past several decades, whereas land in farms 500 acres or less has declined. Land in operations having at least 1000 acres now comprises about 60% of the total farmland in the United States. Much of the increase

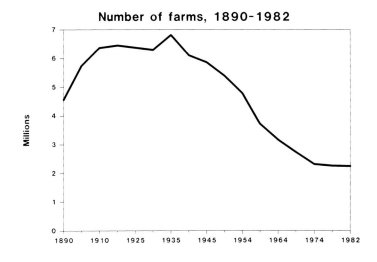

Number of farms, 1890-1982

Millions

Land in farms, 1900-1982

Billions of acres

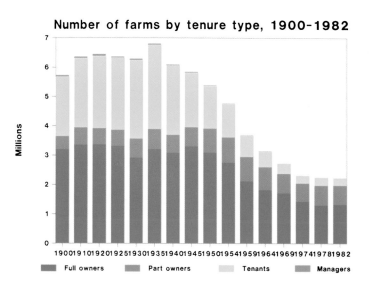

Number of farms by tenure type, 1900-1982

Millions

Full owners   Part owners   Tenants   Managers

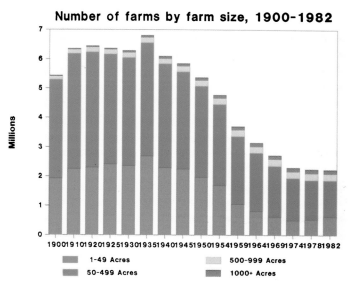

Number of farms by farm size, 1900-1982

Millions

1-49 Acres   500-999 Acres
50-499 Acres   1000+ Acres

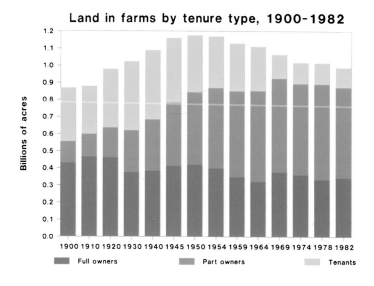

Land in farms by tenure type, 1900-1982

Billions of acres

Full owners   Part owners   Tenants

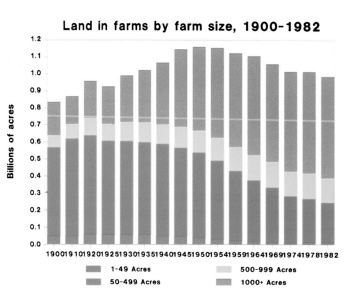

Land in farms by farm size, 1900-1982

Billions of acres

1-49 Acres   500-999 Acres
50-499 Acres   1000+ Acres

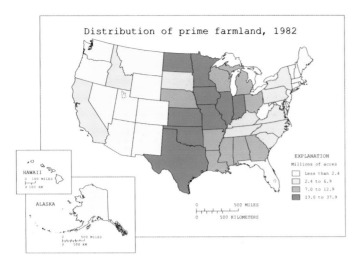

Distribution of prime farmland, 1982

EXPLANATION
Millions of acres
Less than 2.4
2.4 to 6.9
7.0 to 12.9
13.0 to 37.9

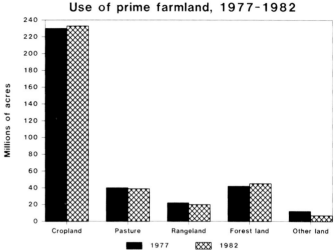

Use of prime farmland, 1977-1982

1977   1982

in farm size is the result of smaller-sized farms being absorbed into larger operations.

The average farm size has increased steadily, from 199 acres in 1860 to 456 in 1986. Mechanized and chemical farming practices have enabled individual operators to farm larger acreages.

The decrease in number of farms and the increase in average farm size have been accompanied by trends toward greater farm-enterprise specialization. The tendency to concentrate production in one enterprise rather than have many different agricultural enterprises on the same farm has evolved as well as the trend toward the regionalization of specialized production where climate, markets, topography, soils, and institutional patterns combine to provide production advantages. Examples of regional production patterns include dairy, feed grains, and specialty crops in the Northeast; cotton, cash crops, and livestock in the Gulf and Atlantic Coastal Plain; fruit, truck crops, and livestock in the Lake States; grains and livestock in the Central Lowlands; wheat in the Great Plains; fruits and vegetables in California, Florida, and south Texas; livestock and irrigated crops in the Basin and Ranges and Columbia Plateau; and dairy and specialty crops in the Pacific Northwest.

4-3
Prime farmland

Prime farmland is the best farmland in the country for producing food, feed, fiber, and oilseed crops. It has an adequate and dependable water supply, a favorable temperature and growing season, acceptable soil acidity or alkalinity, salt, and sodium content, and few or no rocks. Air and water move readily through the soil, and the soil is not subject to excessive erosion. The land is protected from flooding and is not saturated with water for long periods. Prime farmland produces the highest yields with minimal expenditure of energy and economic resources, and farming it results in the least damage to the environment. Land classified as prime farmland includes cropland, pastureland, rangeland, forest land, or other land, but not urban or built-up land or land covered with water. Most of the Nation's crops and a large share of the agricultural exports are produced on prime farmland.

In 1982, there were about 344 million acres of prime farmland in the United States. About 68% of the prime farmland was in cropland; 12% in pasture; 5% in rangeland; 13% in forest land; and 2% in farmsteads, farm roads, feedlots, or similar land.

Losses of prime farmland since 1967 are estimated at 48 million acres (note: losses since 1967 depend on inadequate estimates of prime farmland in 1967). Most of the prime farmland loss resulted from cropland being converted to urban and built-up areas or submerged by water impoundments. The loss of prime farmland puts more pressure on use of less suitable farmland that generally is more susceptible to erosion or drought, more difficult to cultivate, and usually less productive.

The distribution and use of prime farmland varies from state to state. The best farmland in the United States lies in a broad belt extending from the Great Lakes to the Gulf of Mexico. In Arizona, Colorado, New Mexico, North Dakota, and Utah, 90% of the prime farmland is used for crops, and in California, Hawaii, Idaho, Illinois, Iowa, Nebraska, Nevada, Ohio, and South Dakota, 80 to 90% of prime farmland is used for crops. In the remaining states, less than 50% of the prime farmland is used for crops. Instead, much of it is used for timber production and livestock grazing. Some is held idle by speculators anticipating urban or industrial growth.

Conversion of prime farmland to other uses has both regional as well as local impacts. Not every region is equally endowed with prime farmland, and

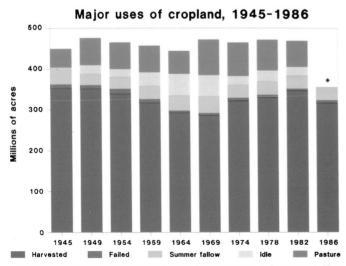

Major uses of cropland, 1945-1986

Harvested   Failed   Summer fallow   Idle   Pasture

* Idle cropland, cropland pasture, and total cropland are estimated only for years coinciding with Census of Agriculture years.

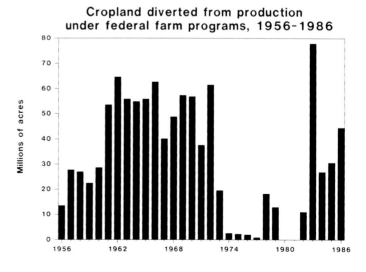

Cropland diverted from production under federal farm programs, 1956-1986

Distribution of cropland acreage changes, 1949–1982

1949-69

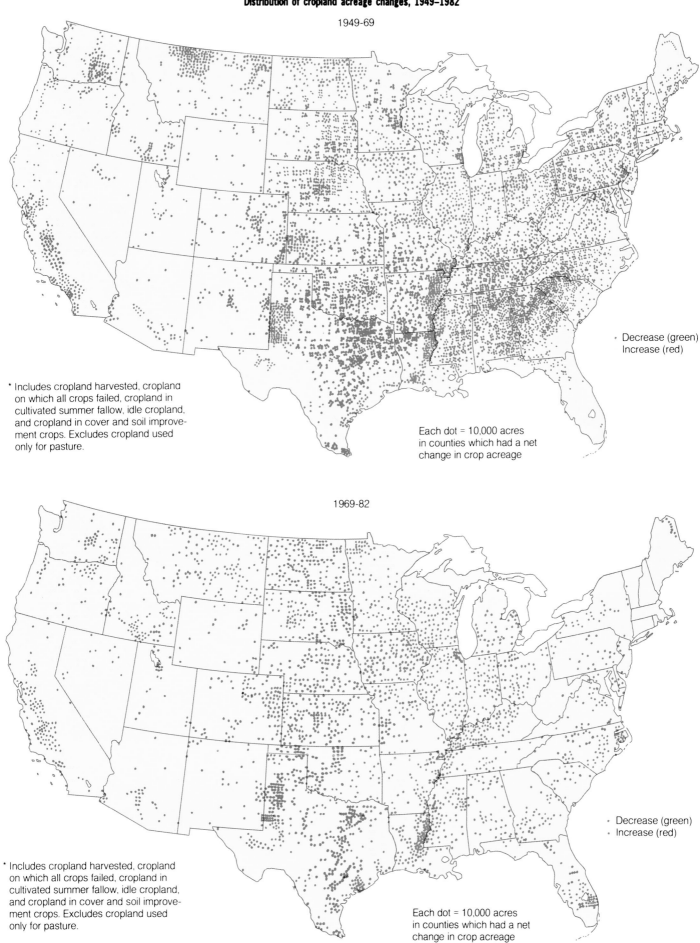

* Includes cropland harvested, cropland on which all crops failed, cropland in cultivated summer fallow, idle cropland, and cropland in cover and soil improvement crops. Excludes cropland used only for pasture.

Decrease (green)
Increase (red)

Each dot = 10,000 acres in counties which had a net change in crop acreage

1969-82

* Includes cropland harvested, cropland on which all crops failed, cropland in cultivated summer fallow, idle cropland, and cropland in cover and soil improvement crops. Excludes cropland used only for pasture.

Decrease (green)
Increase (red)

Each dot = 10,000 acres in counties which had a net change in crop acreage regions with the least resource capability are where most of the prime farmland conversions are taking place. The Northeast, for example, has lost proportionately more prime farmland than any other region. In the West, irrigation is essential to prime farmland and land-use policies must protect not only the land but also the water that makes it prime.

4-4
Cropland

The total cropland base in the United States has remained relatively stable since about 1945. Total cropland in 1945 was 475 million acres, compared to 469 million acres in 1982.

The major uses of cropland include cropland used for crops (harvested cropland, cropland on which crops fail, and cultivated summer fallow), idle cropland, and cropland pasture. Cropland used for crops peaked in total acreage in 1949 and remained at around 380 million acres until 1956 when cropland diversion programs began. In the early 1970s, many growers shifted idle cropland and cropland pasture back into crop production when diversion programs ended and export markets expanded. Cropland used for crops increased to 387 million acres in 1981 but decreased to 357 million acres in 1986. Crop acreages are likely to continue to decline as farmers remove erosion-prone cropland from production and place it into federally sponsored conservation programs through 1990.

About 30 million acres of cropland are usually summer fallowed annually. Summer fallow increased during the 1960s when much cropland was diverted from production.

Crop failure has averaged 6–7 million acres annually over the past 20 years. This represents about 2% of the cropland harvest.

About 20% of all cropland has been idled or put into pasture since 1949, except in 1969 when the proportion reached nearly 30%. Much of this land is readily convertible to crop production. Idle cropland includes land completely idled and land seeded to soil improvement crops but not harvested. Some is idled because of adverse weather and soil conditions at planting time, lack of economic incentives, or personal reasons. Other acreage is idled because of cropland diverted under federal farm programs.

Cropland used for pasture is routinely rotated between crop and pasture, although the length of the rotation period varies. Part of this acreage is marginal for crop use and may remain in pasture indefinitely. The buildup of cropland pasture during 1949–1969 resulted from cropland being planted with soil-improvement crops under federal programs and not returned to crop production.

The use of cropland for agricultural production is influenced by a number of factors, including crop prices and income support relationships; export marketing and trade practices; farm production technologies; soil, water, and climatic conditions; conservation programs; and competition from nonagricultural uses. Although cropland acreages have decreased, acre-yields of grain crops have doubled or tripled as a result of irrigation, fertilizers, more efficient machinery, and more drought-resistant varieties of crops. New land available for conversion to cropland is limited by soil, water, or climatic constraints as well as by economic or regulatory disincentives.

Distribution of cropland acreage changes

Between 1949 and 1969, cropland acreages decreased or remained the same in three-fourths of the Nation's counties. In the Northeast and Appalachian regions, cropland was abandoned and self-seeded to native vegetation, planted to forest land, seeded to pastureland, or converted to urban, residential, and other nonagricultural uses. The largest reductions in cropland acreage occurred in the Southeast, where previously diverted cropland was never returned to crop production and additional cropland was converted to urban and other nonagricultural uses and to forest land. Cropland reductions in the Northern and Southern Plains region resulted from an increase in cropland pasture and permanent pasture. As in the Southeast, much of the pasture was never returned to cropland.

Increases in cropland between 1949 and 1969 occurred principally in the Corn Belt, Mountain, and Delta States regions. The increases resulted from cultivating new land by draining wetlands and clearing forests as well as by returning retired cropland to crop production. Increases in Delta States cropland were confined to the Mississippi Delta

region where bottomland hardwood forests (swamps) were converted to cropland. Additional increases occurred when permanent pasture was converted to cropland in the Northern Plains, and large expanses of forest land in the Southern Plains were cleared for cropland and pasture.

Between 1969 and 1982, the regional picture changed dramatically. All regions of the conterminous United States, except the Plains, experienced net increases in total cropland area. The largest net increases were in the Corn Belt, Lake States, and Delta States regions, but the largest percentage increases were in the Appalachian and Delta States regions. Increases were rather evenly distributed throughout the Corn Belt and Lake States but were concentrated in the Mississippi Delta of the Delta States and in the western and coastal areas of the Appalachian region. Cropland pasture, forest land, and wetlands were the principal sources of additional cropland in all regions, although permanent pasture was also converted. Drainage continued to contribute additions to the cropland base in the Corn Belt, Delta States, and Lake States regions; however, increases in cropland acreage in these regions were offset by losses to urban areas, rural parks, and other nonagricultural uses.

4-5
Materials and energy used in agriculture

Agricultural productivity

Agricultural productivity is the ratio of total outputs (crops, livestock) to total inputs (land, labor, seed, fertilizer, irrigation, energy, or similar factor). Total production is sometimes erroneously measured by outputs only.

The Nation's agricultural productivity has risen steadily over the past two centuries, although the annual growth rate has varied. From the Colonial Period to the Civil War, productivity increased only slightly because agricultural methods were quite primitive, production per acre was low, and large amounts of land and labor were required to meet the Nation's growing demand for food, feed, and fiber. After the Civil War, to about 1920, agricultural productivity increased by about 50%, largely

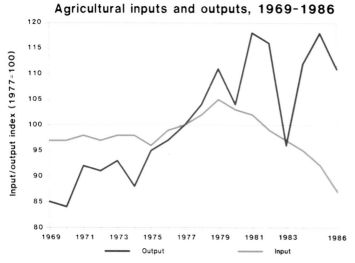

Agricultural inputs and outputs, 1969-1986

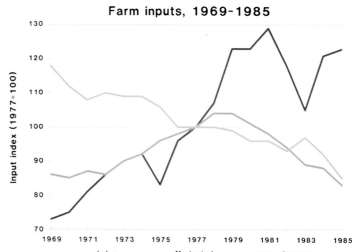

Farm inputs, 1969-1985

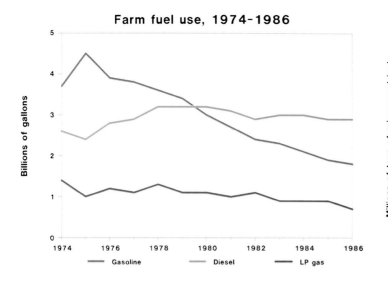

Farm fuel use, 1974-1986

Billions of gallons

Gasoline   Diesel   LP gas

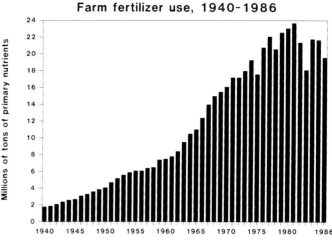

Farm fertilizer use, 1940-1986

Millions of tons of primary nutrients

because of increased use of new and improved farm machinery and equipment. The Great Depression slowed the productivity growth rate, but afterwards and during World War II, the upward trend resumed in response to a number of significant advancements. The tractor replaced draft animals, and lime and fertilizers improved soil conditions. New plant and animal strains were introduced, and disease control was improved.

From 1939 to 1960, total productivity increased 2% each year; however, between 1960 and 1970, productivity rose by only 0.9% per year. The rising costs of production associated with increased use of irrigation water, fertilizer, pesticides, and energy on farms offset much of the gains in total production, and the effect has been a reduction in the productivity growth rate. Since 1970, overall productivity has increased, but there have been declines in certain years as a result of conditions such as a corn blight in 1970, bad weather in 1974, and an acreage reduction program in 1983.

Farm inputs

The principal inputs to agriculture are labor, machinery, and chemicals. The importance of these inputs has changed throughout agricultural history. Today, the Nation's farmers produce more per farmer than ever before but do so with greater use of machinery and chemicals and less use of farm labor. This trend began soon after the Revolutionary War when farmers started inventing ways to reduce labor costs. At that time, farmers made up 90% of the work force in the United States and produced enough to be self-sufficient. The invention of farm machinery, such as planters, cultivators, reapers and threshers, and the development of agricultural chemicals, such as fertilizers, pesticides, antibiotics and other additives, revolutionized farming and increased production while, at the same time, reduced labor requirements. By 1984, farmers represented only 3% of the national work force, but each produced enough food, fiber, and fuel for about 77 people.

Farm fuel use

Energy is another important farm input. It includes gasoline, diesel fuel, liquid petroleum gas, natural gas, and electricity, which are used directly in the production and marketing of crops, livestock, and poultry and in the manufacture of fertilizer and pesticides.

Gasoline use has declined in recent years, whereas diesel and liquid petroleum gas use has remained unchanged. Increased use of conservation and efficiency measures as well as increased participation in acreage reduction programs are responsible for this trend. On-farm fuel use is expected to decline further in the near future with further reductions in planted acreage, continued replacement of older gasoline machinery by diesel-powered machinery, and adoption of energy-saving farm production technologies.

Farm fertilizer use

Fertilizer use on farms in the United States increased steadily over the past several decades until crop reduction programs and farm economic stresses caused a reversal of this trend a few years ago.

Fertilizers consist of primary plant nutrients such as nitrogen, phosphorus, and potash. These nutrients stimulate plant growth and substantially increase yields per acre, even when soil productivity has deteriorated because of soil erosion, compaction, or removal of crop residue. A side effect, however, is that nutrients not taken up by plants remain in the

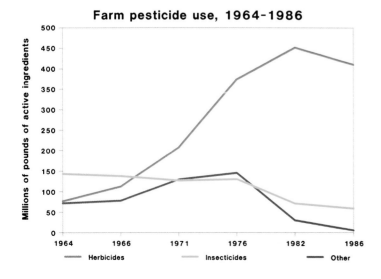

Farm pesticide use, 1964-1986

Millions of pounds of active ingredients

Herbicides   Insecticides   Other

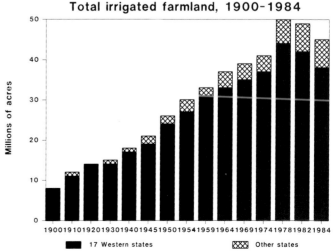

Total irrigated farmland, 1900-1984

Millions of acres

■ 17 Western states   ▧ Other states

Water used for irrigation, 1900-1985

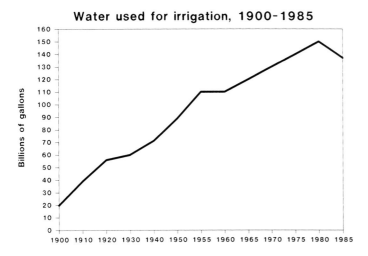

Water applied to irrigated areas, 1969-1984

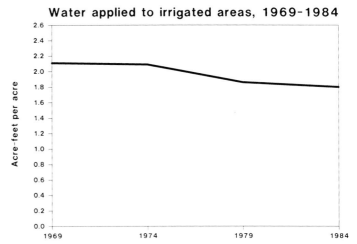

environment, often at levels that exceed optimum, and can adversely affect surface- and ground-water quality and impair human and livestock health. Agricultural fertilizers are among the principal sources of eutrophication of surface water and nitrate contamination of ground water.

Environmental problems stemming from fertilizer use can occur far beyond the farmer's fields and pastures. Areas that have a high potential for nutrient loading to water bodies are generally areas of intensive agricultural use, areas with significant cropland erosion, and (to some extent) areas of dense human populations.

Farm pesticide use

Agricultural pesticides are chemicals used to control plant and animal pests that affect crop and animal production. Pests can destroy commodities, lower market value by causing blemishes or visible detractants, affect nutrient content, or promote the production of toxic substances as a defense mechanism. Pests can also transmit disease and become an irritant, thus affecting growth and output levels in animal production. The principal types of pesticides are herbicides, insecticides, fungicides, and nematocides.

Over the past three to four decades, farmers have become dependent upon the use of pesticides. Total annual pesticide use on farms reached 650 million pounds (of active ingredients) in 1976. However, as a result of a number of factors including the substitution of pesticide materials with low application rates and cropland acreage reduction programs, the pounds applied declined to 475 million pounds in 1986.

Concern about pesticide use relates to the fact that these chemicals act not only against target pests but also pose a threat to human health and reproductive capacity; harm nontarget species; foster the development of resistant pests, especially insects; and accumulate in food chains. Pesticides enter the atmosphere from spray during application and reach the aquatic environment in sediment runoff, effluents from manufacturing plants, and through bioaccumulation. Because data on pesticide buildup in the environment are limited, a national assessment of pesticide impacts is not possible.

Trends in types and amounts of farm pesticides used are variable. Herbicides are used to control weeds on cropland and to eliminate poisonous plants in grazing areas. There are selective herbicides that control only broadleafed plants whereas others control grasses. Preplant or preemergence treatments control emerging weeds, and postemergence treatments are used for weeds that either were not affected by previous treatments or for weeds that emerge later in the growing season. In multiple application cases, both treatments are used and in some cases, the same acreage might receive more than one postemergence application, although this is infrequent.

Herbicides are used extensively on corn and soybeans. Atrazine and alachlor are the products most commonly used in corn production, either alone or in combination. Alachlor and trifluralin are the two most important soybean herbicides.

Annual herbicide use peaked at about 450 million pounds in 1982. The increase in herbicide use occurred primarily because it was a cost-effective means of weed control. In recent years, farmers have adopted no-till conservation tillage practices that require herbicides to control weeds. Conservation tillage reduces erosion and therefore sediment-bound herbicide loss to the environment.

Most herbicides have low toxicity to humans, but some, including alachlor and paraquat are suspected carcinogens. There is also concern about herbicide damage to soil microorganisms and about the subtle, long-term effects of herbicides on aquatic organisms.

Insecticide use has declined steadily since 1964. There has been a shift away from organochlorine compounds such as DDT, which was banned in 1972, and toxaphene, which was banned in 1986, to organophosphates, such as methyl parathion, and to carbamates, such as carbaryl and carbofuran. DDT and toxaphene are persistent compounds that accumulate in the food chain and have reached damaging levels in top predators in the past. With the shifts in insecticide use patterns, this problem has diminished, but the potential for acute toxicity effects on humans and other nontarget species from the use of some of the less persistent compounds may be greater. A variety of biological controls offer alternatives to insecticide use including insect-resistant crop varieties, insect parasites and predators,

insect-controlling bacteria and viruses, and behavior-altering pheromones.

Irrigated farmland

Irrigation has played a significant role in the expansion of agriculture in the western and southeastern portions of the United States. Between 1900 and 1978, the number of acres of irrigated farmland in the Nation increased almost tenfold to reach an all-time peak of 50.3 million acres. Since 1978, depressed commodity prices and rising energy costs have reduced the demand for irrigation in much of the Nation. In 1984, about 43 million acres of cropland and 1.5 million acres of pasture and rangeland were irrigated. An overall reduction in irrigated farmland is expected to continue as participation in acreage reduction programs grows and as water for irrigation becomes more expensive and harder to obtain because of competing uses and declining supplies in some areas.

The Nation's irrigated farmland is concentrated in 17 western states and 3 southeastern states where rainfall is either insufficient or too unreliable to support highly productive agriculture. In 1984, California had the most irrigated land (7.8 million acres), followed by Nebraska (5.8 million), Texas (4.9 million), and Idaho (3.3 million). The southeastern states of Arkansas, Florida, and Louisiana had 1.9 million, 1.4 million, and 0.6 million acres of irrigated land, respectively, in 1984.

Many states have major proportions of harvested cropland under irrigation. Arizona and Nevada each had over 90% of harvestable cropland under irrigation in 1984, and California, Utah, Idaho, Wyoming, and New Mexico each had over half of their harvested cropland acres under irrigation.

The overall national drop in irrigated acreage masks regional differences in irrigation trends. Total irrigated acreage among minor irrigated states grew from 1.4 million in 1974 to over 2.8 million in 1978, and then to 3.4 million in 1982. In contrast, irrigated acreage in the principal irrigated states rose from 39.9 million in 1974 to 47.5 million in 1978, then fell to 45.6 million in 1982. The number of acres under irrigation increased between 1978 and 1982, mainly in the East. In the West, irrigated acreage increased in Nebraska, North Dakota, and South Dakota, but declined elsewhere.

In parts of the humid East, irrigation to supplement rainfall has been expanding rapidly as farmers attempt to increase returns per acre and reduce weather risks. Rainfall in the East is usually sufficient for crop production, but periodic droughts affect production and can be catastrophic for producers. Supplemental irrigation in the East is expected to increase further.

Water used for irrigation rose steadily for the first 80 years of this century, then declined between 1980 and 1985. Irrigators have traditionally used more surface water than ground water to meet their needs. However, growing demands for public water supplies, manufacturing, mining, and energy production have increased competition for surface-water reserves that are already stretched thin. Today, fewer opportunities exist to increase surface-water supply, making ground water an attractive alternative for irrigators. In many areas of the West, where surface-water supplies could not be developed or were inadequate to meet irrigators' demands, ground water has become an increasingly important source of irrigation water.

Ground water became an important source for irrigators starting in the 1930s when engine and pumping technologies advanced and when widespread drought reduced surface-water supplies. During the 1950s and 1960s, additional technological advances and access to cheap energy for pumping ground water to fields facilitated further use of ground water for irrigation. Expansion of ground-water use has led to mining of aquifers in some irrigated regions and, in some cases, has caused a lowering of ground-water levels. The most notable case is the Ogallala aquifer, a huge underground reservoir stretching from northwestern Texas to Nebraska, where water is being pumped out faster than it can be replenished through rainfall. As a consequence of this and the rising cost of pumping deeper wells, some farmers in Texas are being forced back to dryland farming. Other states, such as Florida and Georgia, are expanding their use of ground water for irrigation.

In 1984, irrigators obtained about 56% of their water from surface-water supplies and about 44% from ground water. Small quantities of reclaimed effluent from municipal wastewater treatment facilities also were used. In 1984, 44% of irrigation water was delivered to farms by off-farm suppliers,

such as irrigation districts and private water companies, and another 44% was obtained from pumping facilities located on the farms where the water was used. The remaining 12% of total irrigation water came from on-farm surface-water delivery systems.

4-6
Grazing land

Distribution of lands suited for grazing

Almost one-half of the Nation's land area is suitable for grazing. Grazing lands include rangeland, permanent pasture, grazed forest land, and cropland that is used for pasture for varying lengths of time.

Grazing lands provide a food source for domestic livestock as well as habitat for deer, elk, moose, wild horses, turkey, dove, quail, grouse, and other wildlife. These lands protect water quality and riparian areas, enhance wildlife and fisheries, offer recreational opportunities, and, in some situations, supply wood and energy.

Rangeland is land on which the native vegetation in the climax or natural potential community is predominately grass, grasslike plants, forbs, or shrubs suitable for grazing or browsing. Rangelands include native grasslands, savannas, alpine meadows, tundra, many wetlands, some deserts, certain forb and shrub communities, and areas seeded to introduced species but managed like native rangeland.

Grazed forest lands are those woodlands that produce an understory vegetation that is suitable for forage and can be grazed without significantly impairing wood production and other forest values. The amount and nature of understory vegetation produced in woodlands depend primarily on the amount and duration of sunlight that penetrates through the tree canopy to the ground layer. Forage values are relatively high in open stands with widely spaced trees, such as in ponderosa pine and some of the southern pine forests, where a sufficient crop of forage is produced and climatic conditions permit grazing throughout the year. In contrast, upland hardwood forests with closed canopy produce little forage, although many are grazed as a consequence of their location on farms. Similarly, dense fir, spruce, or hemlock forests produce forage only periodically, such as after clear-cutting, extensive thinning, or fire, and have little utility for grazing.

Pastureland includes improved pasture and native pasture. Improved pasture is land that has been planted to domesticated grasses and forbs and is managed agronomically for intensified production. Native pasture includes former cropland on which the plant cover is changing to native vegetation; improved pastureland that has reverted to a voluntary stand of native vegetation; and grazed woodlands that are not managed for wood production, but where trees have been removed or thinned to increase the grazing resource.

Cropland pasture is cropland seeded to grasses and used for pasture. Much of the cropland used for pasture is routinely rotated between crop and pasture use. However, if the acreage is marginal for crop use, it may remain in pasture indefinitely.

Rangeland

Most of the Nation's rangeland is found west of the Continental Divide and in Alaska. The largest expanse of natural grassland left in the United States is the mixed- or short-grass prairie of the Great Plains. Extending westward from the Continental Divide to the Rocky Mountains, the Great Plains are known for high range quality and cattle production. Livestock are grazed year-round in the southern portion of the Great Plains, but only 8 to 10 months in the central area and 6 to 8 months in the northern area, where supplemental feeds are used the remainder of the time. In earlier days, certain "tall grasses" in the eastern part of the Great Plains furnished excellent grazing lands, but in recent times much of these fertile grasslands have been converted to cropland. Most of the rangeland in the Great Plains is privately owned.

Mountain and cool desert rangelands are found west of the Great Plains and east of the Sierra Nevada and Cascade Mountains. These rangelands encompass all of the states of Utah, Nevada, and Idaho; the western third of Montana, Wyoming, and Colorado; and the eastern third of Washington and Oregon. They include all of the arid and semiarid shrublands of the Basin and Ranges, the foothill grasslands of the Rocky Mountains, and the mountain meadows and alpine grasslands of the Rockies' western slope. Most of this rangeland is public land and is managed for multiple uses, including recreation, wildlife utilization, and timber and livestock production.

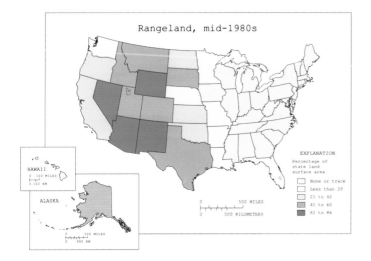

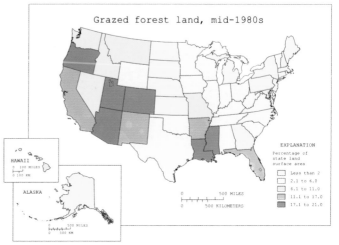

The arid regions of Texas, New Mexico, and Arizona support vast acreages of publicly owned desert grasslands, hot desert shrublands, and shrub-steppe rangelands. The vegetation on these range-lands is adapted to low precipitation, high evapora-tion, and periods of drought. The desert rangelands are rough in topography with hills and broad valleys and support a variety of grass and shrub species. Calf-rearing is the predominant use of the desert grasslands, along with some yearling, steer, and sheep grazing. Many of these ranges also support large wildlife populations, including pronghorn ante-lope, javelina, mule deer, jackrabbits, and a large variety of nongame birds. The natural vegetative cover of hot desert rangelands consists of shrubs (primarily creosote bush) interspersed with succu-lents and low-growing forbs and mesquite woodlands along drainage ways. Forage production depends upon rainfall, and desert rangelands are used for yearlong livestock grazing when production is suffi-cient. The shrub-steppe rangelands represent a tran-sition from the desert grasslands to the hot desert shrublands and the pinyon-juniper woodlands and are covered by a mixture of short grasses and shrubs.

Grazing of grasslands and range is the predom-inant agricultural use of land in Pacific States, Alaska, and Hawaii. Wet grasslands and annual grasslands occur in uncultivated areas of California's Central Valley and surrounding foothills. Pinyon-juniper, chaparral-mountain shrub, desert shrub, and sagebrush rangelands are found in arid portions of California and Oregon. In Alaska, tundra dominated by low shrubs, grasses, sedges, and forbs is grazed. Rangeland in Hawaii is a mixture of trees, shrubs (cactus and mesquite), and grasses. One-third of the land in Hawaii is grazed.

Only a small proportion of the land east of the Continental Divide is rangeland. Included under the traditional definition of rangeland are the northern cordgrass prairies of northeastern states, northern and southern cordgrass prairies of southern and southeastern states, and wet grasslands in poorly drained areas of Illinois, Indiana, Michigan, and Wisconsin. Much of the once vast bluestem prairie and cedar glades in Iowa, Missouri, and Minnesota has been converted to cropland.

Scattered throughout the Southeast is a variety of rangeland types, including palmetto prairie and Everglades sawgrass ranges in Florida, needlegrass prairie in Texas and Oklahoma, shinnery and savanna (mixed grass, shrub, and small trees) in Texas, and plains grasslands in western Oklahoma and northern Texas.

Grazed forest lands

Most forest lands can be managed to increase the production or availability of forage plants for live-stock and wildlife, while continuing to produce timber for harvest.

Redwood, hemlock-Sitka spruce, western white pine, larch, and Douglas fir forests in the West annually produce between 2000 and 4800 pounds of forage per acre. Average annual forage production in Eastern forests is between 1000 and 2000 pounds per acre, except in oak-hickory, loblolly-shortleaf pine, loblolly-slash pine, and elm-ash-cottonwood forests, where annual production is between 2000 and 4000 pounds of forage per acre. Alaskan forests generally produce less forage than counterparts in the conterminous United States. Hawaiian forests, on the other hand, produce much herbage.

In the South, native forage grows beneath pine timber stands, in natural openings, and on cutover lands. Deciduous forests along the Mississippi and Missouri rivers produce suitable forage for grazing, as do pinyon-juniper and oak-hickory stands in cen-tral and western Texas and Oklahoma.

Pinyon-juniper forests in arid regions of Arizona, New Mexico, western Colorado, Utah, and Nevada are important to the livestock industry. Ponderosa pine and associated pinyon-juniper forests in the interior portions of Oregon, Washington, and Califor-nia and the chaparral and wooded lowlands of Cali-fornia are also used for livestock grazing.

Pastureland

Most of the Nation's pastureland occurs east of the Continental Divide. Exceptions are the vast pasture-lands of Hawaii, Texas, and North Dakota.

Native pastures vary greatly in appearance. Some pastures may be virtually free of trees, others with some tree cover, and still others supporting full stands of noncommercial trees. The typical native pasture is a relatively stable ecological community often including grasses foreign to the region. With few exceptions, some control of woody plants is necessary to maintain optimum grazing conditions.

Permanent meadows and improved pasture are sown with grasses, clovers, and alfalfa. Meadow grasses include orchard grass, meadow fescue, smooth brome, timothy, and Johnson grass, and pas-ture grasses include Kentucky bluegrass, Bermuda grass, colonial bent, ryegrasses, carpet grasses, and fescues.

Most of the Nation's cropland pasture is concen-trated in the Southern Plains, Corn Belt, and Appalachian regions.

Ownership of land suitable for grazing

Over one-half (56%) of the Nation's land that is suitable for grazing is in private ownership. This includes 66 million acres of suitable forest land, 133 million acres of suitable pastureland, and 406 million acres of suitable rangeland. Suitable grazing land owned by the federal government includes 162 mil-lion acres of rangeland administered by the Bureau of Land Management, 51 million acres of forest land within the National Forest System (the National Forest System contains 191 million acres, of which 102 million acres are in grazing allotments, but only 51.3 million acres within these allotments are suit-able for livestock grazing), and 259 million acres of land administered by various agencies in the Depart-ment of the Interior and the Department of Defense.

4-7
Grazing land conditions and apparent trends

Many factors affect the health of grazing lands, including soil conditions, climate, topography, fire, drought, floods, insects, grazing, and browsing. Of these factors, intense livestock grazing over the last 100-150 years, especially on semiarid and arid ranges of the West, has had the most profound effect on rangeland conditions. The net result has been a weakened condition of preferred forage plants and a replacement by less desirable plants.

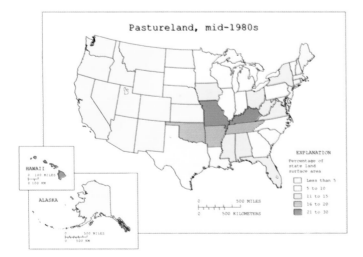

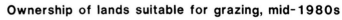

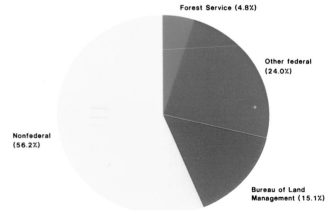

Ownership of lands suitable for grazing, mid-1980s

Total land suitable for grazing = 1.08 billion acres

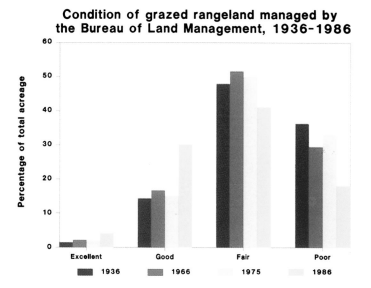

Condition of grazed rangeland managed by the Bureau of Land Management, 1936-1986

Percentage of total acreage

Excellent Good Fair Poor

■ 1936 ■ 1966 1975 1986

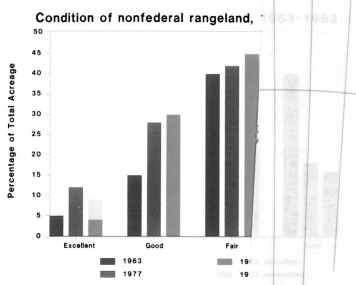

Condition of nonfederal rangeland, 1963-1982

Percentage of Total Acreage

Excellent Good Fair

■ 1963 1982, classified
■ 1977 1982, unclassified

Range conditions reached an all-time low in the 1930s but have been improving slowly ever since. (It should be noted that there are slight differences in the ways that federal and nonfederal rangeland conditions are evaluated; however, attempts are being made to standardize procedures.)

Nonfederal rangelands are assigned to one of four condition classes depending upon the degree of departure from the ecological potential of the site. "Excellent" rangelands are those lands where more than 75% of the vegetative cover and soil conditions is characteristic of the potential for the site. On "good" rangelands, conditions are between 50 to 75% of the potential, and on "fair" rangelands, between 26 to 50%. On "poor" rangelands, 25% or less of the conditions are characteristic of the site's potential. Generally, the correlation between range condition and forage production is positive.

In 1982, one-third of the nonfederal rangeland in the United States was in excellent-to-good condition. Conditions were generally better in the northwestern states than in the southwestern states where rangelands are subjected to arid climate, prolonged grazing seasons, and a long history of sustained grazing. Rangeland conditions in Hawaii and Alaska are gen-

erally better than in most of the conterminous states.

Grazing land conditions on nonfederal lands are improving with proper care and management. In 1982, about 136 million acres (34%) of nonfederal rangeland was adequately protected and needed no special treatment. The remaining acreage was nearly evenly split between land needing improvement achievable through refined grazing practices and land requiring more intensive treatment such as soil improvement, seeding and planting of vegetation, brush management, erosion control, or some combination thereof. Between 1977 and 1982, rangeland requiring nonintensive treatment and rangeland considered beyond treatment decreased by 41 and 10 million acres, respectively, whereas rangeland requiring intensive treatment did not change significantly.

The condition of nonfederal pastureland also improved during this 5-year interval. The amount of pastureland that was adequately protected increased by 19.2 million acres (from 31.1 to 45.3% of the pastureland base in the United States), and the amount requiring intensive treatment decreased by 15.7 million acres (from 29.0 to 17.4% of the pastureland base). Almost 2 million acres of pasture-

land requiring nonintensive treatment and slightly over 1 million acres of pastureland beyond treatment improved enough to be removed from their respective categories.

Uncontrolled livestock grazing on public rangelands in the late 1800s and early 1900s left 95% of these grazing lands in a deteriorated state. These grazing lands are administered by the Bureau of Land Management, and since the 1930s, there has been a steady increase in rangeland in good and excellent condition and decrease in rangeland in poor condition. These changes are attributable to rangeland improvements and better management practices, including a reduction in grazing livestock density. These accomplishments have been achieved through the cooperative efforts of the federal government, livestock operators, and other rangeland users.

The methods used by the Bureau of Land Management to characterize rangeland conditions have changed slightly over the past fifty years. The 1936 ratings were inferred by estimating deviations from virgin or climax conditions. The 1966 figures were derived by comparing the present state of range sites to their potential condition (potential

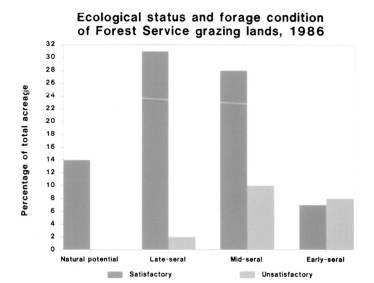

Ecological status and forage condition of Forest Service grazing lands, 1986

Percentage of total acreage

Natural potential Late-seral Mid-seral Early-seral

Satisfactory Unsatisfactory

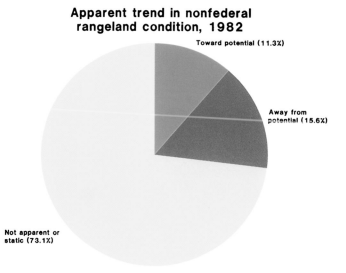

Apparent trend in nonfederal rangeland condition, 1982

Toward potential (11.3%)

Away from potential (15.6%)

Not apparent or static (73.1%)

Apparent trend in Bureau of Land Management grazed rangeland condition, 1986

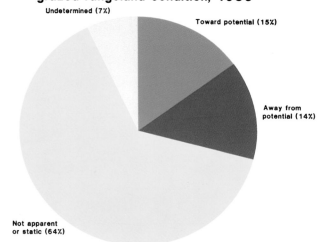

Undetermined (7%)
Toward potential (15%)
Away from potential (14%)
Not apparent or static (64%)

Apparent trend in Forest Service suitable grazing land condition, 1986

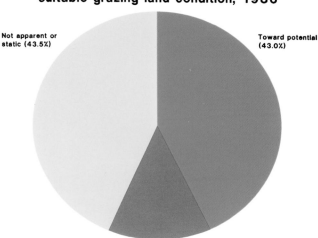

Not apparent or static (43.5%)
Toward potential (43.0%)
Away from potential (13.5%)

condition takes into account disturbance, especially by humans). The 1975 figures were based on an assessment of the site's ability to produce forage for livestock, and the 1986 figures were obtained using methods similar to those used to judge the health of nonfederal rangelands. In the future, the Bureau of Land Management will employ methods similar to those used by the Forest Service.

Since 1981, the Forest Service has defined the condition of grazing lands in terms of ecological status and value for livestock forage. Ecological status is defined as the degree of similarity between the present community and the potential natural community of a site. Ecological status considers the state of the vegetation relative to one of four stages of ecological succession (from early to advanced): early seral, mid seral, late seral, and natural potential. These categories are not equivalent to the condition categories used to judge nonfederal rangelands or rangelands administered by the Bureau of Land Management (that is, poor, fair, good, and excellent).

Forage conditions are defined as being satisfactory or unsatisfactory for livestock use. A satisfactory rating is given according to the following criteria: the soil is adequately protected and the forage species composition and production are at acceptable levels or the trend in forage species composition and production is acceptable.

An apparent trend in rangeland condition is an assessment of what is currently happening to the plant community and the direction of change. Other range condition ratings do not indicate whether the plant community is improving or deteriorating in relation to its potential but report the net result of a sustained trend over a period of time. An apparent trend is a much more sensitive indicator of change and provides important information for range managers.

An apparent trend is detected by examining factors such as changes in plant vigor, species composition, age–class structure, and buildup of organic matter and nutrients in soils. These changes, whether indicating declining or improving range conditions, generally follow a pattern, and usually these patterns can be predicted for specific sites, climates, and grazing use.

The potential natural community is used as the reference plant community, and an apparent trend is described as moving toward or away from potential,

as being static with no apparent change, or as being undetermined. An apparent trend is based on evidence that is obtained from a single observation as opposed to a measured trend that is a quantitative assessment of change based on repeated measurement over time.

4-8
Distribution of forest land

Forest land covers about 720 million acres of the United States. Nineteen forest groups in the conterminous United States make up six major forest types. About 50 coniferous and 90 hardwood tree species grow within these forests.

Climate, topography, and soils are the primary natural environmental factors that influence the distribution and composition of forests. The major climatic factors are moisture, temperature, length of growing season, and length of daylight, although storms and wildfires also tend to be influential. Forests dominate the vegetative cover in areas that receive substantial moisture throughout the year in contrast to arid and semiarid areas, where grasses and shrubs typically associated with rangelands are the dominant cover.

Major forest types

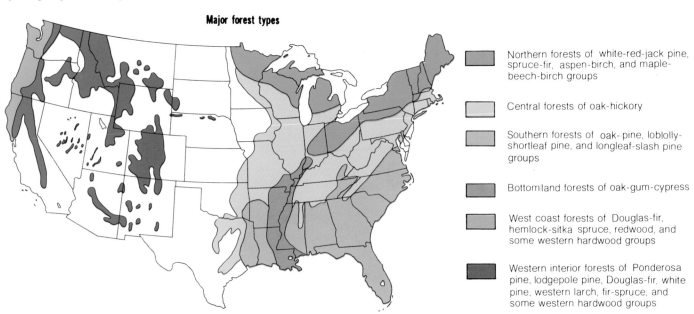

Northern forests of white-red-jack pine, spruce-fir, aspen-birch, and maple-beech-birch groups

Central forests of oak-hickory

Southern forests of oak-pine, loblolly-shortleaf pine, and longleaf-slash pine groups

Bottomland forests of oak-gum-cypress

West coast forests of Douglas-fir, hemlock-sitka spruce, redwood, and some western hardwood groups

Western interior forests of Ponderosa pine, lodgepole pine, Douglas-fir, white pine, western larch, fir-spruce, and some western hardwood groups

The history of land utilization over the past three centuries has been a primary influence in the pattern of forest distribution seen today. Very little remains of the original deciduous forests that covered the eastern United States and the coniferous forests and some western hardwood groups that covered the West coast and western interior of the country because of clearing for farms, harvesting of timber, and conversion to other uses. The greatest impacts to these forests occurred between 1860 and 1900 during the industrial revolution. Since then, much of the overcut forest land has reverted to second-growth forests through natural succession and reforestation. Today, these second-growth forests are being harvested for wood products and cleared for cropland use; urban and residential development; and highway, airport, and reservoir construction.

Human influence, insect pests, disease, fire, and other natural disasters are changing the appearance of forests. For example, the eastern oak-hickory forest has replaced the former oak-chestnut region where the European-introduced chestnut blight eliminated the chestnut in the early part of this century. The gypsy moth, mountain pine beetle, and spruce budworm are but a few of the pests that now threaten forests. In addition, suppression of natural fires that produced and maintained some of the magnificent coniferous forest-land vegetation, such as red and white pine in the Lake States, Douglas fir and ponderosa pine in western interior forests, and the productive southern pine forests, has upset the natural balance in these forest systems.

The northern forests of today are composed of spruce-fir, white-red-jack pine, aspen-birch, and maple-beech-birch forest groups. The spruce-fir or boreal forest is the northernmost group, extending from northern New England and the Lake States into Canada. White pine, red pine, and jack pine prevail on dry sand plain ridges stretching across the north from Minnesota through much of New England to the Atlantic Coast, the Allegheny and Adirondack mountains, and the upper Great Lakes region. Maple-beech-birch forests occur mainly on upland sites in the New England, Middle Atlantic, and Great Lakes regions; and aspen-birch forests dominate some previously logged areas in the Lake States. The southern boundary of the northern forest group is the southern terminus of the last glaciation.

The oak-hickory forest group is the largest eastern forest group. It has a component centered in the Interior Highlands that extends northward and north-eastward to meet the beech-maple-birch group, as well as an eastern component in the Southern Appalachian and Northern Blue Ridge mountains, the Ridge and Valley section, and Piedmont region of the East.

Southern forests consist of the oak-pine, longleaf-slash pine, and longleaf-shortleaf pine groups. The oak-pine forest is so-named because of the predominance of pine in the secondary growth forest, although oaks and hickories dominate old-growth stands. The oak-pine forest type occupies much of the Coastal Plain in Virginia, the Piedmont Plateau south of Virginia, and the Gulf States, where it occurs as a transition between more northern and southern forests. Southeastern pine forests are confined to the Coastal Plain from southern Virginia to Texas. Longleaf-slash pine forests occur in the southern states and along the Atlantic Coast, and loblolly-shortleaf pine forests tend to grow at higher elevations and farther north. Southern bottomland forests of oak-gum-cypress are found primarily along the Mississippi River drainage and in outlying areas such as the Chesapeake Bay area of Maryland and Virginia and the Dismal Swamp and pocosins of Virginia and North Carolina.

West coast forests occupy the western portion of Washington, Oregon, and northern California and are vegetated by Douglas fir, hemlock-Sitka spruce, redwood, and western hardwood species. They are some of the most productive forests in the United States. Western interior forests, which are somewhat less productive, contain ponderosa pine, lodgepole pine, interior Douglas fir, white pine, western larch, fir-Englemann spruce, and some western hardwood groups.

4-9
Ownership of forest land

Federal ownership embraces 39% of forest land in the Nation. The forest industry owns nearly 18% of the nonfederal forest land; state, local, and municipal governments own 8%; and the remainder is owned by individuals or nonforest industry partnerships or corporations. Of the federally owned forest land, the Forest Service manages about 19%; the

Bureau of Land Management manages 12%; and the Department of Defense, the National Park Service, the Fish and Wildlife Service, and other federal agencies together manage about 8%.

Regional ownership patterns vary. Over one-half of western forest land is in the National Forest System, and much of the rest is managed by the timber industry. In the East, three-fourths of the forest land is owned by farmers and other individuals.

Nearly two-thirds of the forest land in the United States is classified as commercial, namely, forest land capable of producing at least 20 cubic feet of industrial wood per acre per year and land that is not reserved by law for uses that are incompatible with timber production. About 3% of forest land that meets the criteria for commercial production has been set aside for parks, wilderness areas, or other uses. The remaining forest land is incapable of producing a sustained crop of industrial wood but is valuable for livestock grazing, wildlife habitat, fuelwood production, watershed protection, and recreational use.

Seventy-two percent of all commercial timberland is privately owned; the remaining 28% is in federal, state, and a variety of other public holdings. Fourteen percent of the commercial timberland is owned by the forest industry, and the remaining 58% of commercial timberland is in farmer and other private ownerships and might not be available for timber harvest. Most of the noncommercial forest land is in private ownership.

Nearly three-fourths of the commercial timberland in the Nation is located in the humid East, where it is equally divided between the North and the South. In the West, commercial timberland is concentrated in the Pacific Northwest States of Oregon, Washington, and California and in the Rocky Mountain States of Montana, Idaho, and Colorado.

One-half of the commercial timberland area is in hardwood forest and more than two-fifths is occupied by southern pine, Douglas fir, hemlock, spruce, and other softwood species. The remainder does not contain a dominant tree cover type and is classified as nonstocked.

Commercial timberland acreage increased in the 1950s and 1960s but has declined since then because of land clearing for farmland and other uses and set asides for wilderness areas and parks. This trend may reverse as more cropland is replanted

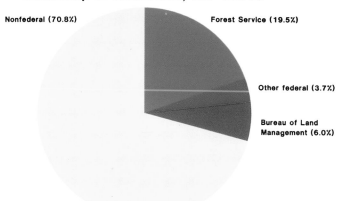

Ownership of forest land, mid-1980s

Nonfederal (70.8%)
Forest Service (19.5%)
Other federal (3.7%)
Bureau of Land Management (6.0%)

Reforestation by planting and direct seeding, 1950-1986

Millions of acres

Reforestation by ownership, 1986

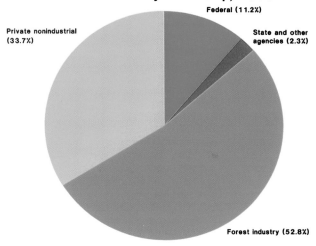

Private nonindustrial (33.7%)

Federal (11.2%)

State and other agencies (2.3%)

Forest industry (52.8%)

Wildfire damage, 1926-1986

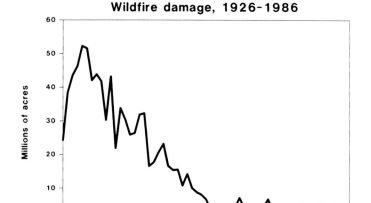

with commercial grade trees on conservation reserves.

4-10
Reforestation

Forest lands planted with tree seedlings and direct seeded have increased since 1955. In 1986, nearly 1.8 billion tree seedlings were produced and 2.7 million acres were reforested. This trend coincides with increasing forest acreage under industry ownership and large-scale reforestation programs. It also reflects improvements made by state, federal, and private nurseries in tree breeding and seed production techniques and increases in the number of genetically improved seedlings grown. Much of this activity is taking place in southern pine forests where most of the seed nurseries are located. In 1986, Georgia led in tree planting with 435,000 acres; followed by Florida, 296,000 acres; Alabama, 288,000 acres; and Mississippi, 220,000 acres.

In addition to industry efforts, the trend in acres planted and seeded in trees reflects participation by farmers in federally sponsored cropland diversion programs where cropland is removed from cultivation and planted to grass, trees, and other vegetative cover. In addition to reducing surplus crop production, these plantings are beneficial in reducing soil erosion and sustaining long-term timber supplies.

The statistics also take into account the growing number of farm acres planted with windbreaks, a trend that has increased more or less steadily over the past 50 years. Windbreaks help reduce erosion, conserve moisture, and provide a source of firewood for human use as well as food and cover for wildlife.

The forest industry is responsible for over one-half of the annual tree planting and seeding activities in the United States. Tree planting and improvement are good investments for clearcut areas, although many areas are still managed under the practice of selective harvest and natural regeneration. Industry nurseries produced over 900 million seedlings, or 53% of the national total, in 1986. Most of the seedlings are planted on company lands, although some are distributed to the public through various company assistance programs.

Nonindustrial forest owners are the second largest tree planting group. This category includes owners participating in soil conservation programs or making investments in tree planting for future financial gain.

State nurseries produced 40% of all seedlings grown in the United States in 1986, yet only 2.1% of all plantings took place on state-owned lands. Many private owners benefit from services and research activities of state agencies in the way of seedlings and planting advice.

Most of the seedlings produced by federal nurseries are planted on national forest lands. In 1986, the Forest Service led the other federal agencies in reforesting over 250,000 acres.

4-11
Wildfire damage

Fire is a part of the natural environment. It is critically important in some forest ecosystems for maintaining open space, mineral soils, vegetative composition, and other conditions that are needed for tree reproduction. Fire also tends to reduce destructive insect populations and diseases and maintains habitat of fire-adapted wildlife species, such as the Kirtland's warbler. In some parts of the country, prescribed burns are used to eliminate unwanted vegetation, make tree planting easier, and reduce competition with undesirable tree species. On the other hand, wildfires destroy vast expanses of forest and other lands, claim lives, and cost millions of dollars in fire prevention, fire fighting, and property damages.

Land use patterns and human activities greatly affect the incidence and spread of fires. Over a recent 20-year period, the major causes of fire in protected areas were arson (36%), debris burning (29%), and smoking (12%). Lightning was responsible for starting 10% of these fires and children, campfires, railroads, equipment, and other miscellaneous causes were responsible for starting the rest.

The overall national trend for wildfire damage has been downward since the 1930s, although there have been occasional reversals of this trend. Forest fire damages increased after World War II as a

major population shift from urban to suburban living occurred and people built homes in closer proximity to forests. Between 1950 and 1970, a combination of improved fire fighting capabilities, fire control, and fire prevention campaigns, such as Smokey the Bear, helped reduce forest fire damage. Recent increases in wildfire damage are correlated with, among other things, a renewed rural migration and an upsurge in primary, secondary, and retirement home construction in rural areas.

4-12
Forest land damaged by insects and diseases

Insects and diseases damage millions of acres of the Nation's forests each year. In addition to tree mortality, infestations reduce timber production and quality, promote replacement by less desirable species, diminish wildlife and recreational use of forest areas, and increase dead wood that fuels fires.

Spruce budworm

The spruce budworm is a major insect pest in the immense boreal forests of the eastern United States and Canada. Since 1909, waves of spruce budworms have moved through forests of mature and overmature spruce and fir, the preferred host trees. The most recent epidemic peaked in 1978 and impacted roughly 12 million acres of the Nation's spruce-fir forest before it ended. The states most heavily affected were Michigan, Minnesota, Wisconsin, Vermont, New Hampshire, and Maine.

The western spruce budworm, a cousin of the eastern variety, is responsible for defoliating mixed coniferous forests in the western states from southern New Mexico to Canada. The first occurrence of the western spruce budworm was reported in 1914, but it was not recognized as a serious threat until 1922. Around this time, the makeup of mixed coniferous forests began to change as fire prevention became more effective and harvest of ponderosa pine, a nonhost species, increased while Douglas fir and true firs, both host species, were left behind. Many outbreaks have occurred since 1922, yet they follow no apparent pattern or trend. The most recent outbreak defoliated over 10 million acres each year between 1983 and 1986.

The battle against the spruce budworm involves integrated pest management techniques of prevention and suppression. Prevention includes thinning mature stands to remove susceptible firs, leaving more resistant spruces, planting trees that are less likely to host the budworm, and monitoring budworm populations so that outbreaks can be detected and treated before heavy losses occur. Suppression involves the use of both chemical and biological controls. Biological controls, such as the bacterium *Bacillus thuringiensis*, are advantageous because they are effective against the budworm yet relatively harmless to other organisms and the environment.

Gypsy moth

The gypsy moth is not native to North America but was imported from Europe in 1869 with the intention of crossing it with the silkworm moth to develop a better silk product. Some moths escaped soon after importation, and since then the gypsy moth has multiplied and spread throughout New England, New Jersey, and Pennsylvania, and more recently into Delaware, Maryland, Virginia, and West Virginia. Infestations have also been found in Arkansas, California, North Carolina, Oregon, and Washington.

Like most other defoliating insects, the gypsy moth does its damage in the larval stage. The larvae prefer the leaves of oak species, yet during an epidemic, they are indiscriminate feeders.

Gypsy moth outbreaks are cyclic, and populations periodically build up to epidemic levels. Defoliation by gypsy moth larvae since 1979 has claimed more acres of hardwoods than all previous gypsy moth defoliations combined. The most recent outbreak peaked in 1981, when a record 12.8 million acres was defoliated. Defoliation is on the rise again as the gypsy moth expands its range on the average of one-half million acres a year.

The impact of the gypsy moth on timber resources depends upon the abundance of host trees present and the condition of the site and stand. Generally, vigorous trees can withstand one or two consecutive defoliations, but those in poor condition can die after one defoliation. Hardwood mortality harms some wildlife species but benefits others. For example, loss of mature hardwoods reduces seed crop consumed by turkeys and squirrels, whereas the proliferation of herbaceous groundcover that occurs when canopy species are removed is often beneficial to deer and grouse.

A number of strategies are used to combat infestations of gypsy moth, including use of natural predators and parasites. A variety of birds, mammals, amphibians, reptiles, and invertebrates feed on the different life stages of the gypsy moth and can help keep populations at low levels. Research continues to improve biological insecticides, such as the bacterium *Bacillus thuringiensis* and a naturally occurring virus that can collapse populations in outbreak areas. In addition, isolated infestations have been successfully eradicated by using a synthetic sex pheromone (sometimes in combination with insecticides) that prevents or disrupts mating or by releasing sterile males who cause wild females to lay infertile eggs. Despite these control techniques, however, the gypsy moth continues to spread and the problem has grown from a regional problem to a national one.

Mountain pine beetle

The mountain pine beetle has always been present in the West but was not considered a serious pest until about 1900. It is found almost everywhere lodgepole and ponderosa pines grow—from the Pacific Coast east to the Black Hills and from western Alberta (Canada) south to Mexico. Stands of mature and overmature lodgepole pine, second-growth ponderosa pine, and western white and sugar pines, as well as mature and overmature stands of whitebark and timber pines, are susceptible to attack. Both the adult and larval stages of the mountain pine beetle cause damage.

By 1965, most of the lodgepole forests in northern Utah, southern Idaho, and western Wyoming were experiencing massive outbreaks of mountain pine beetle infestations that began in 1953. These outbreaks continued to spread northward, sweeping through Yellowstone National Park and into Gallatin National Forest in Montana, and by the 1980s covered over 1.5 million acres in Montana and Idaho. In the Pacific Northwest, most of the damage occurred east of the Cascade Mountains, where from 1955 through 1966 just under one million acres of lodgepole pine were infested. The current outbreak, which started in 1967 in northwest Oregon, has infested more than 3 million acres per year since 1978. The long-term trend in beetle-caused damages is downward, however, primarily because of extensive thinning of second-growth ponderosa pine and because the beetle has already killed most of its host trees. Today, thousands of acres of tree skeletons stand as evidence of previous mountain beetle outbreaks.

Pest management techniques used against the mountain pine beetle include selective harvest to reduce mortality, suppress small infestations, and prevent outbreaks; use of insecticides to reduce beetle populations and minimize future tree mortality; and pretreatment of uninfected trees to prevent the beetle from attacking. In some areas managed for timber, regular harvests coupled with fuelwood cutting and prescribed burning can reduce future epidemics by increasing species diversity and age-class distribution.

Southern pine beetle

The southern pine beetle attacks all southern yellow pines. Shortleaf and loblolly pines are the most susceptible, Virginia and slash pines are less so, the longleaf pine is somewhat resistant, and Eastern white pine growing in southern mountains is often infested. Although the natural range of the southern pine beetle in the United States extends north into Missouri, Illinois, Indiana, Ohio, Pennsylvania, New Jersey, Delaware, and Maryland, it is economically important only south of the Ozark Mountains and the Ohio River. A separate population in Arizona is of little economic importance.

Smaller than most grains of rice, southern pine beetles attack en masse directly through the tree bark and kill the tree. Populations can build up rapidly, and if left unchecked, the infestation can spread to thousands of trees within a few weeks.

Outbreaks of southern pine beetle have occurred historically at 7- to 10-year intervals. In the late 1700s, writers documented widespread tree mortality that has since been attributed to the beetle. After the Civil War, the large-scale conversion of cotton fields to pine forests increased the occurrence of host trees, and the significance of the southern pine beetle increased. Sketchy data indicate that 12

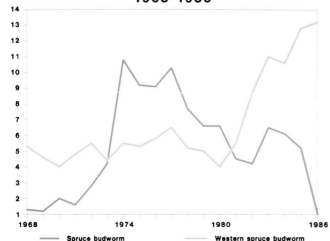

Forest area damaged by spruce budworms 1968-1986

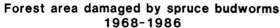

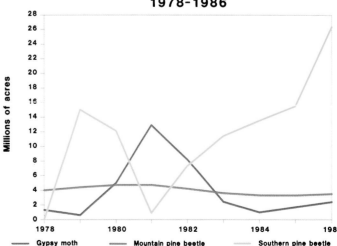

Forest area damaged by other insects 1978-1986

Cumulative area defoliated by gypsy moth 1924–1986

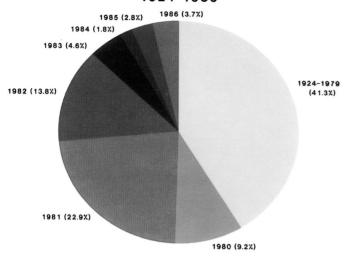

1985 (2.8%)
1986 (3.7%)
1984 (1.8%)
1983 (4.6%)
1982 (13.8%)
1924–1979 (41.3%)
1981 (22.9%)
1980 (9.2%)

Forest area infested by disease, 1986

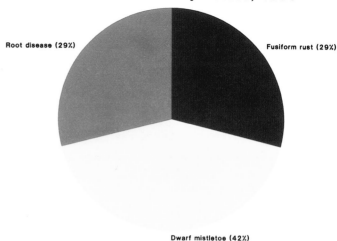

Root disease (29%)
Fusiform rust (29%)
Dwarf mistletoe (42%)

Total area infested by disease = 52 million acres

to 15 outbreaks occurred from 1882 to 1960. In the past 15 years, however, three major documented outbreaks have occurred. Local outbreaks in the 1960s culminated in a widespread epidemic that lasted until 1976. Another outbreak began in 1976 and persisted until 1981. Typically, outbreak acreage drops dramatically after three or more years of high activity. Nonetheless, the South is never completely free of outbreak events. In fact, in 1986 the South was experiencing an outbreak that promised to be the most damaging one yet.

Significant developments in the management of the southern pine beetle have occurred during the past 10 years. Use of airborne Loran-C precision-positioning systems when conducting aerial surveys has increased outbreak detection accuracy, and computer-based hazard-rating systems have enabled foresters to determine if stands need preventive treatment or increased surveillance. Spread of the southern pine beetle can be prevented in stands of 10 to 50 trees by cutting a buffer strip and removing infested trees. Use of insecticides such as lindane and chlorpyrifos also helps resource managers control the southern pine beetle problem.

Fusiform rust

Fusiform rust flourishes across the Southeast, killing or deforming millions of slash and loblolly pines each year. Longleaf and pond pines are sometimes affected, whereas Virginia and shortleaf pines are resistant to infection. Since 1930, both the intensity of rust infection and the acreage affected have increased by about 2 to 3% per year over much of its range. This increase is correlated with increased planting of susceptible pines in plantations and use of fire controls that have enabled oaks, the rust's alternate but not severely damaged host, to increase in number. Genetically resistant trees and more effective management strategies are keys to slowing the current epidemic.

Dwarf mistletoe

Dwarf mistletoe and conifers began evolving together in North American forests about 25 million years ago, yet today, dwarf mistletoe is one of the most widespread of forest diseases in North America. Practically all western members of the pine family,

including the pines, true firs, spruces, Douglas fir, larch, and hemlock, are parasitized, whereas the southern pines are not affected. Cedars, cypress, junipers, redwood, and giant sequoia are immune.

Dwarf mistletoe is a parasitic plant that absorbs nutrients and water from its host through rootlike structures. Each year this parasite accounts for about 8% of the pest-caused tree losses in the United States. The total area infested and annual loss are relatively constant, however, because the dwarf mistletoe spreads very slowly (at a rate of 1 to 2 feet per year). Timber management activities, including direct suppression, also slow the mistletoe's spread.

Root diseases

Root diseases are becoming a national problem, although the incidence of disease remains relatively constant over large areas. Six root diseases produce most of the disease-related losses: annosus root disease (which grows at the wood–bark interface in loblolly and ponderosa pines and spreads between trees by root contact), armillaria root disease (which infects all, but usually stressed, woody plants and causes rapid tree death or gradual decline through associated root and butt decay), red-brown butt rot (which decays the heartwood and the lower trunk, especially in Douglas fir), laminated root rot (which affects Douglas fir, true firs, mountain hemlock, and western red cedar and can survive for decades in roots and stumps and inoculate any new growth on site), and littleleaf disease (which results from the interaction of a fungus and certain soil and nutrient conditions and decays small feeder roots in shortleaf and loblolly pines in the southeastern Piedmont).

Techniques used to reduce the incidence and spread of root disease include planting less susceptible species of trees; removing suitable host tissue; thinning and brush control to reduce stress caused by competition for light, moisture, and nutrients; removing infected stumps and roots; and leaving the infected sites fallow for a prescribed period of time.

4-13
Timber stocks

The Nation's forests contain some 830 billion cubic feet of roundwood. Some 91% of this is in growing

stock (live, sound trees suited for roundwood products). The remaining 9% of all roundwood volume is in rotten, cull, and salvable dead trees. Some of the latter may be suitable for lumber and veneer, but most of it is usable only for pulp, fuel, and other products where there are no significant log quality requirements. There are additional large volumes of fiber in tree tops, limbs, and bark; in trees under 5 in. in diameter at breast height; and in trees on forest land other than timberland (for example in fence rows and in urban areas) that are also usable for fuel, pulp, and other products where there are no significant log quality requirements. Much of the fuelwood now being used for domestic heating comes from these sources.

Timber inventories rise when net annual growth (total growth less mortality) is greater than the volumes removed by timber harvesting, clearing, or changing land use (timber removals). The growth-removals balance for the United States is positive for all species (1.31), for softwoods (1.07), and for hardwoods (1.86). The ratios in the North are vey high, indicating continued substantial increases in growing stock volume. The softwood ratio for the South is approaching 1.00. The growth-removals ratio in the Rocky Mountains exceeds 2.00, and for the Pacific coast, it is .91. Such growth-removals balances and inventory declines on the Pacific coast result from harvesting the mature stands in the region. Net annual growth in such stands is low because mortality tends to offset growth. Once harvested and regenerated, however, the lands in the Douglas fir subregion of Oregon and Washington and those in coastal Alaska have the capacity to grow large volumes of timber.

The Rocky Mountain region has had a positive growth-removals balance for a long time, but inventories have increased slowly because many of the stands are old and net annual growth is low.

4-14
Timber use

In one form or another—as housing, furniture, containers, writing paper, books, and newspapers—products made from timber affect the quality of life for everyone. Over the past centuries, wood has been used for many purposes. Substitutes

Net annual growth of growing stock by ownership, 1952-1986

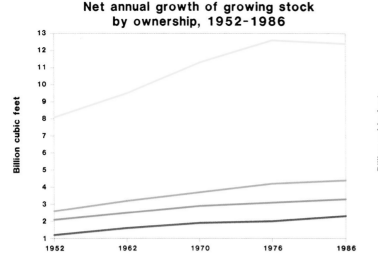

Annual removal of growing stock by ownership, 1952-1986

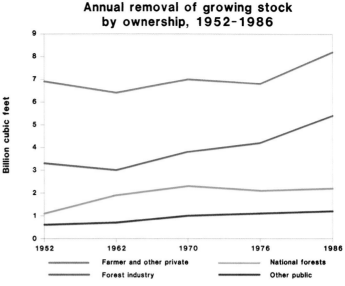

Net annual growth and annual removals in North and South regions, 1952-1986

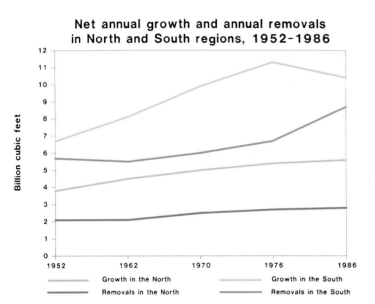

Net annual growth and annual removals in Rocky Mountain and Pacific Coast regions, 1952-1986

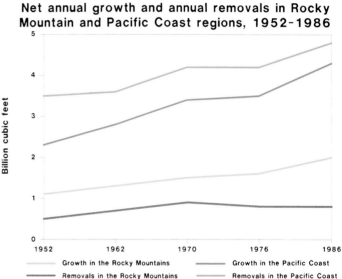

such as steel, plastics, and petroleum-based products have displaced wood in many uses, and wood-based materials have in turn displaced other products. Wood-based products are among those that increase in demand with increased populations and a growing economy. This means that the United States has experienced a continuing growth in demand for timber products.

Between 1950 and 1980, there was a slight upward trend in lumber consumption, punctuated by well-defined short-term fluctuations. Demand for lumber follows cycles in new housing starts and other general measures of the economy. For example, the severe recession of the early 1980s caused a decline in housing that forced a drop in lumber demand. This was followed in the mid-1980s by record consumption brought on by reduced interest rates that stimulated both new housing and repair and remodeling of existing structures. Demand for softwood plywood rose rapidly through the decades of the 1950s and 1960s, reaching a peak in the early 1970s. Much of this growth was the result of

Roundwood harvest by product, 1950-1986

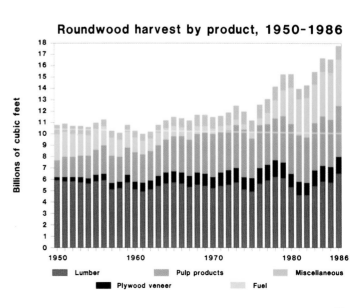

the substitution of plywood for lumber in many end uses. By the 1970s, opportunities for this substitution had largely been captured, and demand for plywood began to follow housing cycles, much as for lumber.

The late 1970s and 1980s were years of major changes in the plywood and structural panel industries. Fiber-based structural panels began to make significant inroads into markets for solid softwood plywood. These fiber-based panels have now been accepted in the marketplace and should have major influences on the species and quality of roundwood needed in the structural panel industry. The new panels can be made of almost any species of wood with the preference being soft hardwoods such as aspen. After the recession of the early 1980s, consumption of structural panels reached record levels in response to the strong markets of the mid-1980s. Future growth in demand for structural panels is expected to be for the new fiber-based panels.

Consumption of wood in the manufacture of pulp, paper, and paperboard grew rapidly in the decades following World War II. This growth in demand was in response to rapid growth in the economy, which stimulated consumption of packaging and other pulp-based products. Much of the increase in consumption of wood fiber during the 1960s and 1970s came from the by-products of lumber and plywood manufacture. In recent years, the use of hardwood roundwood has increased, and this is expected to continue in the future. In the 1970s, demand for pulp, paper, and paperboard demand became more susceptible to economic cycles. By the mid-1980s, however, consumption was again at record levels.

The oil-price shocks of the 1970s caused many structural shifts in the U.S. economy. Undoubtedly the major impact on timber demand in the United States was the reversal of a long decline in the demand for fuelwood. Rising costs for oil and natural gas stimulated both commercial and noncommercial demand for wood as fuel. These structural shifts involved major investments in technology and equipment that are not easily reversed. As a result, consumption of fuelwood continued to increase in the 1980s despite steep declines in crude oil prices. Although there has been a respite in energy price rises in the 1980s, there is a consensus that these prices will increase significantly after the turn of the century, with the result that fuelwood demand is expected to continue to grow over the long term.

4-15
Soil conditions

Soils develop from unconsolidated earthy materials that have accumulated or formed in a given landscape. Sediment particles carried by streams and deposited on a floodplain, for example, become the parent material that forms soils. Rock decomposing or weathering in place also provides materials that mix with organic matter to form soil.

Various soil-forming processes work on the accumulated materials and determine how and what kind of soil will develop. Precipitation influences the breakdown and movement of rock materials when and where it falls. Biological and chemical processes transform rock and soil minerals into different forms, and water moves soluble chemicals deep into the soil. Water, wind, and gravity gradually move materials from one site to another; however, catastrophic events such as landslides and floods transport the same large quantities of materials in a

much shorter time span. Land use and the types of plants and animals that occupy a habitat affect the soils. These soil-forming processes are complex and ongoing, at work today and for the past hundreds, thousands, and even tens of thousands of years. As a result, soils differ from each other in age; color; particle size; chemical and nutrient content; capacity to hold or allow movement of air and water; and resistance to wind and water erosion or downslope creep, slips, and slides.

People are primarily interested in soils that are suitable for plant growth. Not all soils are ideal, so people try to improve the soils or minimize their limitations through fertilization, irrigation, drainage, and reshaping the surface. Environmental factors limit the degree to which these modifications can be made, however, and severe physical or chemical degradation can occur where limits have been ignored or misjudged.

Saline soils

Salinization is a problem in arid and semiarid areas where naturally occurring salts are not leached by precipitation as they are in more humid areas, where irrigated soils are not adequately drained, and where soils are irrigated with low-quality water. High evaporation rates also tend to concentrate salts already in the soil and those carried in by irrigation water. When land is irrigated, the leaching process begins. If too little water is used or if drainage is limited or nonexistent, salts build up in soil at the plant root zone and migrate to the surface by capillary action, eventually causing salt crusts, which tends to reduce crop yields, and the need for farmers to switch to more salt-tolerant crops. On the other hand, when more irrigation water is used or where well-drained soils are involved, salts gradually dissolve and are carried below the root zone and often into ground water. This leaching process can increase salt levels in public water supplies, fish and wildlife habitat, and irrigation water downstream. Use of saline irrigation waters also can cause salts to accumulate in soils.

Irrigation-related salinization of soils is occurring around the Salton Sea and in the Imperial and

Coachella valleys in California, along the lower Gila River in Arizona, in parts of the Rio Grande basin in southern New Mexico and Texas, in parts of the Great Basin in Nevada and Utah, and in parts of the Arkansas and Colorado river basins.

Soil erosion

Over long periods, the natural geological processes of weathering and erosion transform rock minerals into useable plant nutrients and produce sediment. Working under the influence of gravity, the frictional forces of water and wind are the principal agents of erosion.

Accelerated erosion occurs where human activity disrupts the plant cover that usually protects the soil. Wherever the soil is fine, the surface of the ground loose, dry, and bare, and the wind and/or rainfall strong, erosion may be expected unless control measures are adopted. Soils are most susceptible to erosion in late winter and early spring, when the winds usually blow the strongest, snowmelt and spring rains begin, and vegetative cover is the least. Frequent or improper tillage and the growing of cultivated crops incapable of providing sufficient cover on the land also contribute to soil erosion.

Weather causes considerable loosening and structural disintegration of the surface soil. Alternating wetting, drying, and/or freezing/thawing break down the soil aggregates to granules that are more easily eroded by wind and rain. Raindrops loosen surface soil particles, and rainwater flowing over the unprotected land carries the particles away as sheet runoff. Fast-flowing water cuts channels, or rills, in the surface of the soil, and soil particles are carried away as rill erosion. Rills can enlarge to become gullies. Sheet and rill erosion increases as the slope gradient increases.

Wind moving against soil particles dislodges them. The largest particles roll and slide along the surface, disturbing other particles, whereas the smaller particles shoot upwards in a jumping movement. When the small particles fall back to the ground, they either rebound and continue their movement or strike other particles, causing them to rise upward.

SALINE.AREA.PSC1

KJL1>CEQ>DATA>SALINE.AREA

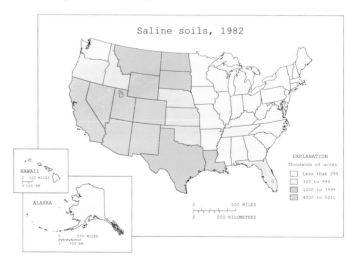

Saline soils, 1982

EXPLANATION
Thousands of acres

Less than 299
300 to 999
1000 to 3999
4000 to 5211

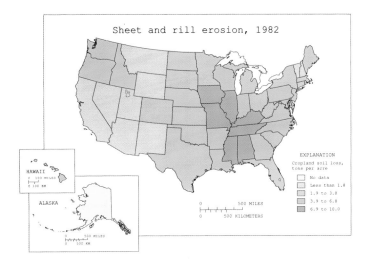

Sheet and rill erosion, 1982

EXPLANATION
Cropland soil loss,
tons per acre

No data
Less than 1.8
1.9 to 3.8
3.9 to 6.8
6.9 to 10.0

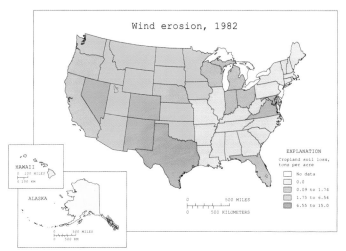

Wind erosion, 1982

EXPLANATION
Cropland soil loss,
tons per acre

No data
0.0
0.09 to 1.74
1.75 to 6.54
6.55 to 15.0

Most of the particles kicked upward by jumping grains are fine grains of dust that rise high, travel far, and drop to earth only when rain washes them down or when the wind subsides.

Sheet, rill, and wind erosion have been and continue to be major national problems. Findings of a 1934 national reconnaissance survey of erosion in the United States indicated that soil erosion had increased at a rate perhaps unequalled in history. Erosion was found in practically every agricultural region and affected, to some extent, the production of nearly every crop. Over 3% of the total land area in the United States had very severe sheet erosion and frequent gullies or very severe wind erosion; 12% had severe sheet erosion and some gullies or severe wind erosion; 41% had moderate sheet erosion and occasional gullies or moderate wind erosion; 37% had slight erosion or none; and the remaining 7% was in mountains, deserts, and similar areas where erosion was not characterized.

More recently, estimates of soil erosion have been made using the soil loss prediction models developed and refined since 1940. In 1977, sheet and rill erosion accounted for 3.5 billion tons of soil lost from nonfederal lands in the United States (excluding erosion from gullies, streambanks, roadsides or construction sites, and from all lands in Alaska). In 1982, the annual rate was reduced to 1.8 billion tons. Wind erosion accounted for a loss of 1.4 billion tons of soil from the 10 Great Plains states in 1977, whereas soil loss from wind erosion in these plus 18 additional states was estimated to be 1.3 billion tons in 1982.

Fifty percent or more of all erosion on nonfederal lands is on cropland. In some states, a disproportionate share of soil erosion is on marginal croplands, lands generally considered unsuited to row crops, cropland without adequate conservation treatment, and soils with a wetness problem or on sloping or steep land. Soil erosion by wind is worst in the Great Plains, the area that extends almost from the Mississippi River to the Rocky Mountains and from the Gulf of Mexico into the prairie provinces of Canada. Other major regions subject to wind damage are the Columbia River plains, some parts of the Pacific Southwest and the Colorado River basin, the peat and sand areas of the Great Lakes region, and the sands of the Gulf and Atlantic seaboards.

Soil loss by erosion equates to more than just depletion of topsoil. Soil washing off cropland, pasture or forest land ends up in surface water, in the air, and on other lands. Sediment in water bodies causes turbidity, siltation, and deterioration of aquatic habitats, decreases water storage capacity in lakes and reservoirs, and clogs water distribution systems. Eroded sediments can carry fertilizers, pesticides, and salts that reduce water quality. Soil particles blown by wind can cause dust storms that physically damage crops, buildings, and equipment and permeate homes, offices, and factories with dust. Windblown particles can also become air quality problems, accentuating respiratory ailments and impairing vision in humans and other animals.

Cropping, livestock grazing, logging, and other activities will continue to cause soil erosion unless appropriate conservation practices are applied. Among the most successful techniques for erosion control are various forms of conservation tillage in which residue from a previous crop is left in the field; contour plowing and stripcropping on sloping lands; maintenance of vegetative buffer strips between fields and along waterways to slow down and filter runoff; not cultivating highly erodible soils but planting the land to permanent tree or grass cover; and keeping a vegetative cover on fallow or idle land. These practices are applicable almost everywhere, but their importance varies with the conditions.

Sources and technical notes

4-1
Land cover and land use

4-1a
Ecoregions

U.S. Department of Agriculture, Forest Service and U.S. Department of the Interior, Geological Survey. *Ecosystems of the United States* (Rare II map, no date). After maps by R. G. Bailey, *Ecoregions of the United States*, 1978, and A. W. Kuchler, *Potential natural vegetation*, 1966.

4-1b
Trends in major uses of land in the United States, 1910–1982

4-1c
Land in special use areas, 1982

4-1d
Land ownership, 1982

4-1e
Land use by ownership, 1982

4-1f
Land use by region, 1982

Frey, H. T., and R. W. Hexem. 1985. *Major uses of land in the United States: 1982*. U.S. Department of Agriculture, Economic Research Service, Natural Resources Economics Division. AER-535 (Washington, D.C.), table 3, Major uses of land, United States, 1950–82, p. 3.

Frey, H. T., 1982. *Major uses of land in the United States: 1978*. U.S. Department of Agriculture, Economic Research Service. AER-487 (Washington, D.C.).

Frey, H. T., 1979. *Major uses of land in the United States: 1974*. U.S. Department of Agriculture, Economic Statistics Cooperative Service. AER-440 (Washington, D.C.).

Frey, H. T., 1973. *Major uses of land in the United States: 1969*. U.S. Department of Agriculture, Economic Research Service. AER- 247 (Washington, D.C.).

Frey, H. T., O. E. Krause, and C. Dickason. 1968. *Major uses of land and water in the United States: Summary for 1964*. U.S. Department of Agriculture, Economic Research Service. AER-149 (Washington, D.C.).

Wooten, H. H., 1953. *Major uses of land in the United States*. U.S. Department of Agriculture, Bureau of Agricultural Economics. TB-1082 (Washington, D.C.).

Wooten, H. H., and J. R. Anderson. 1957. *Major uses of land in the United States: Summary for 1954*. U.S. Department of Agriculture, Agricultural Research Service. AIB-168 (Washington, D.C.).

Wooten, H. H., K. Gertel, and W. C. Pendleton. 1962. *Major uses of land and water in the United States: Summary for 1959*. U.S. Department of Agriculture, Economic Research Service. AER-13 (Washington, D.C.).

Cropland excludes cropland used only for pasture. Grassland, pasture, and range include grassland and other nonforested pasture and range including cropland used only for pasture. Forest land excludes forest land in parks and other special uses of land. Special use areas include rural transportation areas, rural parks, wildlife areas, defense and industrial areas, farmsteads, farm roads, and lanes.

Unclassified areas include urban areas, areas in miscellaneous uses not inventoried, and areas of little usable surface such as marshes, open swamps, rock areas, desert, and tundra. The total land area of the United States increased in 1959 with the addition of Alaska and Hawaii as states. Other changes in total land area result from refinement in measuring techniques. Within a category, changes result from gains and losses from bases. The estimates for different years are not strictly comparable.

4-2
Farmland

4-2a
Distribution of farms, 1982

U.S. Department of Commerce, Bureau of the Census. 1985. *Number of Farms: 1982. 1982 Census of Agriculture, volume 2, part 1, Graphic summary.* AC82-SS1 (Washington, D.C.), figure M1, Number of farms, p. 6.

U.S. Department of Agriculture, Soil Conservation Service. 1981. *1980 Appraisal Part 1—Soil, water and related resources of the United States: Status, conditions and trends* (Washington, D.C.), pp. 7-17.

The term farm denotes all places on which agricultural operations were conducted at any time in the census year under the day-to-day control of individual management and from which $1000 or more in agricultural products were sold or could normally have been sold.

4-2b
Number of farms, 1890–1982

4-2c
Land in farms, 1860–1982

U.S. Department of Commerce, Bureau of the Census. 1976. *Historical statistics of the United States: Colonial times to 1970* (Washington, D.C.), part 1, series K 109 and 142.

U.S. Department of Commerce, Bureau of the Census. 1985. *Statistical abstract of the United States: 1986* (Washington, D.C.), p. 636.

4-2d
Number of farms by tenure type, 1900–1982

4-2e
Number of farms by farm size, 1900–1982

U.S. Department of Commerce, Bureau of the Census. 1976. *Historical statistics of the United States: Colonial times to 1970* (Washington, D.C.), part 1, series K 109-113.

U.S. Department of Commerce, Bureau of the Census. 1985. *Statistical abstract of the United States: 1986* (Washington, D.C.), p. 636.

4-2f
Land in farms by tenure type, 1900–1982

4-2g
Land in farms by farm size, 1900–1982

U.S. Department of Commerce, Bureau of the Census. 1976. *Historical statistics of the United States: Colonial times to 1970* (Washington, D.C.), part I, series K 142-147.

U.S. Department of Commerce, Bureau of the Census. 1986. *Statistical abstract of the United States: 1987* (Washington, D.C.), p. 622.

Rasmussen, W. D. 1984. *A history of agricultural policy: chronological outline.* U.S. Department of Agriculture, Economic Research Service (Washington, D.C.).

U.S. Department of Agriculture, Economic Research Service. 1984. *History of agricultural price-support and adjustment programs, 1933–84.* Agricultural Information Bulletin No. 485 (Washington, D.C.).

Snodgrass, M. M., and L. T. Wallace. 1975. *Agriculture, economics, and resource management.* Third edition. Prentice-Hall, Inc. (Englewood Cliffs, N.J.), pp. 134-144.

Mighell, R. L. 1955. *American agriculture: Its structure and place in the economy.* A volume in the census monograph series. John Wiley and Sons, Inc. (New York), pp. 98-101.

Ball, A. G., and E.O. Heady. 1972. *Size, structure and future of farms.* The Iowa State University Press (Ames, Iowa), pp. 232-239.

Since 1850, when minimum criteria defining a farm for census purposes were first established, the farm definition has changed nine times. The current definition, first used in 1974, is cited under 4-2a above. No adjustments have been made to account for different definitions of a farm.

4-3
Prime farmland

4-3a
Distribution of prime farmland, 1982

U.S. Department of Agriculture, Soil Conservation Service, and Iowa University Statistical Laboratory. 1987. *Basic statistics: 1982 national resources inventory.* Statistical Bulletin No. 756 (Washington, D.C.), table 40a, Prime farmland in 1982 by state, p. 62.

4-3b
Use of prime farmland, 1977–1982

U.S. Department of Agriculture, Soil Conservation Service and Iowa State University Statistical Laboratory. 1982. *Basic statistics: 1977 natural resources inventory.* Statistical Bulletin 686 (Washington, D.C.), table 17, Prime farmland, by land use and state, 1977, p. 59.

U.S. Department of Agriculture, Soil Conservation Service and Iowa University Statistical Laboratory. 1987. *Basic statistics: 1982 national resources inventory.* Statistical Bulletin No. 756 (Washington, D.C.), table 40a, Prime farmland in 1982 by state, p. 62.

Schmude, K. O. 1977. "A perspective on prime farmland." *J. Soil and Water Conserv.,* **32**: 241.

4-4
Cropland

4-4a
Major uses of cropland, 1945–1986

U.S. Department of Agriculture, Economic Research Service. 1988. *Cropland, water, and conservation situation and outlook report.* AR-12 and earlier issues (Washington, D.C.), table 1, Major uses of cropland, United States, p. 5.

Horsfield, J., and N. Landgren. 1987. *Cropland trends across the Nation.* AER-494 (Washington, D.C.).

Acres of idle cropland, cropland pasture, and total cropland are estimated only for years coinciding with Census of Agriculture years. Data are for the 48 conterminous states.

4-4b
Cropland diverted from production under federal
farm programs, 1955–1986

U.S. Department of Agriculture, Economic Research Service. 1988. *Cropland, water, and conservation situation and outlook report.* AR-12 (Washington, D.C.), table 4, Cropland idled under federal acreage reduction programs, by region, p. 8.

4-4c
Distribution of cropland acreage changes, 1949–1982

U.S. Department of Agriculture, Economic Research Service. 1985. *Cropland use and supply outlook situation report.* CUS-2 (Washington, D.C.), figure 7, Cropland acreage changes, 1949–1969, p. 15 and figure 8, Cropland acreage changes, 1969–1982, p. 17.

4-5
Materials and energy used in agriculture

4-5a
Agricultural inputs and outputs, 1969–1986

U.S. Department of Agriculture, Economic Research Service. 1986. *Economic indicators of the farm sector: Production and efficiency statistics, 1984* (updated). ECIFGS 4-4 (Washington, D.C.), table 1, Farm production: Indexes of farm output by enterprise groups, United States, 1939–1984, p. 5 and table 57, Indexes of total farm input and major input subgroups, United States, 1939–1984, p. 56.

4-5b
Inputs, 1969–1986

U.S. Department of Agriculture, Economic Research Service. 1986. *Economic indicators of the farm sector: Production and efficiency statistics, 1984* (updated). ECIFGS 4-4 (Washington, D.C.), table 57, Indexes of total farm input and major input subgroups, United States, 1939–1984, p. 56.

Agricultural chemicals include fertilizer, lime, and pesticides.

4-5c
Farm fuel use, 1974–1986

U.S. Department of Agriculture, Economic Research Service. 1988. *Agricultural resources inputs situation and outputs report.* AR-11 (Washington, D.C.), table 13, Farm fuel use, p. 15.

4-5d
Farm fertilizer use, 1939–1986

U.S. Department of Commerce, Bureau of the Census. 1976. *Historical statistics of the United States: Colonial times to 1970* (Washington, D.C.), part 1, series K 193.

U.S. Department of Commerce, Bureau of the Census. 1985. *Statistical abstract of the United States: 1986* (Washington, D.C.), p. 654.

U.S. Department of Agriculture, Economic Research Service. 1988. *Inputs situation and outlook report.* AR-9 (Washington, D.C.), table 6, U.S. fertilizer consumption, p. 10.

Primary nutrients include nitrogenous, phosphate, and potash fertilizers.

4-5e
Pesticide use, 1964–1986

U.S. Department of Agriculture, Economic Research Service. 1968. *Quantities of pesticides used by farmers in 1964.* AR-131 (Washington, D.C.), pp. 19, 20, 26. 27.

U.S. Department of Agriculture, Economic Research Service. 1970. *Quantities of pesticides used by farmers in 1968.* AR-179 (Washington, D.C.), pp. 22-23.

U.S. Department of Agriculture, Economic Research Service. 1977. *Quantities of pesticides used by farmers in 1971.* AR-252 (Washington, D.C.), pp. 9, 13, 40, 41, 50.

U.S. Department of Agriculture, Economic Research Service. 1982 crop and livestock pesticide usage survey, unpublished data (Washington, D.C.).

U.S. Department of Agriculture, Economic Research Service. 1983. *Inputs situation and outlook report.* IOS-2 (Washington, D.C.).

U.S. Department of Agriculture, Economic Research Service. 1987. *Inputs situation and outlook report.* AR-5 (Washington, D.C.), table 14, Projected pesticide use on major U.S. field crops, p. 16.

For the years 1964, 1966, 1972, and 1976, estimates of pesticide use are for total use on all crops and livestock in the United States. The 1982 estimates are for major field and forage crops only and represent 33 major producing states excluding California. The 1986 estimates are for 10 major field crops.

4-5f
Total irrigated farmland, 1900–1984

U.S. Department of Commerce, Bureau of the Census. 1976. *Historical statistics of the United States: Colonial times to 1970* (Washington, D.C.), part I, series J 86.

U.S. Department of Commerce, Bureau of the Census, 1985. *Statistical abstract of the United States: 1986* (Washington, D.C.), p. 640.

U.S. Department of Commerce, Bureau of the Census, 1986. *1984 farm and ranch irrigation survey.* AG84-SR-1 (Washington, D.C.), 85 pp.

Data are for the 48 conterminous United States.

4-5g
Water used for irrigation, 1900–1985

U.S. Department of Commerce, Bureau of the Census. 1976. *Historical statistics of the United States: Colonial times to 1970* (Washington, D.C.), part I, series J 94.

U.S. Department of Commerce, Bureau of the Census. 1986. *Statistical abstract of the United States: 1987* (Washington, D.C.), p. 186.

Solley, W. B., C. F. Merk, and R. R. Pierce. 1988. *Estimated use of water in the United States in 1985.* U.S. Department of the Interior, Geological Survey Circular 1004 (Reston, Va.), p. 69.

Estimates for years 1900–1940 are for the 48 conterminous United States only.

4-5h
Water applied to irrigated acres, 1969–1984

U.S. Department of Commerce, Bureau of the Census. 1986. *1984 farm and ranch irrigation survey.* AG84-SR-1 (Washington, D.C.), 85 pp.

4-6
Grazing land

4-6a
Rangeland, mid-1980s

4-6b
Grazed forest land, mid-1980s

4-6c
Pastureland, mid-1980s

4-6d
Ownership of land suitable for grazing, mid-1980s

U.S. Department of Agriculture, Extension Service. 1986. *Grazing lands and people* (Washington, D.C.), Appendix a, U.S. grazing lands, pp. 14-15.

U.S. Department of Commerce, Forest Service. 1987. *Condition of U.S. Forest Service rangelands as of 1987* (Washington, D.C.), table 2, Ecological status-suitable acres, p. 2.

U.S. Department of the Interior, Bureau of Land Management. 1987. *Public land statistics, 1986* (Washington, D.C.), summary p. 1.

U.S. Department of Agriculture, Soil Conservation Service and Iowa State University Statistical Laboratory. 1987. *Basic statistics: 1982 natural resources inventory.* Statistical Bulletin 756 (Washington, D.C.), table 2a, Land cover/use of nonfederal land and small water in 1982, by state, p. 24.

Hitchcock, A. S. 1971. *Manual of grasses of the United States.* Second edition (revised by A. Chase). Dover Publications, Inc. (New York), volume 1, pp. 1-6.

U.S. Department of Agriculture, Soil Conservation Service. 1976. *National range handbook.* NRH-1 (Washington, D.C.), section 200, Definitions.

Box, T. W. 1983. "A billion acres of rangeland: Our Nation's multiple use lands," pp. 76-85, in *1983 Yearbook of Agriculture: Using our natural resources,* J. Hayes (ed.). (Washington, D.C.).

Frey, H. T., and R. W. Hexem. 1985. *Major uses of land in the United States: 1982.* U.S. Department of Agriculture, Economic Research Service, Natural Resources Economics Division. AER-535 (Washington, D.C.), pp. 21-22.

Data from sources were reconciled by agency representatives at a workshop convened by the Council on Environmental Quality. Data refer to land cover that is suitable for grazing and should not be confused with land use statistics in Frey and Hexem (1985) that reflect what the land is used for.

4-7
Grazing land conditions and apparent trends

4-7a
Condition of nonfederal rangeland, 1963–1982

U.S. Department of Agriculture, Soil Conservation Service, and Iowa State University Statistical Laboratory. 1987. *Basic statistics: 1982 natural resources inventory.* Statistical Bulletin 756 (Washington, D.C.), table 42a, Rangeland condition by state, 1982, p. 64.

U.S. Department of Agriculture, Extension Service. 1986. *Grazing lands and people* (Washington, D.C.), Appendix a, U.S. grazing lands, pp. 14-15.

Pendleton, D. T. 1978. *Nonfederal rangelands of the United States—A decade of change: 1967-1977,* unpublished data. First International Rangeland Congress (Denver, Colo.: August, 1978).

Pendleton, D. T. 1979. *Rangeland, range condition, and erosion,* unpublished data. 32nd annual meeting of the Society for Range Management (Casper, Wyo.: February, 1979).

4-7b
Condition of Bureau of Land Management grazed rangeland, 1936–1987

U.S. Department of the Interior, Bureau of Land Management. 1987. *Public land statistics, 1986* (Washington, D.C.), summary p. 1.

U.S. Department of the Interior, Bureau of Land Management. 1984. *50 years of public land management, 1934–1984* (Washington, D.C.), 27 pp.

Hess, K., and R. J. White. 1986. "Are the public rangelands ailing?" *J. Range Manage.,* 8(6): 278-281.

4-7c
Ecological status and forage condition of Forest Service grazing lands, 1986

U.S. Department of Agriculture, Forest Service. 1987. *Condition of U.S. Forest Service rangelands as of 1987* (Washington, D.C.), table 2, Ecological status-suitable acres, p. 2.

4-7d
Apparent trend in nonfederal rangeland condition, 1982

U.S. Department of Agriculture, Soil Conservation Service and Iowa State University Statistical Laboratory. 1987. *Basic statistics: 1982 natural resources inventory.* Statistical Bulletin 756 (Washington, D.C.), table 42a, Rangeland condition by state, 1982, p. 64.

4-7e
Apparent trend in Bureau of Land Management grazed rangeland condition, 1987

U.S. Department of the Interior, Bureau of Land Management. 1987. *Range condition and trend report* (Washington, D.C.), table 4, Apparent trend, p. 6.

4-7f
Apparent trend in ecological status of Forest Service suitable grazing land condition, 1986

U.S. Department of Agriculture, Forest Service. 1987. *Condition of U.S. Forest Service rangelands as of 1987,* table 3, Regional summary trend of suitable acres—1987 (Washington, D.C.), p. 3.

Report of the Range Inventory Standardization Committee for the Society of Range Management. 1983. *Guidelines and terminology for range inventories and monitoring* (Albuquerque, N. Mex.), pp. 1-12.

4-8
Distribution of forest land

4-8
Major forest types

Hall, F. C. 1983. "Forest lands of the United States," pp. 130-139, in *1983 Yearbook of Agriculture: Using our natural resources,* J. Hayes (ed.). (Washington, D.C.).

Braun, E. L. 1950. *Deciduous forests of Eastern North America.* The Free Press (New York), 596 pp.

4-9
Ownership of forest land

4-9
Ownership of forest land

U.S. Department of Agriculture, Forest Service. 1989. *The 1989 assessment of the forest and rangeland situation in the United States* (Washington, D.C.), pp 7-8.

U.S. Department of Agriculture, Soil Conservation Service. 1986. *Soil, water, and related resources of the United States: Status, conditions, and trends.* Draft appraisal, part 1 (Washington, D.C.), pp. 19-34.

4-10
Reforestation

4-10a
Reforestation, 1950–1986

4-10b
Reforestation by ownership, 1986

U.S. Department of Agriculture, Forest Service. *U.S. forest planting report,* annual (Washington, D.C.).

4-11
Wildfire damage

4-11
Forest land damaged by wildfire, 1926–1986

U.S. Department of Agriculture, Forest Service. *Wildfire statistics,* annual (Washington, D.C.).

4-12
Forest land damaged by insects and diseases

4-12a
Forest land damaged by spruce budworms, 1968–1986

4-12b
Forestland damaged by other insects, 1968–1986

U.S. Department of Agriculture, Forest Service, Forest Pest Management. *Forest insect and disease conditions in the United States,* annual (Washington, D.C.).

Hoffard, W. H., 1985. "Southern pine beetle," pp. 32-37, in *Insect and disease conditions in the United States 1979-1983,* R. C. Loomis, S. Tucker, and T. H. Hofacker (eds.). (Washington, D.C.).

Kucera, D. R. 1985. "Spruce budworm," pp. 38-43, in *Insect and disease conditions in the United States 1979-1983,* R. C. Loomis, S. Tucker, and T. H. Hofacker (eds.). (Washington, D.C.).

Bridgewater, D. R. 1985. "Western spruce budworm," pp. 44-47, in *Insect and disease conditions in the United States 1979-1983,* R. C. Loomis, S. Tucker, and T. H. Hofacker (eds.). (Washington, D.C.).

Wolfe, R. D. 1985. "Gypsy moth," pp. 8-15, in *Insect and disease conditions in the United States 1979–1983*, R. C. Loomis, S. Tucker, and T. H. Hofacker (eds.). (Washington, D.C.).

McGregor, M. D. 1985. "Western pine beetle," pp. 16-23, in *Insect and disease conditions in the United States 1979–1983*, R. C. Loomis, S. Tucker, and T. H. Hofacker (eds.). (Washington, D.C.).

4-12c
Defoliation by gypsy moth, 1924–1986

R. C. Loomis, S. Tucker, and T. H. Hofacker (eds.). 1985. *Insect and disease conditions in the United States 1979–1983*. U.S. Department of Agriculture, Forest Service, Forest Pest Management (Washington, D.C.).

U.S. Department of Agriculture, Forest Service, Forest Pest Management. *Insect and disease conditions in the United States, annual* (Washington, D.C.).

4-12d
Infestation by disease, 1986

R. C. Loomis, S. Tucker, and T. H. Hofacker (eds.). 1985. *Insect and disease conditions in the United States 1979–1983*. U.S. Department of Agriculture, Forest Service, Forest Pest Management (Washington, D.C.).

U.S. Department of Agriculture, Forest Service, Forest Pest Management. *Insect and disease conditions in the United States, annual* (Washington, D.C.).

Johnson, D. W., and F. G. Hawksworth. 1985. "Dwarf mistletoes," pp. 48-55, in *Insect and disease conditions in the United States 1979–1983*, R. C. Loomis, S. Tucker, and T. H. Hofacker (eds.). (Washington, D.C.).

Anderson, R. L. 1985. "Fusiform rust," pp. 56-63, in *Insect and disease conditions in the United States 1979–1983*, R. C. Loomis, S. Tucker, and T. H. Hofacker (eds.). (Washington, D.C.).

DeNitto, G. A. 1985. "Root diseases," pp. 76-84, in *Insect and disease conditions in the United States 1979–1983*, R. C. Loomis, S. Tucker, and T. H. Hofacker (eds.). (Washington, D.C.).

4-13
Timber stocks

4-13a
Net annual growth of growing stock by ownership, 1952–1986

U.S. Department of Agriculture, Forest Service, 1989. Supporting table 28, Net annual growth of growing stock on timberland in the United States, by ownership, region, and species group, for 1952, 1962, 1970, 1976, and 1986. Prepared by D. R. Darr, *The 1989 RPA assessment of the forest and range land situation in the United States* (Washington, D.C.), 88 pp.

4-13b
Annual removals of growing stock by ownership, 1952–1986

U.S. Department of Agriculture, Forest Service, 1989. Supporting table 29, Annual removals of growing stock on timberland in the United States, by ownership, region, and species group, for 1970, 1976, and 1986. Prepared by D. R. Darr, *The 1989 RPA assessment of the forest and range land situation in the United States* (Washington, D.C.), 88 pp.

4-13c
Net annual growth and removals by region (North and South), 1952–1986

4-13d
Net annual growth and removals by region (Mountain and Pacific), 1952–1986

U.S. Department of Agriculture, Forest Service, 1989. Supporting table 28, Net annual growth of growing stock on timberland in the United States, by ownership, region, and species group, for 1952, 1962, 1970, 1976, and 1986. Prepared by D. R. Darr, *The 1989 RPA assessment of the forest and range land situation in the United States* (Washington, D.C.), 88 pp.

U.S. Department of Agriculture, Forest Service, 1989. Supporting table 29, Annual removals of growing stock on timberland in the United States, by ownership, region, and species group, for 1970, 1976, and 1986. Prepared by D. R. Darr, *The 1989 RPA assessment of the forest and range land situation in the United States* (Washington, D.C.), 88 pp.

4-14
Timber use

4-14
Roundwood harvest by product, 1950–1986

U.S. Department of Agriculture, Forest Service. 1988. *U.S. timber production, trade, consumption, and price statistics, 1950-1986* (Washington, D.C.), table 4, p. 13.

U.S. Department of Agriculture, Forest Service, 1989. Supporting table 30, Volume of roundwood products harvested in the United States, by source of material, species group, region, and product, 1986. Prepared by D. R. Darr, *The 1989 RPA assessment of the forest and range land situation in the United States* (Washington, D.C.), 88 pp.

4-15
Soil conditions

4-15a
Saline soils, 1982

U.S. Department of Agriculture, Soil Conservation Service, and Iowa State University Statistical Laboratory. 1987. *Basic statistics: 1982 natural resources inventory*. Statistical Bulletin 756 (Washington, D.C.). table 44a, Saline and/or alkali areas in 1982, by state, p. 66.

Walker, C. H., 1986. *Irrigation water conservation and soil and water salinity*. A technical report prepared for the 1985 Resources Conservation Appraisal (RPA). U.S. Department of Agriculture (Washington, D.C.), 18 pp.

4-15b
Sheet and rill erosion, 1982

U.S. Department of Agriculture, Soil Conservation Service, and Iowa State University Statistical Laboratory. 1987. *Basic statistics: 1982 natural resources inventory*. Statistical Bulletin 756 (Washington, D.C.). table 17a, Estimated average annual erosion on all 1982 cropland, by state, p. 39.

Dideriksen, R. I. 1981. "Resources inventory—Sheet, rill and wind erosion." *Trans. Am. Soc. Agric. Eng.*, 24(5): 1246-1252.

4-15c
Wind erosion, 1982

U.S. Department of Agriculture, Soil Conservation Service, and Iowa State University Statistical Laboratory. 1987. *Basic statistics: 1982 natural resources inventory*. Statistical Bulletin 756 (Washington, D.C.). table 17a, Estimated average annual erosion on all 1982 cropland, by state, p. 39.

Chepil, W. S. 1957. "Erosion of wind by soil," pp. 308-314, in *1957 yearbook of agriculture*, U.S. Department of Agriculture (Washington, D.C.).

Chapter 5
Wetlands and Wildlife

5-1
Wetlands

The term wetlands applies to a variety of low-lying areas where the water table is at or near the surface of the land, soils are saturated or covered by water during parts of the year, and there is a predominance of hydrophytic plants. Wetlands include tidal marshes, swamp forests, peat bogs, prairie potholes, wet meadows, and similar transitional areas between aquatic and terrestrial environments.

Water is the primary factor controlling the type of soils that develop in wetlands and the kinds of plants and animals that can live there. Water regimes in wetlands vary depending on local conditions, but most wetlands are flooded at some time during the year. Tidal wetlands are inundated with water over each tidal cycle, and plants and animals must tolerate long periods of flooding. Standing water—from a few inches to a foot or more—is not uncommon in swamp forests, especially in winter. Some wetlands, such as vernal ponds and prairie potholes, are wet only periodically, either seasonally or cyclically, and at other times resemble dry meadows or prairies. Wetlands occurring on groundwater-seepage slopes may never be flooded, but the soils remain saturated for all or most of the growing season.

Wetlands are among the most biologically productive ecosystems in the world. Net primary production of plants in salt marshes and freshwater wetlands rivals that of tropical rainforests and the Nation's most productive agricultural lands. This production is an important component of aquatic and terrestrial food webs. Seeds of many wetland plants

are eaten by waterfowl and other animals. The underground roots and rhizomes of some plants are consumed by muskrats and waterfowl, and the shoots and leaves of certain marsh plants are grazed by muskrat, nutria, deer, moose, bears, and, in some places, domestic livestock. A large fraction of the wetland plant biomass is decomposed by microorganisms to form detritus that is stored and utilized within the wetland habitat or is exported out of the system for use elsewhere. Detritus is consumed by zooplankton, insects, and shellfish which, in turn, are in the diets of fishes and shorebirds.

Many types of animals depend upon wetlands for at least part of their life cycle. Wetlands provide cover, freedom from disturbance, food, and other habitat factors that are vital to certain animals. It is estimated that over one-half of all the saltwater fish and shellfish harvested annually in the United States as well as most of the freshwater game fish use wetlands for feeding areas, spawning grounds, and nurseries for young. About one-third of the North American bird species are wetland associates. In addition to providing year-round habitats for resident birds, wetlands are important breeding grounds, overwintering areas, and feeding areas for migratory birds, particularly waterfowl. Of the 10 to 20 million waterfowl that nest in the conterminous 48 United States, 50% or more reproduce in the prairie pothole wetlands of the Midwest. Bald eagles, ospreys, hawks, egrets, herons, kingfishers, and a variety of shore, marsh, and passerine birds are other components of the wetland avifauna.

Many mammals are wetland-dependent also. Muskrats, nutria, beaver, marsh rice rats, and swamp rabbits are totally wetland-dependent species that spend their entire life cycle in wetlands. Other mammals, such as otter, mink, raccoon, bobcat, meadow mouse, moose, and white-tailed deer, are partially dependent, visiting wetlands for a specific purpose, such as feeding, or at certain times of the year. Moose, for example, obtain sodium (a dietary nutrient) from aquatic plants. Many other forms of animal life make their homes in wetlands, including turtles, snakes, alligators, frogs, salamanders, and insects. Nearly all of the approximately 190 species of amphibians in North America are wetland-dependent, at least for breeding purposes.

The wetlands of the United States are important for other reasons as well. Wetlands produce oxygen and play a significant role in converting atmospheric nitrogen into a form that can be used by plants and animals to make protein. Wetlands naturally trap nutrients and sediments and help maintain or improve water quality. Some wetlands are capable of performing other wastewater treatment functions, such as removing coliform bacteria, heavy metals, pesticides, and toxic chemicals that pass through the system. Wetlands associated with estuaries, rivers, and streams as well as some isolated wetlands and lakes provide flood protection by slowing and storing floodwaters and reducing flood peaks. Wetlands anchor shorelines and provide erosion protection by binding and stabilizing substrates, dissipating wave and current energy, and trapping sediments.

Wetlands also provide many economic and social benefits to the Nation. Fishing, hunting, and trapping are among the more traditional contemporary uses of wetlands, although wetlands have provided food and fiber throughout history. Wetland plants were used by Indians and colonists for food, teas, medicinal purposes, ornaments, and baskets. Many of these uses still prevail. Wild rice is harvested for its grain, and elderberries, cranberries, blackberries, and the fruits of other wetland plants are used to make condiments and wine. Valuable wood products come from wetlands. Cypress lumber, for example, has always been in great demand because of its durability. The bottomlands along the Mississippi River have been heavily harvested for valuable hardwoods for lumber, furniture making, and firewood and to make way for conversion of wetlands to cropland. In certain places, peat is mined for agricultural use and to provide a source of energy.

Wetlands are some of the last remaining wilderness areas in the Nation. Their beauty and allure inspire artists, authors, and naturalists—professionals and amateurs alike. Wetlands provide places to spend leisure hours bird watching, photographing, canoeing, and enjoying nature. Studies on plants and animals and other aspects of wetlands and opportunities to visit wetlands have helped to reshape public perception of them. Once viewed as insect-ridden places that should be drained or filled and converted to other uses, wetlands are now

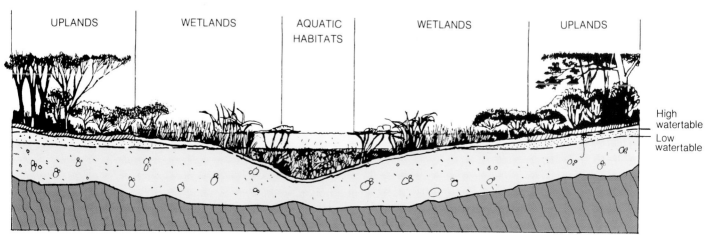

UPLANDS   WETLANDS   AQUATIC HABITATS   WETLANDS   UPLANDS

High watertable
Low watertable

Identifying features of wetlands

regarded as playing a vital role in maintaining environmental quality.

5-2
Distribution of wetlands

Wetlands occur in every state in the Nation. Alaska, Florida, and Louisiana have the greatest wetland acreages, with over 25% of the land surface area in each of these states covered by wetlands. Other states with considerable wetland area include Alabama, Arkansas, Georgia, Maine, Michigan, Mississippi, North Carolina, South Carolina, and Wisconsin.

Wetlands exist in a variety of sizes, shapes, and types as the result of regional differences in climate, vegetation, soils, and hydrology. For classification purposes, wetlands are either estuarine or freshwater systems. Within each of these systems, there are marshes that are characterized by soft-stemmed herbaceous plants, swamps and bogs that are dominated by trees or shrubs, nonvegetated flats of sand or mud, and open water habitats with depths less than 6 feet.

Estuarine wetlands are found in coastal areas and are influenced daily or periodically by the rise and fall of the tide. There are estuarine wetlands along the open coast, such as salt marshes, mangrove forests, and tidal flats, where salinities are only slightly lower than that of ocean waters. Estuarine wetlands also include brackish marshes and swamps that are moderately saline because of freshwater input from upstream headwaters as well as freshwater marshes and swamps where the tidal effect is still significant, but salinity is that of freshwater.

Inland, or nontidal, freshwater wetlands occur in a variety of areas: in tributaries above tidal influence; along river and lake shorelines; on slopes with ground-water seeps; in isolated bogs and landscape depressions such as glacial kettles, limestone sinkholes, and peat bogs; and on isolated wetland domes fed primarily by rainwater. In Alaska, inland freshwater wetlands are found in freeze-and-thaw basins and areas underlain by permafrost at a shallow depth. Farm ponds and beaver impoundments with water depths less than 6 feet are also considered inland freshwater wetlands.

Some of the major wetland types have regional distribution patterns. Salt marshes, for example, occur in the following regions: New England (from Maine to New Jersey); Coastal Plain (southward from New Jersey along the southeastern coast of the United States, except along the southern tip of Florida where salt marshes are replaced by mangrove forests, and to Louisiana along the Gulf of Mexico); West Coast (far less developed because of the precipitous nature of the coastline); and Arctic (in Alaska). Salt marshes are dominated by the few plant species that can tolerate salt stress (for example, cordgrasses, saltworts, and salt bushes).

Freshwater marshes are found throughout the interior and coastal regions of the United States. There are large concentrations of freshwater marshes in the north-central Prairie Pothole region, especially in the Dakotas, in southern tip of Florida (for example, the Everglades), and along the Pacific flyway in the West. Freshwater wetlands produce a much more diverse plant assemblage than their saltwater counterparts, primarily because of the reduced salt stress. It is not uncommon to find over 30 different plant species in a square meter of freshwater marsh, whereas the same size area in a salt marsh supports only 1 or 2 different plant species. Freshwater marshes also support much of the fisheries, waterfowl, and wildlife harvested from wetlands in the United States.

Forested wetlands are widely distributed throughout the Nation. There are coniferous wetland forests with evergreen cover and deciduous wetland forests, which sport brilliant autumn colors before the leaves fall. Most forested wetlands have an herbaceous ground cover of marsh plants.

Northern forested wetlands occur throughout the Northeast, as far south as the Appalachians, west to the Great Lakes States, and beyond the grasslands in the far West. Northern boreal swamps are dominated by spruce, fir, and northern white cedar. Slightly more southern hardwood swamp forests are dominated by red maple. Atlantic white cedar swamps extend from Cape Cod southward along the coast. In the far West, western hemlock, red alder, and other evergreens are dominant in the wetland forests. Northern swamp forests also occur where extensive floodplains have developed along major rivers such as the Connecticut, Wabash, Tippecanoe, and upper Mississippi. Willows, cottonwoods, silver maple, and their associates make up these wet forests.

Southern swamp forests occur on the coastal plain from Virginia south to Florida and westward along the Gulf of Mexico to the Mississippi River. They fringe the major southern rivers, including the Roanoke, Pee Dee, Altamaha, Suwannee, Apalachicola, Chattahoochee, and lower Mississippi. The wetlands vegetation occurs in distinct bands or zones above the river, and this distribution pattern reflects the plants' ability to tolerate saturated conditions. The most water-tolerant trees, such as water tupelo and bald cypress, occur at the river's edge where the substrate is almost continuously flooded. A short distance away, where flooding occurs over 80 to 90% of the year, slightly less tolerant species such as water elm, Carolina ash, and pumpkin ash occur. Higher up, where flooding occurs over perhaps one-third of the year, the dominant species are even less tolerant and include overcup oak, water hickory, water locust, black willow, red and silver maples, magnolias, and bays. On nearby uplands, where flooding occurs for only short periods, the least water-tolerant species—sweetgum and a variety of oaks as well as loblolly pine— occur.

Bald cypress swamps, another type of southern swamp, are best developed in Florida where they cover over 10% of the state. They also occur along the Gulf Coast to eastern Texas and north into Arkansas and Tennessee, in the Mississippi River valley up to southern Illinois and Indiana, and along the East coast to as far north as Delaware.

Shrub swamps are typical of forested regions and are found throughout the Northeast and into the Great Lakes region as well as in the Southeast from Virginia south to Florida and locally in the West. These wetlands are characterized by scrubby, low-lying thickets of evergreens or deciduous shrubs. Some shrub wetlands are successional areas—on their way to becoming forests—whereas others are more persistent, lasting for decades or centuries. Alder and leatherleaf thickets are typically associated with northern shrub wetlands, and hollies, bays, and scraggly cedar and pines are found in the southern shrub wetlands or pocosins.

Bogs are another distinctive kind of wetland. They are characterized by a canopy of evergreen trees or shrubs and a ground cover of sphagnum moss. Bogs form in shallow depressions and are very wet. They tend to be acidic, which facilitates the accumulation

Wetland ecoregions

- Pacific
- Great Basin/Desert and Montane
- Plains/Prairie Potholes
- Northeast/Midwest
- Southeast/Southern Florida

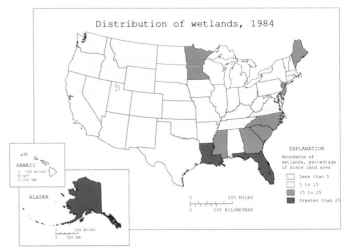

Distribution of wetlands, 1984

HAWAII
0   100 MILES
0   100 KM

ALASKA
0   500 MILES
0   500 KM

EXPLANATION
Abundance of wetlands, percentage of state land area
Less than 5
5 to 15
15 to 25
Greater than 25

0   500 MILES
0   500 KILOMETERS

Marshes

Shrub swamps

Bogs

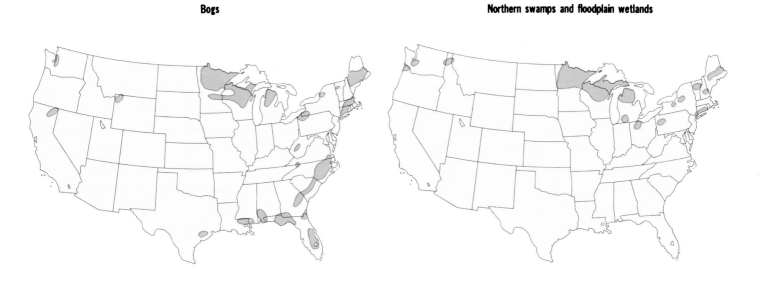

Northern swamps and floodplain wetlands

Southern swamps

Cypress swamps

Status of wetlands by type, 1954-1974

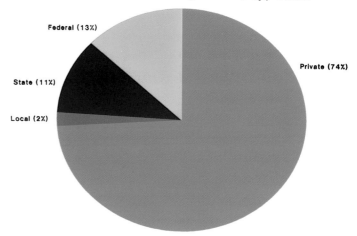

Status of wetlands by ownership, 1985

Total wetlands = 95 million acres

of peat, and are nutrient poor because of slow decomposition rates. Bogs are common in parts of the United States that were once glaciated, and most occur in New England and across the Great Lakes region. One of the largest peatland complexes is in northern Minnesota. Bogs also occur in isolated areas from the Appalachian Mountains into the Gulf Coast region and throughout the mountains of the West and the Pacific Northwest.

5-3
Wetland status and trends

The current analysis of wetland status and trends in the conterminous United States is based on the results of the last national inventory of wetlands that used aerial photography from the mid-1950s and mid-1970s. Wetland acreages for the mid-1980s are estimated because exact figures will not be available until after 1990 when the results of another national inventory are finalized.

In the mid-1970s, there were an estimated 99 million acres of wetlands in the conterminous United States, which accounted for roughly 5% of the total land surface cover. About 95% of these wetlands was classified as inland freshwater wetlands. Over one-half of the inland freshwater wetlands were

forested and about one-third were emergent marshes. The rest of the wetlands in the freshwater category were shrub wetlands, ponds, and unvegetated flats.

Estuarine wetlands covered 5.2 million acres of the land in coastal conterminous states in the mid-1970s. Nearly 75% of the estuarine wetlands was marshes, 10% was forested or shrub wetlands, and the remainder was tidal flats and ponds.

Of the total wetland area in the conterminous United States in the mid-1970s, most (70.3 million acres) was in private ownership. An estimated 12.5 million acres of wetlands were under federal ownership or control and another 12.2 million acres were owned or managed by state and local governments. Much of the federal wetland area was found in wildlife refuges and the rest was in national parks, national forests, military reservations, and other public lands. State and local government wetlands were found in a variety of protected areas, including wildlife management areas, natural areas, and parks.

The amount of wetlands present in the conterminous United States when settlement occurred in the early 17th century is estimated to be between 127 and 215 million acres. The wide range in estimates reflects differences in wetlands definitions, classifica-

tion systems, and survey methods used to generate the figures. Nonetheless, the estimates are often compared with existing wetland acreage to determine how many acres of wetlands have been lost since Colonial times. Using the 215-million-acre figure (which is considered a reliable estimate of original wetland area), 56% of the original wetlands was lost by the mid-1980s.

Between the mid-1950s and mid-1970s, an average of 458,000 wetland acres were lost each year in the conterminous United States. This annual loss is equivalent to approximately one-half of the size of Rhode Island. Over the 20-year interval, the total wetlands acreage lost is equivalent to an area the size of Massachusetts, Connecticut, and Rhode Island combined.

The reasons for wetland losses are many and varied. Wetlands are subjected to both natural and human stresses, which may affect their abundance as well as the quality of the habitat and functions they provide. Natural events, such as erosion, fire, land subsidence, sea level rise, beaver and muskrat activity, and natural succession, can alter wetland conditions. Most of the wetland losses that have occurred since settlement, however, are attributed to drainage and other human activities.

Trend in wetland acreages for the conterminous United States, 1700s-1980s

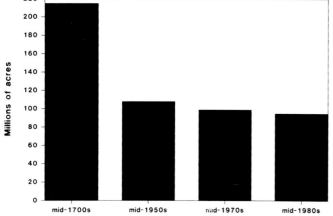

Net losses and gains in wetlands by type, 1954-1974

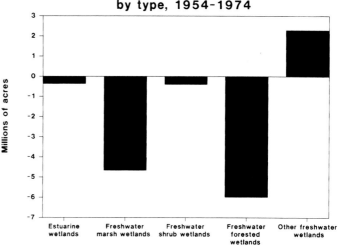

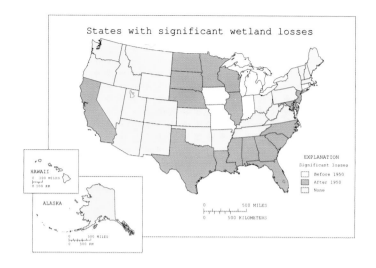

States with significant wetland losses

EXPLANATION
Significant losses
☐ Before 1950
▨ After 1950
☐ None

HAWAII
0 100 MILES
0 100 KM

ALASKA
0   500 MILES
0 500 KM

0   500 MILES
0   500 KILOMETERS

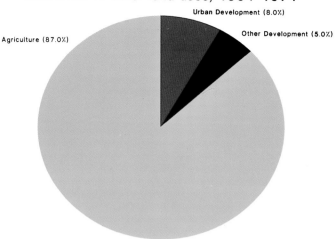

Fate of wetlands
converted to other land uses, 1954-1974

Agriculture (87.0%)

Urban Development (8.0%)

Other Development (5.0%)

Over the past four centuries, wetlands have been drained to produce agricultural land, dredged and filled for industrial and residential development, and filled with sanitary landfill and other unwanted debris. Prior to the mid-1970s, some federal, state, and local government policies actually provided incentives for the destruction of wetlands. Since then, however, improved scientific understanding and more public awareness of wetland values have led to the passage of many wetland protection laws and regulations and the gradual elimination of many of the government incentives that encouraged wetland conversion. Wetland losses continue to occur in the 1980s, but at a slower annual rate and, in some instances, with compensatory action to create or restore lost or damaged wetlands.

Wetland losses have affected certain wetland types more than others. Inland freshwater marshes and forested wetlands have been affected the most. Between the mid-1950s and mid-1970s, approximately 4.67 million acres of inland freshwater marsh (or about 14% of the total coverage of this wetland type in the conterminous United States) were lost. Inland drainage for agriculture was the most significant cause of freshwater marsh destruction in the Prairie Pothole region of the Dakotas and Minnesota, in Nebraska's Sandhills and Rainwater Basin, and in Florida's Everglades. By the mid-1950s, it was estimated that over one-half of the wetlands in the Prairie Pothole region had been lost since settlement. On the West Coast, the wetlands of the Central Valley of California also have been greatly reduced by drainage as well as from the impact of pollutants washing off adjacent agricultural fields.

Over the 20-year period between 1950 and 1970, approximately 5.99 million acres of forested wetlands (10% of the total cover) were lost. The greatest losses of forested wetlands took place in the lower Mississippi River Valley with the conversion of bottomland hardwood forests to farmland.

Wetland losses also occurred in estuarine vegetated wetlands and inland freshwater shrub wetlands between the mid-1950s and mid-1970s. There was a net loss of 372,000 acres of estuarine vegetated wetlands, and most of this loss occurred in estuarine marshes along the Atlantic and Mississippi flyways and on the Gulf Coast in Louisiana, Texas, and Florida. Urban development and change to open water habitat were responsible for most of these losses. Estuarine shrub wetlands were hardest hit in North Carolina where pocosin wetlands were converted to cropland or pine plantation or mined for peat.

Some wetland types gained in total area between mid-1950 and mid-1970. Open water lake acreage increased by 1.4 million acres with 94% of this gain occurring in the eastern half of the Nation. Coastal open waters increased by 200,000 acres. Most of this gain occurred in Louisiana where estuarine marshes became permanently flooded as a result of numerous and complicated causes, including sea level rise, local subsidence, levee construction, channelization, and oil and gas extraction. Also increased were nonvegetated wetland flats (by over 46,000 acres) and inland open water (by 2.1 million acres). Most of the increase in open water acreage occurred in the Central and Mississippi flyways where uplands were impounded or excavated to create farm ponds, although 145,500 acres of forested wetlands and 385,000 acres of marsh also were changed to open water ponds.

Agricultural activities were responsible for 87% of the wetland losses that occurred in the conterminous United States between the mid-1950s and mid-1970s. Most of these losses were associated with draining, clearing, filling or otherwise converting wetlands to cropland. Over this period, approximately 5.8 million acres of forested wetlands, 2.7 million acres of marshes, and 0.4 million acres of scrub–shrub wetlands were converted to agricultural use.

Urban development, another major human-induced cause of wetland loss, accounted for 8% of the total wetland loss observed between the mid-1950s and mid-1970s. Dredge and fill for residential development in coastal areas was significant in Florida, Texas, New Jersey, New York, and California. During this same period, wetlands were destroyed to make way for marinas, reservoirs, highways, airports, industrial facilities, sewage treatment plants, and many other land uses.

5-4
Wetland losses by selected type

Along the coast of Louisiana, large expanses of marsh are disappearing at an alarming rate. As much as 30 square miles of coastal marsh are con- verted to open water every year. For a state whose coastal fisheries depend on coastal marshes and whose seafood industry produced 1.7 billion pounds valued at over 313 million dollars in 1986, this is a serious problem.

Coastal subsidence, sea level rise, and cyclical processes in the growth and deterioration of the Mississippi River Delta are some of the natural forces responsible for the wetlands loss. Human-induced causes include channelization and levee construction along the Mississippi River; canal dredging for navigation and energy operations; and subsidence associated with extraction of minerals, oil, natural gas, and ground water. Channelization and canal construction have increased marsh erosion and salt-water intrusion along the coast, and subsidence has exacerbated the effects of sea level rise. Man-made levees prevent sediment-rich waters from flowing over the marshes, and thus the marshes are unable to accumulate sediments and accrete vertically to keep pace with sea level rise.

Bottomland hardwood forests of the lower Mississippi River floodplain constitute the largest remaining contiguous wetland habitat in the conterminous United States. They are also one of the most rapidly diminishing wetland ecosystems. Of the over 12 million acres of bottomland hardwood forests that once existed in the lower Mississippi River floodplain, about one-half have been destroyed, and current information indicates a continued loss at a rate of 100,000 acres each year. Such losses are having detrimental effects on the remaining and adjacent ecosystems. Loss of wildlife habitat and natural flood storage capacity, foregone timber production, lost recreational opportunity, and poor downstream water quality are among the frequently cited impacts. Various types of development have contributed to a great reduction in bottomland hardwood forests since the 1930s. Intensive forestry, water control projects, and draining and clearing for agricultural development are responsible for much of this reduction.

The Prairie Pothole region of North America covers approximately 300,000 square miles and includes a large portion of North Dakota, South Dakota, Minnesota, and three Canadian provinces as well as a small portion of Montana and Iowa. Prairie potholes are depressions created by glaciation thousands of years ago. These wetlands are the most valuable

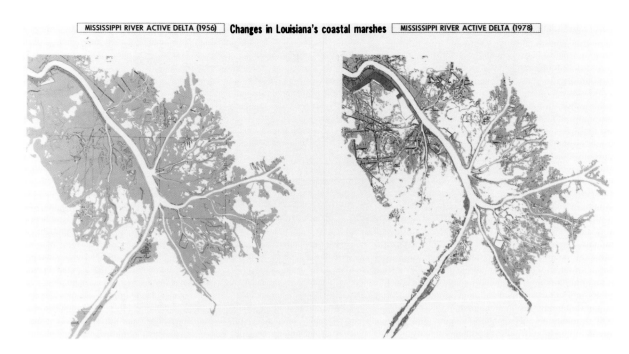

inland marshes for waterfowl production in North America and serve as the primary breeding habitat for many kinds of ducks, including: mallard, pintail, wigeon, gadwall, shoveler, teal, canvasback, and redhead.

Estimates of original prairie pothole acreage indicate that between 15 and 17 million acres once existed in the United States. Currently, there are approximately 5.6 million acres remaining in the Dakotas and western Minnesota, and only about 5 to 10% of the original prairie pothole wetlands remain in Iowa. Agricultural drainage is the principal cause of prairie pothole loss and is the greatest threat to the remaining pothole marshes.

Marshes in the Great Lakes Basin are declining at a rate of 20,000 acres per year. Industrial, residential, and agricultural development and rising lake levels are the principal reasons for the decline.

California has lost over 90% of its original wetlands. Although California's coastal wetlands are now generally protected by state law, they are still under heavy pressure for urban and industrial development. Inland wetlands remain subject to agricultural

pressures, and degradation of remaining wetlands from urban and agricultural runoff remains a problem.

The Rainwater Basin covers 4,200 square miles of flat or gently rolling plains in the south-central part of Nebraska. Survey maps from the early part of the 20th century indicate that the Rainwater Basin once contained nearly 4,000 individual marshes covering about 94,000 acres. By the 1960s, only 18% of these wetlands was left, and by 1981, estimates indicate that less than 10% remains. Roughly 9 out of every 10 original marshes have been destroyed and those remaining are remnants of formerly larger marshes. Wetland destruction in the Rainwater Basin accelerated after World War II because of intensive drainage for agriculture, improved earth-moving equipment, and deep well irrigation.

Wetlands within the Rainwater Basin are important to migrating waterfowl in the Central flyway (about 2.5 million ducks and geese move through the Basin each spring). Wetlands loss in this region

has forced ducks and geese to concentrate in the remaining wetlands and has adversely affected breeding populations. Late winter storms in 1975 prevented waterfowl from migrating farther north and more than 20,000 waterfowl died from an outbreak of avian cholera that was aggravated by crowded conditions. Since then, outbreaks of avian cholera have been common, and in 1980, between 72,000 and 80,000 waterfowl were lost to this disease. Currently, wetland resources and breeding waterfowl populations are at critical levels.

Pocosins are isolated wetland bogs that have a mixture of evergreen shrubs and trees and are found along the southeastern Coastal Plain. Named by Indians for their occurrence on broad, flat uplands away from large streams, pocosins (meaning "swamp on a hill") support a number of endangered and threatened wildlife, including the red cockaded woodpecker, pine barrens tree frog, eastern cougar, and American alligator.

About 70% of the Nation's pocosins occur along the coastal plain of North Carolina. They stabilize

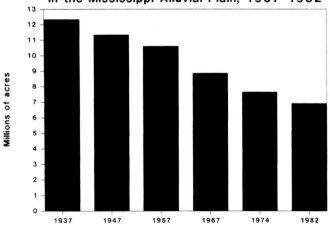

Losses of bottomland hardwood wetlands in the Mississippi Alluvial Plain, 1937-1982

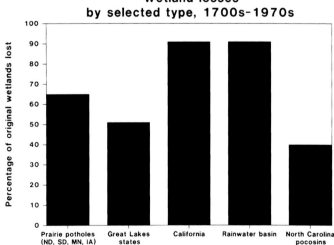

Wetland losses by selected type, 1700s-1970s

salinity levels in nearby estuaries by absorbing, storing, and gradually releasing floodwaters. This stability is critical to estuarine-dependent fish and shellfish and to North Carolina's multimillion dollar commercial fisheries. In 1962, pocosins comprised about 2.2 million acres or one-half of North Carolina's freshwater wetlands. In the early 1980s, only 1 million acres of pocosins remained in their natural state. Thirty-three percent of the original pocosins was converted to cropland or managed forest and another 36% was partially drained, cleared, or planned for development.

5-5
Population trends for selected bird species

Birds are the most visible of the vertebrates. Of the more than 9000 species worldwide, between 1000 and 1350 bird species occur in the United States and its territories. Birds live almost everywhere—from remote offshore islands, to grasslands and agricultural fields, to deep woods forests, to the central parts of large metropolitan areas.

Most seabird populations in the continental United States are less abundant than they were historically, yet many have been holding their own or increasing in the past several decades. Scavenging birds, such as seagulls and fulmers, are flourishing because of increasing food provided by man from fishing boats at sea and garbage dumps on land. Grebes appear to be stable whereas terns seem to be declining. In addition to suffering from competition from gulls, terns are particularly susceptible to disturbance and loss of nesting habitat. The greatest immediate concerns for seabirds are for species nesting in temperate and tropical areas where increased human disturbance, exploitation of birds, introduction of competing predatory species, and loss of nesting areas are severe. Also of concern is the substantial number of seabirds that are being killed or injured in some areas as a result of entanglement in, or injestion of, man-made debris, particularly plastics.

Approximately one-half of the North American avifauna consists of songbirds such as warblers, thrushes, and finches. Some songbird species are declining whereas others are expanding in number and range. Loss of habitat, human disturbance, contamination by pesticides and other toxic substances,

and adverse weather conditions are the most frequently cited causes of declines. Introductions, hybridizations, land use conversions to suitable habitat, and backyard feeding stations are reasons for increases.

Some field birds, such as the horned lark, have adapted to changing agricultural practices and are stable or increasing, but many other field bird species are declining. The upland sandpiper, which prefers to nest in hayfields, meadows, or hilly pastures in the eastern United States and the prairies of the Midwest, was slaughtered by market hunters in the late 1800s and has never recovered to its former status. Interior populations appear to be stable or increasing slightly; however, eastern populations, which have always been low compared to populations in the Midwest and whose preferred habitats have declined as farms and pastures revert to woodlands, appear to be declining. Lark sparrow and grasshopper sparrow populations have declined significantly since 1970. The lark sparrow inhabits prairies, abandoned fields, and brushy pastures of the midwestern and southwestern United States and apparently has not adapted to land use changes, primarily conversion to tilled farmland. The grasshopper sparrow is a secretive species dependent upon meadows, hayfields, pastures, and prairies. Its preferred habitat has been lost to intensive agricultural practices, urbanization, and reversion of grassland to shrub land and forest land. The lark bunting, also a prairie bird, is declining for similar reasons. The brown-headed cowbird, which was originally confined to prairies and grasslands, expanded its range when forested lands were cleared in the late 19th and early 20th centuries but is now stable or declining slightly. The cowbird is of concern because it parasitizes the nests of other birds and has been implicated in the decline of the black-capped vireo and in hindering the recovery of the endangered Kirtland's warbler.

The eastern bluebird is a weather-sensitive species that inhabits farmland, cutover woods, orchards, hedgerows, and roadsides. Its population has been depressed since the harsh winter of 1955. Since 1970, the population has been stable, if not increasing, except for 1977 and 1978 when exceptionally cold winter temperatures, especially in the Midwest and Mid-Atlantic states, caused mortality.

The construction of bluebird boxes has benefited the species whose second greatest problem is competition from introduced starlings and house sparrows.

Fragmentation of forests and loss of suitable habitat seem to have played a major role in the decline of forest-dwelling birds. The red-eyed vireo, the most common summer inhabitant of eastern deciduous forests, is particularly sensitive to forest fragmentation. Between 1966 and 1979, the population increased on the average of 2.8% annually; however, since 1979, it has declined at an average rate of 0.9% per year. The wood thrush, also a typical inhabitant of eastern deciduous forests and sensitive to forest fragmentation, has experienced even more dramatic declines since 1979, losing an average of 5.1% of the population annually. The blue jay population, which is also declining, has shown an average loss of 1.3% per year. The continental population of yellow-billed cuckoo, which prefer dense tangles of undergrowth, particularly brushy roadsides and willow thickets bordering streams and ponds, is apparently stable, whereas local populations in the West, particularly in California, are in serious trouble because of loss of riparian woodland habitat.

Some woodland species have adapted to human encroachment. The black-capped chickadee and the tufted titmouse now inhabit woods in residential neighborhoods and city parks and are frequent visitors to winter feeding stations.

The European starling was introduced into Central Park of New York City around 1890. This adaptable and aggressive species began to breed immediately and by 1952 had expanded its range throughout most of the United States. Large concentrations of starlings are nuisances in cities and residential areas, and they compete with native species, such as bluebirds and woodpeckers, for cavity nests. Heavy mortality during the cold winters of 1977 and 1978 contributed to a decline in starling numbers. The population has increased slightly to a relatively stable level since then.

Overall, the health of most North American raptors (birds of prey) appears good, although some species are declining or remain below historical levels. Raptors tend to require extensive natural areas for nesting and are severely impacted by habitat loss. They are top-of-the-food-chain predators and

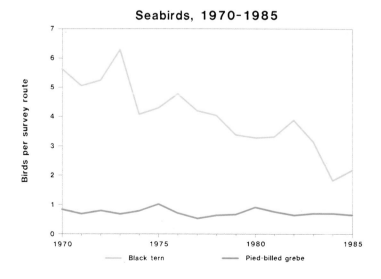

Seabirds, 1970-1985

Black tern — Pied-billed grebe

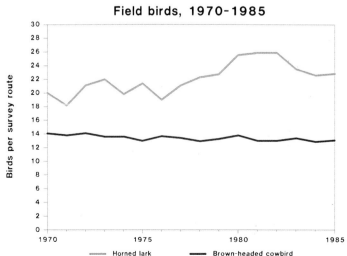

Field birds, 1970-1985

Horned lark — Brown-headed cowbird

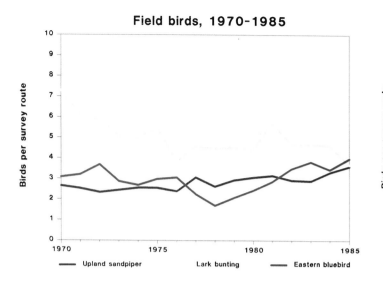

Field birds, 1970-1985

Birds per survey route

— Upland sandpiper   Lark bunting   — Eastern bluebird

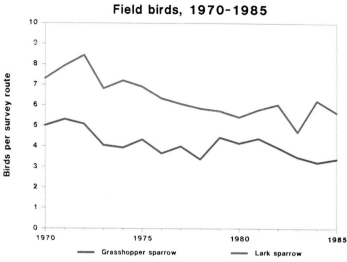

Field birds, 1970-1985

Birds per survey route

— Grasshopper sparrow   — Lark sparrow

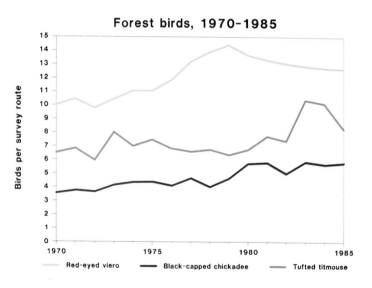

Forest birds, 1970-1985

Birds per survey route

— Red-eyed viero   — Black-capped chickadee   — Tufted titmouse

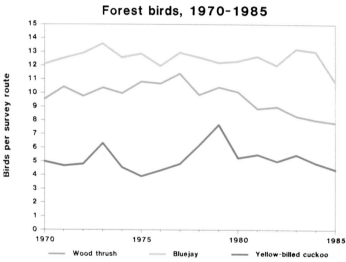

Forest birds, 1970-1985

Birds per survey route

— Wood thrush   — Bluejay   — Yellow-billed cuckoo

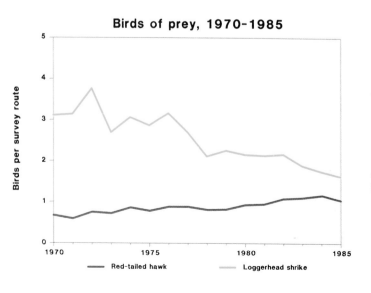

Birds of prey, 1970-1985

Birds per survey route

— Red-tailed hawk   — Loggerhead shrike

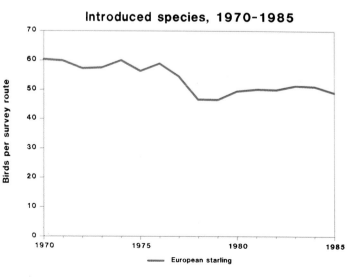

Introduced species, 1970-1985

Birds per survey route

— European starling

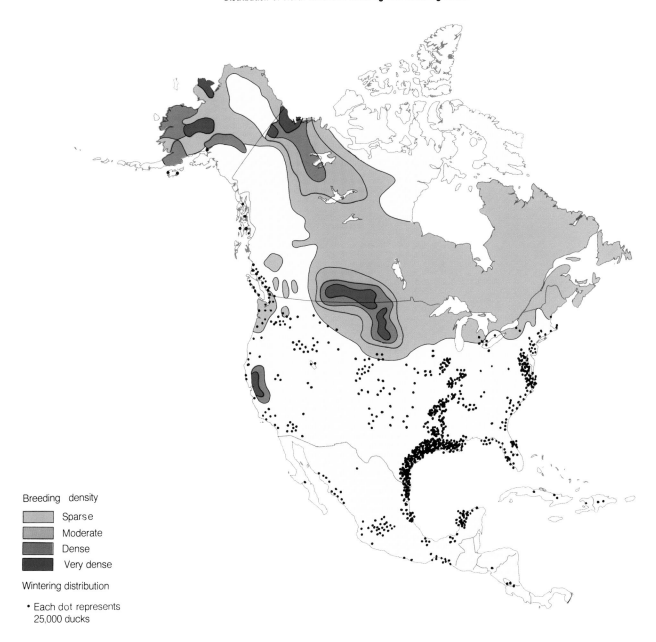

Breeding density
Sparse
Moderate
Dense
Very dense

Wintering distribution

• Each dot represents
  25,000 ducks

thus are vulnerable to man's persecution and chemical contamination. Because they have delayed sexual maturity and low annual productivity, raptors recover slowly from population declines.

The red-tailed hawk is one of the more widely distributed hawks in North America and is more tolerant of habitat modification. The red-tailed hawk has increased in number since DDT was banned in 1976. The closely related red-shoulder hawk, however, has not shown a recovery to pre-DDT population levels.

The loggerhead shrike is the only predatory songbird that consistently preys on vertebrates. It breeds throughout most of the United States and has declined significantly over its range. Although there is no precise reason for this decline, the shrike's diet of small mammals and insects may expose it to chemical contaminants that accumulate to toxic lev-

els. Loss of hedgerows and thorn trees in which shrikes prefer to nest, as well as changes in agricultural practices that have increased grass height, may have impacted reproductive performance.

5-6
Distribution of North American breeding and wintering waterfowl

The range of migratory bird species is customarily divided into breeding range, where the species nests, and winter range, where the species occurs between fall and spring migrations. In North America, the major breeding grounds for waterfowl extend from the northern United States to arctic Alaska and Canada. The major wintering areas are in the southern United States and Central America. To reach

their winter range, migratory waterfowl proceed south in broad fronts along migratory pathways, which are delineated as flyway corridors for administrative and regulatory purposes.

Four major flyways are recognized in the United States. These are the Atlantic Flyway, which extends from the coasts of Newfoundland, Nova Scotia, New England and New Jersey southward along the Atlantic seaboard; the Mississippi Flyway, which is centered around the Mississippi River; the Central Flyway, which extends southward from the Northern Great Plains and east of the Rocky Mountains; and the Pacific Flyway, which extends southward from Alaska and western Canada along the Pacific coast states and portions of the states west of the Rockies. Some species use mainly one route; others use two or three. This pattern of migration requires wetland habitats for breeding and wintering as well as

Flyways of North American ducks

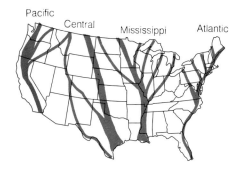

Pacific
Central
Mississippi
Atlantic

areas of food and refuge along the way. Annual production of waterfowl is highly dependent upon weather conditions and habitat quality.

5-7
Waterfowl breeding population estimates in North America

Duck breeding populations in North America have declined erratically but continually since 1955, and since 1979, the annual harvest of ducks in the United States has been below average. Populations of mallard, northern pintail, canvasback, and black duck continue to decline.

The mallard duck is widely distributed throughout North America and is a popular game bird. Mallards are adapted to a wide range of breeding habitats, including ponds, sloughs, potholes, and roadside ditches. Despite its ability to adapt, habitat destruction is largely responsible for the decline of mallards. Draining and filling of wetlands and lakes and farming on marginal lands bordering wetlands has reduced the habitat available to nesting waterfowl and facilitated predation by foxes and other preda-

tors. The use of chemicals on adjacent farmland has also contributed to the toll. Mallard numbers normally fluctuate in response to precipitation; however the population has not recovered even in wet years. Mallard populations reached a record low of 5.5 million birds in 1985.

The black duck, which is closely related to and hybridizes readily with the mallard, breeds exclusively in the northeastern United States and Canada and traditionally has comprised a large part of the hunting take along the Atlantic Flyway. Since 1955, the population has declined by 60%. Overhunting and loss of a high proportion of young females as well as acidification of nesting areas and reduced viability of ducklings have been suggested as causes, but man-induced habitat changes and increased hybridization with introduced mallards have probably played greater roles.

The northern pintail duck has followed the same trend as the mallard, declining since 1955 to a record low in 1985 of 2.9 million breeds. Like the mallard duck, reduction in wetlands cover, protection, and quality in the breeding range is largely responsible for the decline of the northern pintail.

Canvasback ducks have exhibited dramatic reductions since 1980. These declines appear to be directly related to the degradation of waterfowl habitat in selected areas and to a decline in their preferred food—submerged aquatic plants such as wild celery—throughout much of the range. Declining water quality and increased siltation are the suspected causes of the decline in submerged aquatic plants and consequently contribute to changes in feeding and staging areas of the canvasback.

In contrast to ducks, goose populations are healthy and are either stable or increasing, mainly because their breeding grounds are north of areas of human impact. In eastern North America, Canada goose populations have quadrupled in number over the past four decades and have invaded new habitats.

Populations of tundra swan are also healthy and are either stable or increasing in numbers throughout their range. The trumpeter swan, which was on the verge of extinction in the 1930s, now numbers approximately 10,000. Introduced mute swans, which are not hunted, have increased in the

eastern United States in the past several decades. The mute swan and Canada goose have become nuisances in some areas.

5-8
Recreational fishing

Saltwater fishing provides an enormous recreational opportunity for many in the United States. The statistics for marine recreational fishing have fluctuated only slightly over the past decade. The 1986 marine recreational finfish catch in the United States (excluding Alaska and Hawaii and Pacific coast salmon) was an estimated 466 million fish. These fish were taken on an estimated 72 million fishing trips. The estimated number of marine recreational fishermen in the United States has also been relatively stable over the past several years at 17 million. Excluding catches of freshwater and industrial species, such as anchovies and menhaden, the marine recreational catch comprised approximately 20% of the total U.S. finfish landings used for food in 1986.

The Atlantic and Gulf coasts accounted for approximately 88% of the total U.S marine recreational finfish catch by number and 85% of the estimated recreational fishing trips taken in 1986. In 1985, flounders were the most frequently caught fish on the Atlantic and Gulf coasts, comprising over 14% of the total catch. Porgies accounted for 8.4%, sea basses for 7.8%, bluefish for 7.1%, croakers and other drums for 24.9%, and other fish for 37.1% of the total catch. On the Pacific coast, the total 1985 recreational catch contained 26.6% rockfishes, 13.1% sea basses, 17.0% tuna and mackerels, 7.0% croakers, 4.6% smelts, and 31.7% other fishes.

Private and rental boats accounted for over one-half of the total U.S. marine recreational finfish catch in number in 1985. That same year, shore catches accounted for about 20% and party and charter boats accounted for the rest.

In 1985, about 46.6 million, or more than one in four, adult Americans fished. Eighty-four percent fished in freshwater, whereas 26% fished in salt water. Fishermen spent a total of 28.2 billion dollars on their sport, or an average of 604 dollars per fisherman. In comparison, 16.7 million, or one in

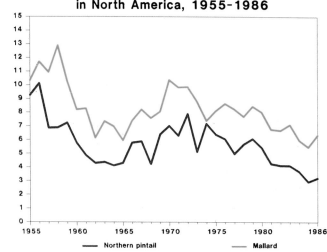

Waterfowl breeding population estimates in North America, 1955-1986

Northern pintail — Mallard

Waterfowl breeding population estimates in North America, 1955-1986

Tundra swan — Canvasback

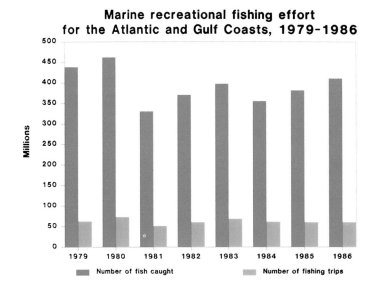

Marine recreational fishing effort for the Atlantic and Gulf Coasts, 1979-1986

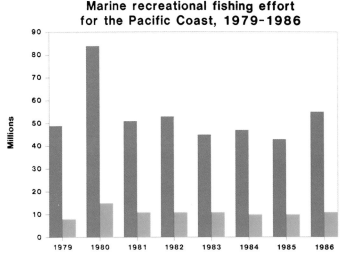

Marine recreational fishing effort for the Pacific Coast, 1979-1986

ten, adult Americans hunted in 1985 and spent an average of 604 dollars per hunter for their sport. Fisherman spent 830,000 days fishing in freshwater streams and lakes. The majority of anglers (60%) lived in urban areas, whereas most hunters (55%) lived in rural areas. However, participation rates for both fishing and hunting were highest among residents of rural areas. Estimates indicate a substantial increase in the number of fishermen between 1980 and 1985 but a slight decline in the numbers of hunters. Participation in other wildlife-related activities, such as feeding, observing, or photographing wildlife, has increased since 1980. In 1985, 109 million, or over one-half of all adult Americans, actively participated in nonconsumptive wildlife activities.

5-9
Commercial fisheries

Commercial landings of edible and industrial fish by domestic fishermen at ports in the 50 United States in 1986 amounted to 6.04 billion pounds valued at 2.8 billion dollars. In terms of volume, the five

major species of fishery resources caught by commercial fishermen were menhaden (an oily fish used primarily for industrial purposes), salmon, crab, shrimp, and herring. Shrimp, salmon, crabs, lobsters, and scallops were the top five species in terms of value. Landings of major finfish, such as Pacific cod, flounders, menhaden, halibut, Atlantic herring, haddock, Alaska pollock, and clams, fluctuate from year to year.

Because of the transitory nature of most finfish and the impact of economics on fishing effort, trends for selected species of fish cannot always be used as a direct measure of environmental quality. An exception to this rule is the case of the striped bass, a popular commercial and game fish on the Atlantic seaboard. From 1929 to 1973, commercial landings of striped bass trended upward, only to decline continuously since 1973. Initially the decline was blamed on overharvest and chemical contamination. Recently, however, evidence indicates that declining pH levels in seawater and tributaries (which indicates increasing acidity) may also be a contributing factor. Localized factors such as dam construction, highway development projects, and hybrid-

ization with other fish species are also implicated as causes for the decline in striped bass numbers. Harvest of striped bass is now limited over much of its range, and state and federal efforts are being made to augment natural recruitment processes by spawning striped bass in hatcheries and releasing the young in the same tributaries where their parents were captured.

Shellfish, such as scallops and oysters, are also susceptible to water quality and habitat degradation and are used as indicators of coastal environmental conditions. In 1985, U.S. landings of all species of scallops were 29.7 million pounds of meats for a 50% decline compared to 1984 landings and the lowest scallop landings since 1975. Catch per unit effort for scallops also reached historically low levels in 1985.

Oyster harvests from coastal waters around the United States have declined over the past years to the concern of biologists, fishermen, and seafood dealers. The effects of drought, disease, hurricanes, water pollution, loss of coastal habitat, and overharvesting are among the reasons cited for the decline in oyster numbers.

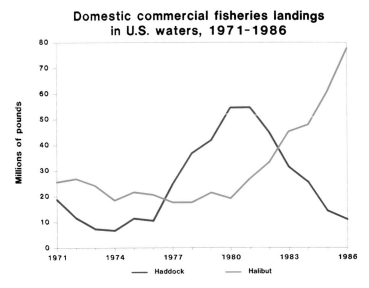

Domestic commercial fisheries landings in U.S. waters, 1971-1986

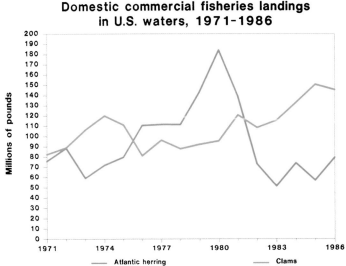

Domestic commercial fisheries landings in U.S. waters, 1971-1986

107

Domestic commercial fisheries landings in U.S. waters, 1971-1986

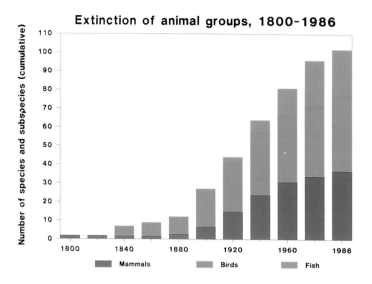

Extinction of animal groups, 1800-1986

5-10
Extinction of animal species

Extinction is a natural evolutionary process. All organisms are replaced sooner or later by better adapted, newly evolved forms. Although some species like the horseshoe crab have remained relatively unchanged for hundreds of millions of years, the unchanged existence of most species is very much shorter. The average species of bird, for example, lasts for about 40 thousand years. A species may become extinct and be replaced by another species, or it may gradually evolve into one or more new species.

Extinctions are naturally slow in rate and low in number of organisms that usually disappear. With the entrance of humans as an ecological factor, however, extinctions have been accelerated. The current rate of extinction of warm-blooded vertebrates is 100 or more birds and mammals per 100 years, which is 7 times greater than the rate estimated for the late Pleistocene, a time of great geological and ecological change at the end of the last ice age. Between 1780 and 1986, 102 species

and subspecies of vertebrates are known to have become extinct in the United States.

A variety of factors has led to extinction of wildlife species in the United States. Direct assault by hunters for food, fur, trophies, and live animal trade; habitat destruction; toxics contamination; and competition with man and introduced species have eliminated or threatened many species. Some of those lost include the eastern elk (last reported in the 1880s), the passenger pigeon (1890s), the Carolina parakeet (1920s), the plains wolf (1920s), and the Leon springs pupfish (1930s). The black-footed ferret is probably extinct in the wild as are the Penasco chipmunk and the Palos Verdes blue butterfly. Well-known cases of extinction of the last two decades include the ivory-billed woodpecker whose virgin hardwood forest habitat of the river bottomlands in the southeastern United States was lost to logging; the dusky seaside sparrow whose coastal river marshes of Florida's east coast were diked and drained for development, roads, and mosquito control; and Bachman's warbler whose extensive canebrake habitat in the Southeast was cleared for agriculture.

Extinction is a worldwide problem. Only about 1.6 million of species and subspecies of plants and animals have been classified and named by scientists. Of these, 20% are likely to become extinct by the end of the century, and in 50 years more than one-half will be gone if the current rate of destruction continues. It is estimated that as many as 30 million species are not yet discovered. Many of these could become extinct before they are even known to science.

5-11
Endangered and threatened plant and animal species

Many species of plant and animal species are dangerously close to extinction in the United States. An endangered species is one that is in danger of becoming extinct through all or a significant part of its natural range, and a threatened species is one that is likely to become endangered in the foreseeable future. In 1986, 328 species of animals were federally listed as endangered in the United States and 84 were listed as threatened. Since 1980, 165 endangered animal species and 53

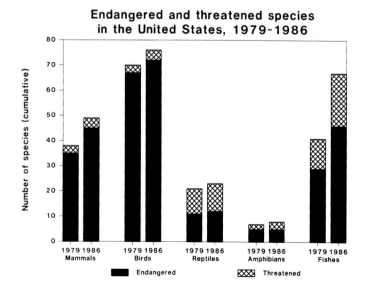

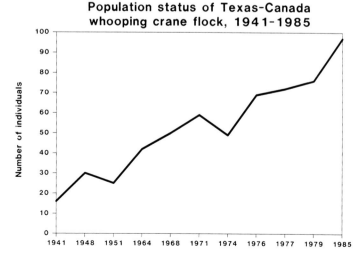

threatened animal species have been added to the list. Between 1977 and 1986, 113 plant species in the United States were listed as endangered and 25 plant species were listed as threatened. Nearly 4000 additional species of plants and animals are potential candidates for listing.

The time period from World War II to 1985 has witnessed the rescue of some wildlife species that were perilously close to extinction. The whooping crane, which was reduced to a low of 16 birds in 1941, has increased to almost 100 birds. Never especially abundant, a combination of habitat destruction from prairie marsh drainage and hunting nearly eliminated the species. Captive breeding programs and the establishment of a wildlife refuge in Texas to protect the whooping crane's wintering range have aided in the recovery of the species.

By the early 1970s, nesting bald eagles had declined to their lowest known levels throughout most of the United States. The main causes of the population decline were the pesticide DDT, persecution by man, and habitat destruction. DDT interfered with calcium deposition during eggshell production, resulting in thin-shelled eggs that easily broke during incubation. Since the late 1970s, the 1972 ban on the use of DDT and improved natural productivity, augmented by "reintroduction" programs and habitat protection programs in both nesting and wintering resting areas, have resulted in increasing numbers of bald eagles.

Some animals have recovered to the point of delisting them. The eastern brown pelican, for example, has recovered well enough from the devastating effects of DDT in most of the southeastern United States that it is no longer given special protection in Alabama, Florida, Georgia, North Carolina, South Carolina, and points northward along the Atlantic coast. Throughout the remainder of its range, which includes the coastal areas of Mississippi, Louisiana, Texas, California, the West Indies, both coasts of Mexico, Central America, and South America, brown pelican populations are not secure and remain listed as endangered.

The American alligator also has responded well enough to widespread protection to be removed from the endangered list over most of its range.

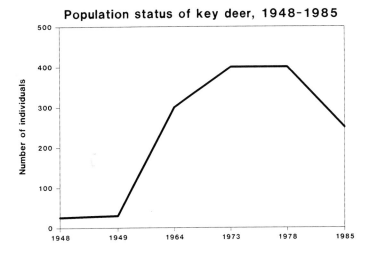

Population status of key deer, 1948-1985

Some species are losing ground despite conservation efforts. The recovery of the key deer, which inhabits the Florida Keys, is threatened by development pressure. Recent declines in the population indicate that the carrying capacity within its limited range has been reached. For the California condor, the situation is even more critical. Decimated in the late 1800s and early 1900s, the California condor population has been declining ever since. In 1982, the wild population was estimated to be between 21 and 24 birds. By 1986, numbers had dropped to 3. The remaining California condors are now in a captive breeding flock.

5-12
Status of selected wildlife populations by region

Eastern black bear

The black bear is the most numerous of the three species of bears that inhabit North America. The black bear population is estimated at 200,000 animals for the lower 48 states; 40,000 of them inhabit the eastern United States. Usually a shy resident of remote forested regions, black bears are more tolerant of human intrusions than grizzly bears.

Historically, black bears ranged over much of the North American continent, except for the Great Plains. Today, they exist in only 30 of the 49 states in which they formerly roamed. Their range continues to shrink as a result of land clearing for crops, grazing, and uses associated with urbanization, especially in many areas of the eastern United States. Uncontrolled hunting, timber harvesting, and forest fires also contribute to the reduction of black bear numbers.

In recent years, black bears have made a comeback in the states where viable populations remain. Black bear populations have been aided by the establishment of national parks and national forests

Population status of bald eagles, 1964-1985

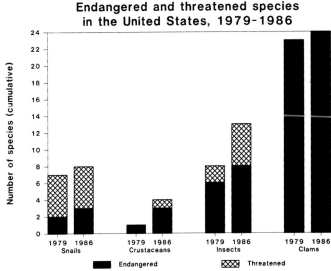

Endangered and threatened species in the United States, 1979-1986

Eastern black bear

Prairie chicken

in Kentucky, Georgia, North Carolina, Tennessee, Virginia, and West Virginia. These reserves, in combination with regulated hunting and the abandonment of farmlands that have reverted back to woodland, have been credited with saving the black bear in much of the eastern United States.

Prairie chicken

The prairie chicken is a "chicken-like" bird with special habitat needs for reproduction and survival. Its tolerance of environmental change is limited.

Unlike many species of wildlife, the prairie chicken expanded in number and range following settlement of the Midwest and the initial introduction of agricultural grain crops. Prairie chickens probably reached peak numbers between 1860 and 1880. Since then, the prairie chicken has become far less numerous and widespread. Its decline is primarily attributed to a reduction in the amount and quality of prairie chicken habitat.

Historically, four subspecies of prairie chickens occurred in the United States; now only three exist and of these one subspecies is endangered. The eastern heath hen of the Northeastern states has

been extinct since 1932, and the Attwater's prairie chicken is endangered in its Gulf Coast range in Texas and no longer found in Louisiana. The ranges of the lesser prairie chicken of southeastern Colorado, southwestern Kansas, and the eastern New Mexico, Texas, and Oklahoma Panhandle region and ranges of the greater prairie chicken that once inhabited the former eastern and central prairies are much reduced today.

The prairie chicken is currently found in ten states. Wisconsin, Minnesota, and Missouri have the highest numbers of birds, and South Dakota, Nebraska, Kansas, and Oklahoma have huntable populations. Remnant populations are found in North Dakota, Illinois, and Colorado; whether they can be saved is uncertain. Nationwide, the long-term survival of the prairie chicken is in question.

Rocky Mountain elk

The Rocky Mountain elk is a majestic animal, prized as a hunting trophy as well as a prime attraction for wildlife observers. Before the Nation was settled by Europeans, there were an estimated 10 million elks in North America and six subspecies in the

United States. By the early 1900s, fewer than 50,000 elks remained in North America and only two subspecies remained in the wild in the United States—the Roosevelt elk, which is native to the area between the Cascade Range and the Pacific Ocean, and the Rocky Mountain elk, which survived in remote areas of Idaho, Montana, Wyoming, and Colorado. The reasons for the decline included overhunting, loss of habitat, indiscriminate logging, and suppression of forest fires.

Over the past several decades, however, the Rocky Mountain elk population has risen steadily. Estimates indicate that the population has grown from 90,000 individuals in 1922 to about 420,000 by 1976. Recovery has been greatly facilitated by the large proportion of forested public lands in the Rocky Mountain region. Because much of the forested land upon which the elk is dependent is in national park or forest, the outlook for the Rocky Mountain elk herds is promising.

Desert bighorn sheep

The desert bighorn sheep is the only native ungulate that inhabits the southwestern desert mountain

Rocky Mountain elk

Desert bighorn sheep

ranges of the United States and Mexico. The desert bighorn sheep is an indicator of the wilderness character that still exists in the area that stretches from Baja California to northern Nevada and Utah, and southeast to New Mexico, west Texas, and into Mexico. This sheep is well adapted to the desert environment; it feeds on desert shrubs and grasses and can endure temperatures up to 115°F and little water.

At the end of the 19th century, there were an estimated one million desert bighorn sheep in North America. By 1960, however, only 1% of the population remained, and most were in isolated remnant herds. Several causes are cited in the decline of the desert bighorn sheep, including overhunting; disease; competition from livestock, feral burros, and other introduced species; human disturbance; and competition for use of the land.

Today, conservation efforts, habitat protection, and reintroductions into former ranges are aiding the desert bighorn sheep. Much of its habitat—about 100 million acres in Arizona, California, Nevada, New Mexico, and Utah—is now on public lands.

Southern sea otter

The sea otter historically ranged from Baja California, Mexico, northward along the Pacific coast of North America to the Alaskan Peninsula, across the Aleutian Island chain to the northern Japanese archipelago. The worldwide population was estimated at about 159,000 to 300,000 animals prior to commercial exploitation. The preexploitation population of the southern or California sea otter was estimated to number between 16,000 and 20,000 individuals. Intensive commercial harvest in the 18th and 19th centuries reduced the worldwide population to an estimated 1000 to 2000 animals and the California population to 50. In 1911, the California sea otter became fully protected outside of the 3-mile territorial sea by international treaty and, in 1913, within the 3-mile territorial sea by California state law. Between the late-1930s and the mid-1970s, the California sea otter population has increased at an average rate of 4 or 5% yearly. From 1938 to 1986, the population also expanded its range, from a residual population centered around Pt. Sur northward to Ana Nuevo Point and southward to the mouth of the Santa Maria River. By 1960, the California population had grown to approximately 1000 individuals. Since the mid-1970s, however, census data indicate that the population ceased to increase and may have declined. The 1986 spring survey yielded 1570 independent otters and dependent pups whereas the 1986 fall count was 1201.

The California sea otter was listed as threatened in 1977, and there are indications that the population may be somewhat worse now than at the time of its original listing. In addition to problems of drastically reduced population size and range, the most probable cause of the otter population's failure to grow is incidental entanglement and drowning in commercial gill and trammel set-nets. Other problems affecting the sea otter include vulnerability to oil spills, illegal shooting, environmental contaminants, and great white shark attack. Because of strong measures to eliminate the entanglement and drowning hazard to sea otters, the sea otter population is expected to begin growing again.

The presence of sea otters along the California coast has rather profound environmental as well as socio-economic impacts. The sea otters are part of the natural coastal environment where they inhabit a narrow zone of shallow, subtidal waters and forage along the bottom as well as within kelp forests for large invertebrates, including abalone, kelp crabs, rock crabs, clams, mussels, and sea urchins. Sea otter predation on sea urchins appears to have a beneficial result in limiting sea urchin destruction of kelp, which is commercially harvested. Heavy otter predation on shellfish, however, causes reduction in the densities and individual sizes of many commercially and recreationally important species. The sea otters' presence has also affected the halibut fishery, not because of direct competition, but because of a ban on commercial set-net fishing within the otter range to minimize entanglement. The overlap of otter range with offshore oil and gas development tracts and tanker shipping lanes and the impact of possible oil spills on the population are other issues that have yet to be reckoned with. Another aspect of sea otter presence, currently unquantified, is the major tourist attraction the otters provide along the central California coast, where they are observable from many public access points.

Caribou

Historically, the caribou was found throughout much of the Alaskan mainland. The caribou spends its summers in tundra areas north of the tree line and in the alpine zone. During the winter months, the caribou moves into open spruce forests south of the tree line and into the foothills of mountain ranges or subalpine highlands.

The caribou has declined in number during this century for reasons that are not well known. Prior to 1970, the largest caribou herd on the North American continent was Alaska's Western Arctic herd, which numbered approximately 240,000 animals and occupied a vast area of 140,000 square miles in the northwestern corner of the state. By 1976, the size of the herd had declined to between 50,000 and 60,000 animals. Several other Alaskan caribou herds also experienced dramatic declines during this time period. The Fortymile herd, for example, which may have numbered over 200,000 caribou in the early 1900s, declined in number to about 50,000 animals by the middle of this century and to approximately 5,000 animals by the mid-1970s. The decline of the caribou is attributed to a combination of increased predation, overgrazing of preferred foods by the herds themselves, construction of transportation corridors, oil and gas development, and other development pressures.

The Western Arctic herd and several other Alaskan herds that had declined to low population levels in the 1970s appear to be recovering. The Western Arctic herd now numbers approximately 170,000. Large acreages used by caribou, but not the entire range, were set aside in 1980 in national wildlife refuges, parks, and preserves. However, many fear that continued development of transportation corridors, industry, and urban and agricultural areas may ultimately lead to major disruptions of caribou range use patterns or migrations.

Southern sea otter

Caribou

Sources and technical notes

5-1
Wetlands

5-1
Identifying features of wetlands

Niering, W. A. 1986. *Wetlands.* The Audubon Society. Alfred A. Knopf, Inc. (New York), 638 pp.

Cowardin, L. M., V. Carter, F. C. Golet, and E. T. LaRoe. 1979. *Classification of wetlands and deepwater habitats of the United States.* FWS/OBS-79/31 (Washington, D.C.), 103 pp.

Tiner, R. W. 1984. *Wetlands of the United States: Current status and recent trends.* U.S. Department of the Interior, Fish and Wildlife Service, National Wetlands Inventory (Washington, D.C.), 58 pp.

Odum, W. E., T. J. Smith, III., J. K. Hoover, and C. C. McIvor. 1984. *The ecology of tidal freshwater marshes of the United States east coast: A community profile.* FWS/OBS-83/17 (Washington, D.C.), pp. 1-12.

5-2
Distribution of wetlands

5-2a
Wetland ecoregions

Niering, W. A. 1986. *Wetlands.* The Audubon Society. Alfred A. Knopf, Inc. (New York), p. 127.

5-2b
Distribution of wetlands, 1984

Tiner, R. W. 1984. *Wetlands of the United States: Current status and recent trends.* U.S. Department of the Interior, Fish and Wildlife Service, National Wetlands Inventory (Washington, D.C.), figure 25, Relative abundance of wetlands in the United States (1984), p. 28.

Percent of each state represented by wetland is shown.

5-2c
Marshes

Niering, W. A. 1986. *Wetlands.* The Audubon Society. Alfred A. Knopf, Inc. (New York), p. 45.

5-2d
Shrub swamps

Niering, W. A. 1986. *Wetlands.* The Audubon Society. Alfred A. Knopf, Inc. (New York), p. 87.

5-2e
Bogs

Niering, W. A. 1986. *Wetlands.* The Audubon Society. Alfred A. Knopf, Inc. (New York), p. 37.

5-2f
Northern swamps and floodplain wetlands

Niering, W. A. 1986. *Wetlands.* The Audubon Society. Alfred A. Knopf, Inc. (New York), p. 94.

5-2g
Southern swamps

Niering, W. A. 1986. *Wetlands.* The Audubon Society. Alfred A. Knopf, Inc. (New York), p. 76.

5-2h
Cypress swamps

Niering, W. A. 1986. *Wetlands.* The Audubon Society. Alfred A. Knopf, Inc. (New York), p. 103.

5-3
Wetland status and trends

5-3a
Status of wetlands by type, 1954–1974

Tiner, R. W. 1984. *Wetlands of the United States: Current status and recent trends.* U.S. Department of the Interior, Fish and Wildlife Service, National Wetlands Inventory (Washington, D.C.), figure 26, Extent of wetlands in the conterminous U.S. in the mid-1970s, p. 29.

5-3b
Status of wetlands by ownership, 1985

U.S. Department of the Interior, Fish and Wildlife Service, *National Wetland Inventory* (Washington, D.C.). 1986. Unpublished data.

5-3c
Trend in wetland acreage for the conterminous United States, 1700s–1980s

5-3d
Net losses and gains in wetlands by type, 1954–1974

Frayer, W. E., T. J. Monahan, D. C. Bowden, and F. A. Graybill. 1983. *Status and trends of wetlands and deepwater habitats in the conterminous United States, 1950s to 1970s.* Department of Forest and Wood Sciences, Colorado State University (Ft. Collins, Colo.), table 1, Area, in thousands of acres, by kind of surface area for the conterminous United States, pp. 20-21.

Roe, H. B., and Q. A. Ayres. 1954. *Engineering for agricultural drainage.* McGraw-Hill (New York), 501 pp.

U.S. Department of the Interior, Fish and Wildlife Service, *National Wetlands Inventory* (Washington, D.C.). 1986. Unpublished data.

5-3e
States with significant wetland losses

U.S. Department of the Interior, Fish and Wildlife Service, *National Wetlands Inventory* (Washington, D.C.). 1986. Unpublished data.

5-3f
Fate of wetlands converted to other uses, 1954–1974

Frayer, W. E., T. J. Monahan, D. C. Bowden, and F. A. Graybill. 1983. *Status and trends of wetlands and deepwater habitats in the conterminous United States, 1950s to 1970s.* Department of Forest and Wood Sciences, Colorado State University (Ft. Collins, Colo.), table 1, Area, in thousands of acres, by kind of surface area for the conterminous United States, pp. 20-21.

5-4
Wetland losses by selected type

5-4a
Changes in Louisiana's coastal marshes

Tiner, R. W. 1984. *Wetlands of the United States: Current status and recent trends.* U.S. Department of the Interior, Fish and Wildlife Service, National Wetlands Inventory (Washington, D.C.), figure 34, Lousiana's coastal marshes are being permanently flooded by Gulf of Mexico waters at an accelerating rate, p. 38.

Example shows marsh changes between 1956 and 1978.

5-4b
Losses of bottomland hardwood wetlands in the Mississippi alluvial plain, 1937–1982

MacDonald, P. O., W. E. Frayer, and J. K Clauser. 1979. *Documentation, chronology and future projections of bottomland hardwood loss in the Lower Mississippi alluvial plain.* U.S. Department of the Interior, Fish and Wildlife Service (Washington, D.C.), 2 volumes.

U.S. Department of the Interior, Fish and Wildlife Service, *National Wetlands Inventory* (Washington, D.C.). 1986. Unpublished data.

5-4c
Wetland losses by selected type, 1700s–1970s

U.S. Department of the Interior, Fish and Wildlife Service, *National Wetlands Inventory* (Washington, D.C.). 1986. Unpublished data.

5-5
Population trends for selected bird species

5-5a
Seabirds, 1970–1985

5-5b
Field birds (horned lark and brown-headed cowbirds), 1970–1985

5-5c
Field birds (upland sandpiper, lark bunting, and eastern bluebird), 1970–1985

5-5d
Field birds (grasshopper sparrow and lark sparrow), 1970–1985

5-5e
Forest birds (red-eyed vireo, black-capped chickadee, and tufted titmouse), 1970–1985

5-5f
Forest birds (wood thrush, blue jay, and yellow-billed cuckoo), 1970–1985

5-5g
Birds of prey, 1970–1985

5-5h
Introduced species, 1970–1985

U.S. Department of the Interior, Fish and Wildlife Service, Office of Migratory Bird Management. 1987. *Migratory nongame birds of management concern: The 1987 list.* (Washington, D.C.), data tables.

5-6
Distribution of North American breeding and wintering waterfowl

5-6a
Distribution of North American breeding and wintering ducks

Executive Office of the President, Council on Environmental Quality. 1981. *Environmental trends* (Washington, D.C.), figure 8-8, Distribution of North American breeding and wintering ducks, 1970s, p. 156.

5-6b
Flyways of North American ducks

Executive Office of the President, Council on Environmental Quality. 1981. *Environmental trends* (Washington, D.C.), figure 6-7, Waterfowl flyways, p. 97.

5-7
Waterfowl breeding population estimates in North America

5-7a
Waterfowl breeding population estimates in North America (northern pintail and mallard), 1955–1986

5-7b
Waterfowl breeding population estimates in North America (tundra swan and canvasback), 1955–1986

U.S. Department of the Interior, Fish and Wildlife Service, Office of Migratory Bird Management in conjunction with the Canadian Wildlife Service. 1985. *Status of waterfowl and fall flight forecast* (Washington, D.C.), table 6, Breeding population estimates for 10 species of ducks, 1955-85 (updated).

U.S. Department of the Interior, Fish and Wildlife Service. 1987. (Draft) *Environmental Impact Statement: Issuance of annual regulations permitting the sport hunting of migratory birds* (Washington, D.C.).

5-8
Recreational fishing

5-8a
Marine recreational fishing effort for the Atlantic and Gulf Coasts, 1979–1986

5-8b
Marine recreational fishing effort for the Pacific Coast, 1979–1986

U.S. Department of Commerce, National Oceanic and Atmospheric Administration. *Fisheries of the United States: Current fishery statistics*, annual issues (Washington, D.C.).

5-9
Commercial fisheries

5-9a
Domestic commercial fisheries landings in U.S. waters (haddock and halibut), 1971–1986

5-9b
Domestic commercial fisheries landings in U.S. waters (Atlantic herring and clams), 1971–1986

5-9c
Domestic commercial fisheries landings in U.S. waters (Alaskan pollock), 1971–1986

U.S. Department of Commerce, National Oceanic and Atmospheric Administration. *Fisheries of the United States: Current fishery statistics*, annual issues (Washington, D.C.).

5-10
Extinction of animal species

5-10
Extinction of animal groups, 1800–1986

U.S. Department of the Interior, Fish and Wildlife Service, Office of Endangered Species (Washington, D.C.). 1986. Unpublished data.

5-11
Endangered and threatened plant and animal species

5-11a
Endangered and threatened species in the United States (mammals, birds, reptiles, amphibians, and fishes), 1979–1986

5-11b
Endangered and threatened species in the United States (snails, crustaceans, insects, and clams), 1979–1986

5-11c
Population status of key deer, 1948–1985

5-11d
Population status of bald eagles, 1964–1985

5-11e
Population status of Texas–Canada whooping crane flock, 1941–1985

U.S. Department of the Interior, Fish and Wildlife Service, Office of Endangered Species (Washington, D.C.). 1986. Unpublished data.

5-12
Status of selected wildlife populations by region

5-12a
Eastern black bear

Pelton, M. 1987. "The black bear," pp. 521-530, in *Audubon wildlife report 1987.* W. J. Chandler (ed.). Academic Press, Inc. (New York), 697 p.

Raybourne, J. W. 1987. "The black bear: Home in the highlands," in *Restoring America's wildlife 1937–1987.* H. Kallman (ed.). U.S. Fish and Wildlife Service (Washington, D.C.).

5-12b
Prairie chicken

Westemeir, R. L., and W. R. Edwards. 1987. "Prairie-chickens: Survival in the Midwest, in *Restoring America's wildlife 1937–1987.* H. Kallman (ed.). U.S. Fish and Wildlife Service (Washington, D.C.).

5-12c
Rocky Mountain elk

Thomas, J. W., and L. D. Bryant. 1987. "The elk," pp. 495-508, in *Audubon wildlife report 1987.* W. J. Chandler (ed.). Academic Press, Inc. (New York), 697 pp.

5-12d
Desert bighorn sheep

Cooperrider, A. 1985. "The desert bighorn," pp. 472-485, in *Audubon wildlife report 1985.* R. L. DiSilvestro (ed.). National Audubon Society (New York), 671 pp.

5-12e
Southern sea otter

Ladd, W. N., Jr. , and M. L. Riedman. 1987. "The southern sea otter," pp. 457-478, in *Audubon wildlife report 1987.* Chandler, W. J. (ed.) 1987. Academic Press, Inc. (New York), 697 pp.

5-12f
Caribou

Scott, M. 1985. "The woodland caribou," pp. 494-507, in *Audubon wildlife report 1985.* R. L. DiSilvestro (ed.). National Audubon Society (New York), 671 pp.

Chapter 6
Protected Areas

6-1
Federal lands

The history of federal lands is complex, with many special laws and unique situations. By 1867 the United States had completed major acquisitions and had expanded from thirteen colonies along the Atlantic coast to own the entire mid-continent of North America plus Alaska. Much of this land was transferred to state governments for public purposes, such as higher education; to the transcontinental railroads; and to homesteaders. This disposal process ended in 1934 when the remaining public lands were withdrawn from private entry.

Today the U.S. Forest Service within the Department of Agriculture and the U.S. Fish and Wildlife Service, Bureau of Land Management, and National Park Service within the Department of the Interior manage most of the 732 million acres of federally owned land. Other federal landowners include other bureaus in the Department of the Interior, as well as the Department of Defense, Department of Energy, and Tennessee Valley Authority. In addition, state

and local governments own 154 million acres of land. This means that nearly 40% of the Nation's land is publicly owned.

6-2
National parks

The National Park System was established to conserve natural and historic features of national significance for the enjoyment and benefit of present and future generations. Four of the Nation's best known national parks were established by 1900: Yellowstone (1872), Yosemite (1890), Sequoia (1890), and Mount Rainier (1899). The National Park Service, which inherited these natural wonders when it was created in 1916, is responsible for protecting and managing the National Park System. By 1986 the System had grown to encompass 339 units, which collectively cover more than 79 million acres in 49 states, the District of Columbia, Guam, Puerto Rico, Saipan, and the U.S. Virgin Islands. National Park System units range in size from over 13 million acres in the Wrangell–St. Elias National Park and Preserve in Alaska to a fraction of an acre in the Thaddeus Kosciuszko National Memorial in Pennsylvania.

The National Park System includes a variety of unit types. Areas are added to the System because

of their natural values; such areas are expanses of land or water of great scenic or scientific quality or significance to the Nation's heritage and are designated national parks, preserves, seashores, or riverways. These areas contain one or more distinctive attributes, such as forest, grassland, tundra, desert, estuary, or river systems, or they may contain "windows" on the past for a view of geological history, or imposing landforms such as mountains, mesas, thermal areas, and caverns. They may be habitats of abundant or rare wildlife and plant life. There are 117 such units in the National Park System, and the System is perhaps best known for them.

More than one-half of the units (139) in the System, however, preserve historic places and commemorate important persons, events, or activities. These units include archaeological sites associated with prehistoric civilizations as well as sites related to the lives of modern Americans. Historical areas are customarily preserved or restored to reflect their appearance during the period of their greatest historical significance. The National Park System also includes national recreational areas, two areas set aside for the performing arts, and national parkways or roadways.

Generally, a national park covers a large area and contains a variety of resources, whereas national preserves are established primarily for the protection

Distribution of public lands

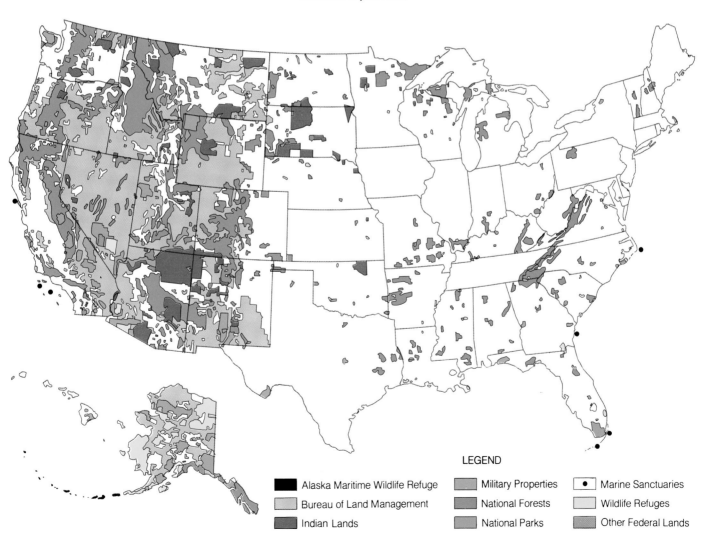

LEGEND

■ Alaska Maritime Wildlife Refuge	Military Properties	● Marine Sanctuaries
Bureau of Land Management	National Forests	Wildlife Refuges
Indian Lands	National Parks	Other Federal Lands

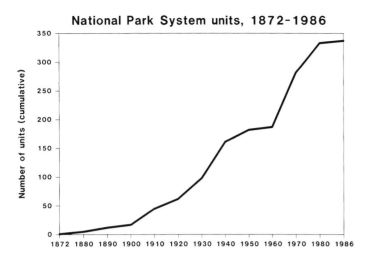

National Park System units, 1872-1986

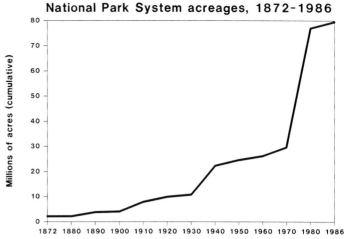

National Park System acreages, 1872-1986

of certain resources. National seashores and national lakeshores preserve shoreline areas and offshore islands and focus on the preservation of natural values while providing water-oriented recreation. National rivers and National Wild and Scenic Rivers preserve ribbons of land bordering free-flowing streams that have not been dammed, channelized, or otherwise altered by man. These areas provide opportunities for such outdoor activities as hiking, canoeing, and hunting. National scenic trails are generally long-distance footpaths winding through areas of natural beauty, and national parkways are roadways flanked by ribbons of land, which offer scenic vistas. National battlefields and national monuments are usually associated with sites important in the military history of the United States.

National parks are extremely popular, and visitation has increased dramatically since the end of World War II. In 1986 at least 364 million people visited national park units. This popularity, however, has led to calamitous overuse of some parks at certain times. Heavy and somewhat uncontrolled visitor use has created problems for the National Park System, which is designed for the protection of natural, historic, and cultural resources. This problem will accentuate if visitor use continues to increase.

6-3
National wildlife refuges

National wildlife refuges are established to preserve, restore, and enhance species of animals and plants that are endangered or threatened with becoming extinct; perpetuate migratory bird resources; and preserve a natural diversity and abundance of fauna and flora on refuge lands. The National Wildlife Refuge System is a network of over 430 refuges, encompassing nearly 90 million acres in 49 states and 5 trust territories. Administered by the U.S. Fish and Wildlife Service, these refuges range in size from the tiny first refuge, 3-acre Pelican Island in Florida, to vast areas of the Yukon Delta, which comprises 19.6 million acres in Alaska. Also associated with the refuge system are 58 "coordination areas," encompassing 423 thousand acres, which are federally owned lands managed under cooperative agreements with the states in which the areas are located, and 1.7 million acres of waterfowl production area located primarily in the Prairie Pothole region of Iowa, Michigan, Minnesota, Montana, Nebraska, North Dakota, South Dakota, Wisconsin, and Wyoming. These areas are managed to preserve wetland habitat, increase waterfowl production, sustain indigenous wildlife, and benefit the public.

Collectively, the National Wildlife Refuge System represents the most comprehensive and diverse land-management program for wildlife in the world. The System includes maritime islands, which harbor pelagic birds and marine mammals; coastal and inland wetlands, which provide nesting and wintering habitat for waterfowl, shorebirds, and wading birds; grasslands and range, which are habitat for bison and other big game populations; and desert oases, which serve as the sole habitat for pupfish and other highly specialized animals. Some refuges are intensely managed to provide benefit to a single species, such as the Key Deer Wildlife Refuge in Florida, which protects the habitat of the endangered key deer, or the Aransas National Wildlife Refuge on the Gulf Coast of Texas, which provides wintering habitat for the endangered whooping crane. About three-fourths of all refuges are managed to provide seasonal habitat for waterfowl as they migrate along the four major continental flyways. Most refuges are managed as ecosystems for all wildlife and plants, however, and the majority of refuge lands (primarily those in Alaska) are not subject to intensive forms of management because they are highly productive in their current natural condition.

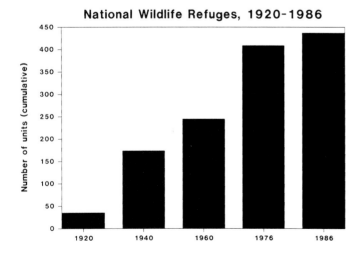

National Wildlife Refuges, 1920-1986

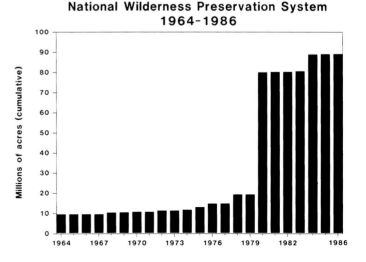

National Wilderness Preservation System 1964-1986

116

Ownership of wilderness areas, 1986 excluding Alaska

Park Service (14%)

Forest Service (83%)

Bureau of Land Management (1%)

Fish and Wildlife Service (2%)

Total acreage = 32.2 million acres

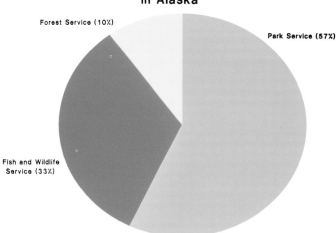

Ownership of wilderness areas, 1986 in Alaska

Forest Service (10%)

Park Service (57%)

Fish and Wildlife Service (33%)

Total acreage = 56.5 million acres

Another goal of the National Wildlife Refuge System is to provide an understanding and appreciation of fish and wildlife ecology and man's role in the environment. More than 20 million visitors annually enjoy a variety of wildlife-oriented activities on national wildlife refuges. Recreational uses include fishing, wildlife observation, nature study, hunting, hiking, and photography. Some refuges provide visitor centers, interpretive trails, auto tour routes, and specialized observation platforms and photography blinds. Public-use activities vary widely among refuges, depending on the season of the year, proximity to urban centers, types of facilities on site, and the nature of ongoing wildlife management programs.

6-4
Wilderness areas

Wilderness areas are undeveloped, federally owned, and generally over 5000 acres in size. They are affected primarily by the forces of nature, where man is a visitor who does not remain and where natural ecological processes are allowed to operate freely. Wilderness areas contain ecological, geologi-

cal, or other features of scientific, educational, scenic, or historical value and possess outstanding opportunities for solitude or primitive and unconfined recreation. Wilderness areas symbolize the last places where man can breathe clean air, drink freely from streams, and get away from other people.

Most wilderness areas have been designated since 1964. In 1986 the National Wilderness Preservation System contained about 89 million acres at 465 locations. Wilderness areas are administered by the Forest Service, Fish and Wildlife Service, National Park Service, and Bureau of Land Management.

When the Wilderness Act was passed, many assumed that simply designating an area as wilderness would assure its protection. Today, however, steadily increasing use and other human influences are impacting wilderness qualities. Preserving these qualities requires careful management of the resources to minimize user impact. Permanent structures and installations, such as campgrounds, buildings, or radio antennas, are not allowed (except for some primitive cabins in Alaska); motor vehicles, mechanical transport, and motorized equipment are prohibited (except in emergencies); permanent or temporary roads are not permitted; and visitor use

is managed to protect the wilderness resource. Timber harvest is excluded, and fires are allowed to burn under preplanned prescribed conditions. Aircraft and motorboat use, livestock grazing, and development of valid and existing mineral rights are allowed within individual wilderness areas under special conditions, such as where use or rights existed prior to wilderness designation. Hiking and certain other uses, such as hunting, fishing, and trapping, are permissible under state and federal laws. In some cases, horseback riding and primitive camping are permitted.

6-5
Wild and scenic rivers

The National Wild and Scenic River System was established in 1968 to protect rivers or river segments of national significance. For a river or river segment to be eligible for protection, it must be free flowing, have high water quality, and possess one or more outstanding scenic, recreational, geologic, fish and wildlife, or cultural values. In 1986, 7363 miles of waterways were designated as wild and scenic preserves.

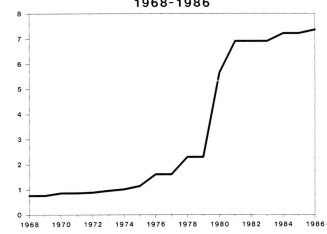

National Wild and Scenic River System 1968-1986

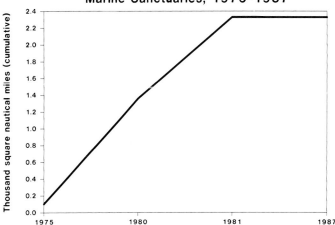

Marine Sanctuaries, 1975-1987

Rivers in the System are classified in three ways: wild, scenic, and recreational. Wild rivers have pristine shorelines and watersheds and unpolluted waters, are undisturbed by impoundments, and are generally inaccessible except by trail. Scenic rivers are free of impoundments and have largely primitive watersheds and undeveloped shorelines, but they may be accessible by road or railway. Recreational rivers have undergone some impoundment or diversion in the past, are accessible by road or railroad, and may have some development along their banks.

The National Wild and Scenic River System is administered by the National Park Service and Forest Service in cooperation with state agencies.

6-6
Marine sanctuaries and estuarine reserves

Off the coasts of the United States, from the frigid, ice-scoured shores of the North Atlantic and Arctic Ocean to the warm tropical waters of the Florida Keys, Caribbean Sea, and Pacific islands, a great variety of underwater habitats exists, each supporting a myriad of marine plants and animals adapted to the rigors of the particular ocean biome. This variety of habitats includes submarine canyons; limestone outcroppings; coral reefs; seagrass beds; oyster, clam, and scallop beds; worm reefs; salt domes; rocky bottoms; broad sand or mud bottoms; and shipwrecks. Marine sanctuaries protect nationally significant examples of many of these ecosystems by managing human activities that may damage their integrity. Through directed research and education programs, scientists and the general public are gaining a better understanding of the characteristics of these systems and how they change over time in response to natural and human influences. On-site and off-site interpretive programs provide education on the unique resources and values of marine ecosystems within sanctuaries and on the need to minimize user impacts.

Since 1975 seven marine sanctuaries have been designated. Sanctuaries range in size from the less-than-one-square-mile *U.S.S. Monitor* marine sanctuary off North Carolina to the 1252-square-mile Channel Islands marine sanctuary off California. Some are located near shore in relatively shallow waters (less than 70 ft) and receive many visitors who fish, scuba dive, or observe sanctuary resources

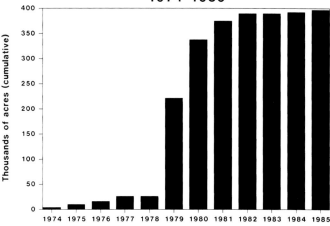

National Estuarine Research Reserve System 1974-1985

through glass-bottom boats. Others are located farther offshore, in deeper waters, and are primarily of interest to fishermen and scientists. One unique site protects the sunken remains of the famous Civil War ironclad, *U.S.S. Monitor,* which rests upside down in 220 ft of water and can be reached only by submersible. Marine sanctuaries are managed by the National Oceanic and Atmospheric Administration within the Department of Commerce with the cooperation of state governments.

The nearshore coastal zone of the United States is every bit as rich and diverse in aquatic life as the oceanic realms. The estuaries, which incise the coast, receive incoming salty ocean water on each flooding tide and outflowing fresh water from rivers. In the estuary, waters meet and mix and produce conditions that make estuaries some of the most biologically productive ecosystems in the world. Over one-half of the Nation's recreationally and commercially important fish and shellfish species spend part of their lives in the bays, lagoons, tributaries, marshes, seagrass beds, oyster reefs, clam beds, or mud and sand flats that are part of estuarine ecosystems. The coastal zone is also important to national defense and water-dependent industries and is a desirable place to live and recreate. These

human uses of the coastal zone, however, threaten the natural productivity and health of the estuary through point and nonpoint pollution and habitat degradation and loss unless managed properly.

The desire to study the natural dynamics and characteristics of estuaries in undisturbed settings and the need to provide technical information for use in addressing coastal management issues has led to the establishment of a national network of natural field laboratories called research reserves. The network contains representatives of the diversity of coastal habitats found in the United States. Reserves can be single sites within an estuary or multiple sites that collectively represent the full spectrum of habitats within the estuary. Currently, 17 estuarine areas are designated as research reserves, and 3 of these areas have more than 1 reserve site. Research reserves are managed by the coastal state in which they are found, with assistance from the National Oceanic and Atmospheric Administration.

6-7
Historic places

The National Register of Historic Places is the official list of the Nation's most significant historic,

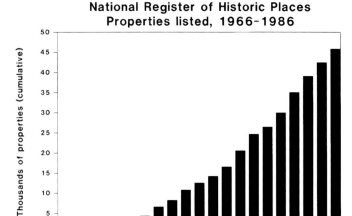

National Register of Historic Places Properties listed, 1966-1986

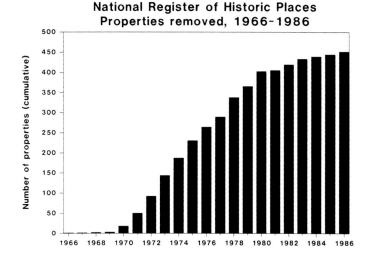

National Register of Historic Places Properties removed, 1966-1986

archaeological, architectural, engineering, and cultural resources. It is an outgrowth of public and private efforts to identify, evaluate, and protect these valuable resources. Sites eligible for listing include historic landmarks, buildings, structures, and objects that are nationally important and contribute to the understanding of the Nation's historical and cultural foundations.

Since 1966 thousands of historic places have been located, inventoried, and nominated by federal, state, and local preservation authorities. By 1986 nearly 47,000 properties had been listed on the National Register. Some 79% of the properties were recognized for their architectural, artistic, or engineering significance and 49% were listed for their association with events that have made a significant contribution to American history. Seventeen percent were recognized because of their association with the lives of persons significant in historical events, and seven percent were listed because they have yielded or are likely to yield information important in prehistory or history.

Some properties listed on the Register are lost each year. Most of the losses result from demolition, usually for public or private redevelopment, whereas others are the result of fire, wind, flood, or other natural events. As of 1986, 452 properties originally listed on the Register had to be removed for one or more of these reasons. The Register is maintained by the National Park Service.

6-8
Threats to public lands

Thousands of threats jeopardize the quality of public lands. Water and air pollution are the biggest threats that national parklands are facing, whereas contaminant impacts on fish and wildlife resources have become increasingly critical concerns on wildlife refuges. Other abuses that have received increasing public attention in recent years include defacing statues and buildings in public places, vandalism and looting of archaeological sites, poaching and other wildlife crimes, littering, and general carelessness and thoughtlessness with regard to fire safety and wilderness preservation.

Pollution became a major concern in the national parks long after surfacing in more-developed parts of

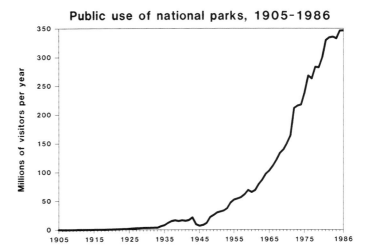

Public use of national parks, 1905-1986

the United States. During the early years of the environmental movement, attention was focused mainly on handling the pressure of rising visitation in national parks. In 1969, however, 4 studies of pollution in parks were reported (3 on pesticides and 1 on water quality), and by 1977 the number had grown to 48 (28 on water quality, 14 on air quality, 3 on pesticides, and 3 on radiation). In 1980, 4345 threats to park resources were identified, and in 1985 most of these problems still remained.

The majority of the threats to national parks come from outside the park boundaries. Even some of the most pristine wilderness areas are threatened. Air-pollution injury to vegetation and cultural resources and acidification of lakes and streams have become widespread concerns. Acid rain threatens vegetation in several eastern parks, and haze or plumes created primarily by fine particles of sulfates, carbon, and soil-derived material affect visibility, especially in the East. Much of the visibility impairment is caused by man-made pollutants transported from urban areas and industrial developments, although natural climatic conditions also con-

tribute to reduced visibility in some areas and seasons. Landfills, chemical spills, agricultural runoff, mining, and other activities pose threats to surface water and ground water in many national parks, and commercial and residential developments along park boundaries threaten wildlife habitat and scenery. In many parks, exotic plants and feral animals are menacing native species.

Other problems in national parks occur within the park boundaries and arise from visitor abuse or inadequate maintenance. Increasing numbers of tourists threaten wildlife and plant life and overburden facilities. Buildings, trails, and other public facilities are suffering from litter, vandalism, and neglect. The theft of human artifacts from prehistoric Indian sites, Civil War battlefields, shipwrecks, and other archaeological sites and the collection of dinosaur bones, petrified wood, and other fossils are problems in national parks as well as other federal lands where these resources occur. National parks and other public lands are also losing resources to persons who engage in illegal wildlife hunting, deliberate killing of endangered and threatened species, and illegal wildlife trafficking.

Visibility impairment in national parks

Current status

Scenic vistas are affected by man-made pollution over 90% of the time. The worst visibility is in the East. The best visibility is in eastern Nevada, western Utah, and southern Idaho. The next best area is the Colorado Plateau.

Visibility is worst in summer when meteorological conditions are such that more pollution is transported to remote areas from urban areas and industrial developments. Natural climatic conditions also contribute to reduced visibility during the summer.

Fine particulates (<2.5 μm in diameter) are generally responsible for most of the visibility impairments. Fine sulfate particles from sulfur oxide emissions are the single most important contributor to visibility impairment, except in the northwestern United States where fine carbon particles play a more prominent role. Fine sulfates are responsible for 40 to 70% of visibility impairment. On the average, soil-derived materials are responsible for 10 to 30% of visibility impairment.

Source: U.S. Department of the Interior, National Park Service, Air and Water Quality Division, 1986, *Highlights of findings of National Park Service visibility research*, table 3-1, p. 3-3, Denver, Colo.

Contaminant issues of concern on national wildlife refuges, 1986

Level of concern	Number of refuges	Examples of contaminant issues of concern on refuges
Evidence indicates the need for corrective action	9	Industrial wastes (DDT, PCBs) Agricultural drainwater (selenium, other trace elements) Military activities (nerve gas, mustard gas, dioxin, plutonium, DDT) Waste dumps (asbestos) Asbestos insulation (refuge buildings)
Evidence indicates the need for in-depth monitoring and analysis of impacts	26	Municipal/industrial/military wastes and discharges (PCBs, trace metals) Agricultural drainwater (ag-chemicals, selenium, arsenic, mercury, boron, other trace metals) Waste dumps (heavy metals, mercury, pesticides, cyanide, nutrients, petroleum, other landfill effluents) Mining activities (mercury, arsenic, other trace elements) Cattle feedlots (nutrients)
Circumstantial evidence indicates a priority need for additional reconnaissance monitoring	43	Agricultural drainwater (ag-chemicals, trace elements, nutrients, toxic chemicals, metals, pesticides, selenium) Industrial dumps and discharges (petroleum by-products, mercury, heavy metals, chemicals, trace elements) Industrial emissions Municipal wastes (trace elements, heavy metals, chemicals) Municipal and military landfills (polychlorinated compounds, trace elements) Buried drums (ag-chemical, PCBs, fuel, unknown contents) Mosquito control spraying (chemicals) Mining activities (cyanide, placer mining) Oil and gas activities

Source: U.S. Department of the Interior, Fish and Wildlife Service, 1986 (updated by agency). *Preliminary survey of contaminants issues of concern on national wildlife refuges*, Washington, D.C., pp. 10-14.

Sources and technical notes

6-1
Federal lands

6-1a
Distribution of public lands

Clawson, M. 1983. *The federal lands revisited*. Resources for the Future (Washington, D.C.), pp. 15-62.

Executive Office of the President, Council on Environmental Quality. 1986. *Environmental quality: 17th annual report* (Washington, D.C.), pp. 178-179.

6-2
National parks

6-2a
National park system (units), 1872–1986

6-2b
National park system (acreages), 1872–1986

U.S. Department of the Interior, National Park Service. *Areas administered by the National Park Service*, annual (Washington, D.C.).

6-3
National wildlife refuges

6-3
National wildlife refuge system, 1920–1986

U.S. Department of the Interior, Fish and Wildlife Service, Office of Refuge Management (Washington, D.C.). 1986. Unpublished data.

6-4
Wilderness areas

6-4a
National wilderness preservation system, 1964–1986

6-4b
Ownership of wilderness areas (conterminous United States), 1986

6-4c
Ownership of wilderness areas (Alaska), 1986

U.S. Department of Agriculture, Forest Service (Washington, D.C.). 1986. Unpublished data.

6-5
Wild and scenic rivers

6-5
National wild and scenic river system, 1968–1986

U.S. Department of the Interior, National Park Service. 1988. *River mileage classifications for components of the National Wild and Scenic River System* (Washington, D.C.).

6-6
Marine sanctuaries and estuarine reserves

6-6a
Marine sanctuaries, 1975–1986

6-6b
National estuarine research reserves, 1974–1985

U.S. Department of Commerce, National Oceanic and Atmospheric Administration, Marine and Estuarine Management Division (Washington, D.C.). 1986. Unpublished data.

6-7
Historic places

6-7a
National Register of Historic Places: Properties listed, 1966–1986

6-7b
National Register of Historic Places: Properties removed, 1966–1986

U.S. Department of the Interior, National Park Service. 1988. *The National Register of Historic Places* (Washington, D.C.).

6-8
Threats to public lands

6-8a
Public use of national parks, 1906–1986

U.S. Department of the Interior, National Park Service, Statistical Office. *National Park statistical abstract*, annual (Denver, Colo.).

6-8b
Visibility impairment in national parks

U.S. Department of the Interior, National Park Service, Air and Water Quality Division. 1986. *Air quality in the national parks: A summary of research findings* (Washington, D.C.), table 3-1, Highlights of findings of NPS visibility research, p. 3-3.

6-8c
Contaminant issues of concern on national wildlife refuges, 1986

U.S. Department of the Interior, Fish and Wildlife Service. 1986. *Preliminary survey of contaminant issues of concern on national wildlife refuges* (Washington, D.C.), pp. 10-14.

Chapter 7
Population

7-1
Population distribution in the United States

The basic pattern of population distribution in much of the United States has not changed greatly since the turn of the century, although the West has gained proportionately more population than the North or South. Population increases have occurred in major urban areas, and urban clusters have grown larger in area. In rural areas, where populations are more spread out, changes in population have been sporadic. During the 1970s, many rural areas of the country experienced population growth, some of them after decades of decline. Since 1980, this rural "turnaround" has waned, but many rural counties and small towns continue to grow. Some exceptional rural areas have witnessed extensive new settlement and growth, notably in Florida and portions of the Far West. In the Northeast, rural areas continue to grow faster than metropolitan areas.

In the eastern half of the conterminous United States, settlement is fairly even and covers all but a few areas. Overall population density is greater in the North because of the greater number of large urban areas. This is especially evident along the northeastern seaboard between Boston and Washington, D. C., and around the southern shores of the Great Lakes. Less of the South's population is urban, with 50 million as compared to 81 million urban population in the North. Rural populations in the North and South are similar, with 28 million in the North and 25 million in the South.

In the western half, many areas are sparsely populated or unpopulated. This contrast is a reflection of the scanty rainfall and rugged terrain in much of the West, both of which reduce the likelihood of settlement. Except for the rainy Pacific Northwest states, areas of rural settlement and most urban centers in the West are dependent upon the availability of irrigation water. The rural popula-tion of the West is only 7 million, and five out of six people live in urban centers.

Hawaii is densely populated with 1 million people, whereas Alaska, with nearly one-sixth of the Nation's land area, has only 500,000 population, which is fewer people than in many metropolitan areas in the conterminous United States.

7-2
Total population, including Armed Forces overseas

The total population of the United States includes the resident population of the 50 states and the District of Columbia plus the Armed Forces stationed in foreign countries, Puerto Rico, and the outlying areas. Estimates exclude residents of the Commonwealth of Puerto Rico, residents of the outlying areas under United States sovereignty or jurisdiction (principally American Samoa, Guam, Virgin Islands of the United States, and Commonwealth of Northern Marianas Islands), and other U. S. citizens (military and civilian) living overseas.

The United States population has shown continuous growth over a long period of time and is continuing to grow at this time, although at a slower

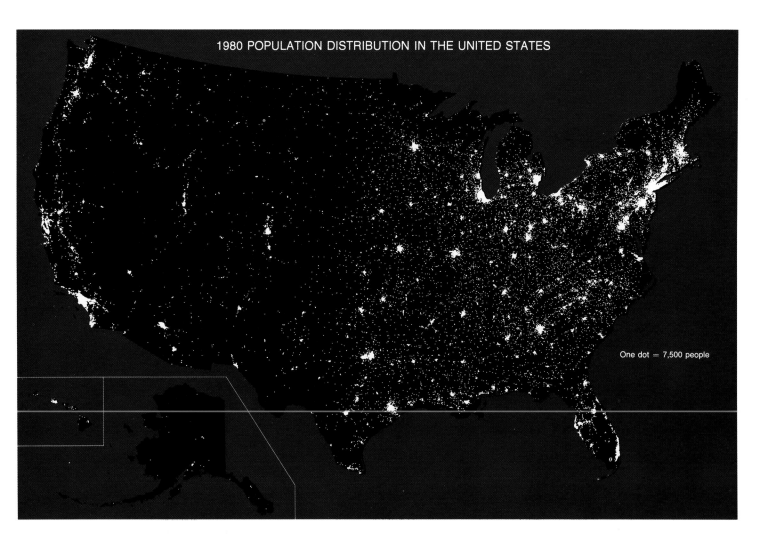

1980 POPULATION DISTRIBUTION IN THE UNITED STATES

One dot = 7,500 people

Total population including armed forces overseas, 1900-1986

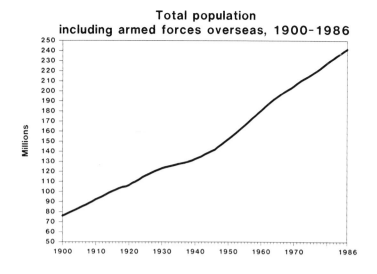

Population growth rate, 1901-1986

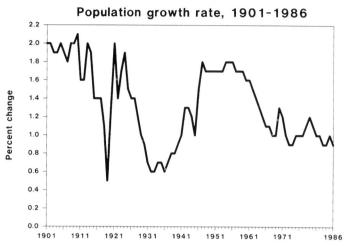

rate. The components of population change are births, deaths, net civilian immigration, and military inductions less discharges overseas. After 1980, population estimates contain an allowance for net undocumented immigration of 200,000 per year.

The United States is the fourth most populous country in the world, behind China, India, and the Soviet Union. By December 1, 1986, the total population of the United States was estimated to be approximately 242.6 million.

7-3
Population growth rate

The effects of several historic events are reflected in the statistics on population growth rate in the United States. During the first decade of the 1900s, the rate of population growth averaged about 2% per year, only to fall significantly during the World War I period. The 1920s witnessed high levels of growth, followed by much lower growth rates during the Great Depression. The renowned Baby Boom period after World War II is apparent as the growth rate shows a sharp increase in the late 1940s, followed by a sustained elevation during the 1950s and

into the 1960s. As more family planning choices became available to America's adults of child-bearing ages in the late 1960s and early 1970s, the growth rate experienced a rather sharp decline and moderation. Since 1980, the rate of growth has averaged slightly less than 1% annually.

Annual population increases of 2% or more are considered by demographers to be "rapid." At this rate, a population will double in 35 years. Compared to growth rates in less developed regions of the world, where growth rates in many countries have exceeded 2% since 1950 (although the rate has declined significantly from around 2.5% per year in 1965-1970), the current rate of growth of the U. S. population is far from rapid.

7-4
Components of population change

The fluctuations in population growth rate in the United States since World War II have been largely due to changes in birth rates. The annual number of births peaked in 1957 at 4.3 million, followed by a period of decline in births between 1960 and 1975.

Since 1975, the annual number of births has generally increased. This reflects larger numbers of women in the childbearing age group rather than an increase in fertility rates.

From 1940 to 1985, the crude death rate has declined slowly from as much as 11.0 per 1000 in 1940 to between 9.7 and 9.1 per 1000 during the 1950s, 1960s, and 1970s to 8.7 per 1000 in 1986. Since 1980, the total annual number of deaths has increased slightly. The recent increase was due to both the growth in the size of the U. S. population and its continued aging.

Life expectancy at birth continues to rise. In 1986, the latest year when empirical data are available, life expectancy was 74.9 years for the total resident population. This represents an increase in life expectancy of 1.6 years since 1977.

Almost 33% of the net change in population in 1980 was due to immigration, as large numbers of Cuban and Haitian people came into the United States in that year. Net changes in population for other years are explained by fluctuations in the birth rate rather than a rise in immigration rates, which remained relatively stable after the end of World War II until the 1980s.

7-5
Age structure of the total population

The age structure of the United States population mirrors the birth history of the Nation. Although deaths and net civilian immigration play a role, past births are the single most important determinant of the age structure. Changes in age structure over time, therefore, reflect differential patterns of reproductive strength, as children from low-birth and high-birth periods grow older over time.

The greatest effect on the contemporary age structure was the "baby boom" period after World War II. The impact can be seen, first, as a bulge in the under-5-years age group in 1950 and 1960, next, when these children are school age (at 5-14 years), and then, when they enter high school and college (at 15-24 years). The 15-24 age group experienced significant growth between 1980 and 1986 as the leading edge of the baby boom reached age 39 in 1986; this cohort now constitutes over 30% of the population. Beginning in 1980, the upswing in the under-5-years population is the echo

Components of total population change 1940-1986

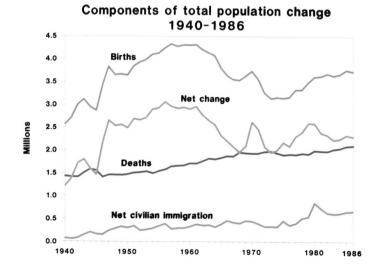

Age structure of total population 1940-1986

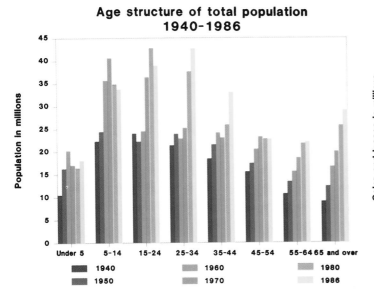

Population in millions

	1940	1960	1980
	1950	1970	1986

Net population migration by region, 1960-1985

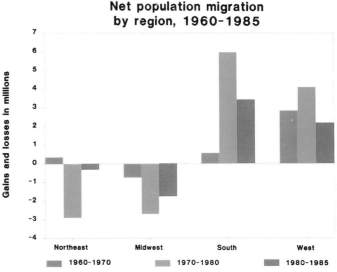

Gains and losses in millions

| | 1960-1970 | 1970-1980 | 1980-1985 |

effect from the baby boom; that is, these children are the offspring of the baby boom generation.

The growth of middle-aged population (45-54 age group) remains slow in the 1980s because of the small numbers of those born in the Depression era who are entering this age group. The population 65 and over has been growing steadily, however, and will continue to grow in the foreseeable future. This is attributed to increasing longevity.

7-6
Net population migration by region

Net population migration includes interregional migration, immigration from abroad, and emigration from the United States. Since 1960, the pattern has been one of net migration from the Northeast and Midwest and net migration to the South and West. The Northeast and Midwest experienced particularly heavy losses during the 1970s, but their losses diminished during the first half of the 1980s.

Approximately 40 million Americans (17% of the total population) moved to a different residence each year between 1980 and 1985. Slightly less than 6.4 million persons (3% of the total popula-

tion) moved to a different state, 3.5 million (less than 2%) moved to a different region of the country, and an additional 1 million persons moved to the United States from other countries in each of these years.

States with the largest net population gains during the 1980-1985 period were located in the South and West, with California, Texas, and Florida gaining 4.1 million persons collectively. The pattern is not consistent for every state within these regions. For example, Oregon and West Virginia lost about 2% of their populations. In the Northeast, all but five states lost migrants. Losses in Michigan, Illinois, and Ohio totaled 1.2 million persons. Four of the five Northeastern states gaining population were in New England (Vermont, New Hampshire, Rhode Island, and Maine). The fifth Northeastern state with net in-migration was New Jersey.

The 1970s and the first half of the 1980s witnessed a sharp distinction in population growth between the North and the rest of the Nation. In the 1970s, most Northern areas had only modest growth, and metropolitan New York along with several other large metropolitan areas experienced

population losses. So far this decade, several metropolitan areas in the North have reversed their declines of the 1970s. Pennsylvania was the only state in the Northeast to lose population during the 1980-1985 period, probably partly because of declines in its energy and steel industries.

In contrast, much of the South and nearly all of the Far West had above average population growth in the 1970s and nearly 90% of national population growth is still occurring in the South and West in the 1980s. Much of the population increase is due to net migration, both from other states and from abroad. Since 1982, the annual growth rate has decelerated in several Southern and Western states where energy development and production are an important part of the economy.

During the 1970s, population fell in certain rural areas of the Middle South and in many counties of the Midwest (most of them sparsely populated) where agriculture plays an important role in the local economy, such as in the Great Plains and the western Corn Belt. Losses continued into the 1980s, with only a slight recovery from this trend by 1985. An exception to this decreasing trend has been population growth in nonmetropolitan areas that are attractive to retirees, such as the Ozarks, the Texas Hill Country, and northern Michigan and Wisconsin. Other counties recovering from earlier population declines in the 1970s attracted new industry (especially in the South) or new or revived mining activity (particularly in the West).

7-7
Population density by county

A striking contrast is apparent between population density by counties in eastern and western halves of the conterminous United States. In the eastern half, only a few counties have densities below 10 per square mile, and most of the area has a population density of between 10 and 50 per square mile. Higher densities occur in the northern manufacturing belt which runs from Boston, New York City, and Washington, D.C., to Chicago and Minneapolis, and around many individual large metropolitan centers. Relatively high population densities can be found in rural tobacco growing areas of eastern North Carolina, mining areas of West Virginia, and the Cajun country in southern Louisiana.

Net population migration, 1980 - 1985

EXPLANATION

Percentage loss (-) or gain (+)

-1.5 and over
None to -1.4
None to +0.9
+1.0 to +4.9
+5.0 and over

Most of the counties in the West have population densities less than 10 per square mile, with substantial areas at less than 2 (including most of Alaska). On the Pacific coast, densities are similar to those in the East. Patches of higher density in the interior West are associated with large cities, such as Denver, or reflect irrigated farming development, such as in eastern Washington and in the northern Texas Panhandle. The actual density pattern in parts of the West is somewhat distorted because many counties are very large in areal extent. For example, some Southern California counties include much of the Mojave Desert, and the dense areas of southern Arizona are less extensive than they appear.

7-8
Population density along major coasts

Most major American urban centers are located on the Pacific, Atlantic, Gulf, and the Great Lakes coasts, and growth in these coastal regions continues to accelerate. Population in coastal counties increased by 61% between 1950 and 1980 and is still growing rapidly. In 1984, over one-half (52.3%) of the residential population in the United States lived within 50 miles of a coastline.

Population density along the Atlantic coast far exceeds that of the other coasts. This density pattern can be explained by a variety of historical, social, and economic factors, including colonial settlement patterns and the industrial revolution. Of the 12 largest metropolitan areas today, all but Washington, D.C., and Dallas–Fort Worth are active ports for ocean-going commercial vessels.

This propensity for major cities to be located on or close to the coast accounts for a much higher population density along coasts than in the interior (noncoastal) regions of the Nation. The lower population density in noncoastal areas also reflects the sparsely populated portions of the Midwest. The average population density in coastal counties is 267 persons per square mile, compared to 46 persons per square mile in noncoastal counties.

The rapid population growth in coastal counties in the South and West which occurred during the 1970s reflects the rapid growth in these regions as a whole, although many individual coastal counties have not witnessed the same degree of growth. Coastal growth in the South is dominated by the rapid expansion in Florida.

7-9
Metropolitan and nonmetropolitan population patterns

Since the turn of the century, the United States has become predominantly a metropolitan Nation. In 1985, 76% of the U. S. population lived within officially recognized metropolitan areas. (The term metropolitan area includes "inside central cities" and "outside central cities," the latter of which consists mainly of the suburbs although it includes some nonsuburban territory.)

The population in metropolitan areas has doubled since 1950, from 85 million to 180 million. Most of this increase occurred outside central cities in metropolitan areas where the population grew from 23% of the Nation's total population in 1950 to 45% of the total in 1985. In contrast, the part of the metropolitan population living inside central cities has changed much more slowly, and its proportionate share of the national total has dropped

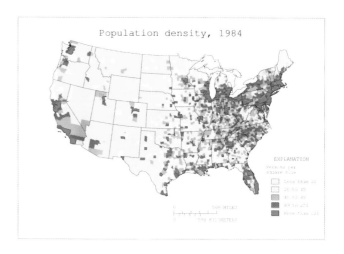

Population density, 1984

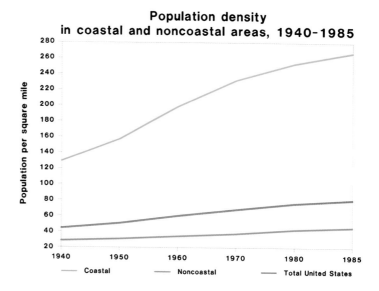

Population density in coastal and noncoastal areas, 1940-1985

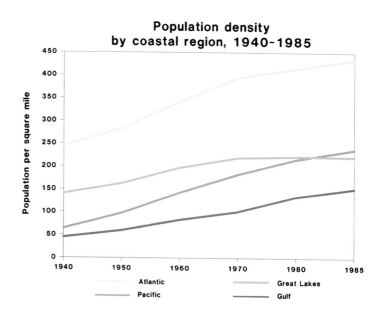

Population density by coastal region, 1940-1985

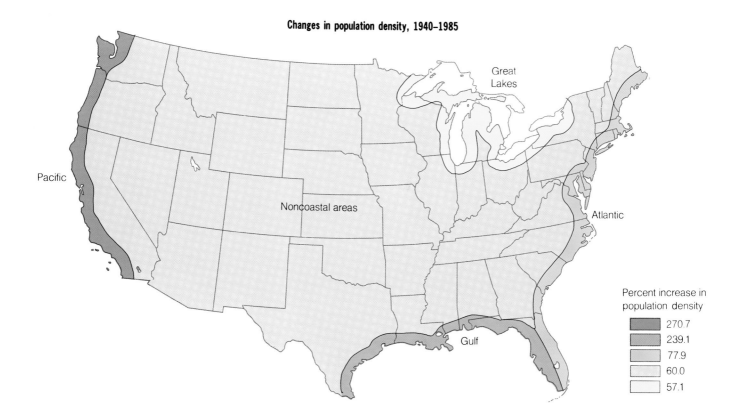

Changes in population density, 1940–1985

Great Lakes

Pacific

Noncoastal areas

Atlantic

Gulf

Percent increase in
population density

▨	270.7
▨	239.1
▨	77.9
▨	60.0
□	57.1

slightly from 33% in 1950 to 32% in 1985. At the same time, the population in nonmetropolitan portions of the country decreased from 44% of the U. S. total in 1950 to 23% in 1985.

Much of the apparent increase in metropolitan population since 1950 has resulted from the expansion of metropolitan territorial boundaries through the addition of areas and counties as new suburban development reached them and through the reclassification of small cities as they grew large enough to qualify as metropolitan.

Between 1980 and 1985, many large central cities experienced smaller population losses or had only small gains, while their suburban areas had slower growth than in recent decades. This slackening of the move to the suburbs was due in part to the high mortgage-interest rates of the early 1980s,

thus slowing suburban home construction significantly in many areas.

7-10
Trends in housing types

Since 1930, 30 million single-family and multifamily units have been built. This number is roughly equal to the number of units constructed before 1970 that still exist. New home construction accounts for most of the new housing, but conversions of commercial buildings and mobile home sales have played an increasing role in adding to the Nation's housing inventory.

Traditionally, the United States has had a very strong single-family housing market, and from cabin to mansion, diversity is the hallmark of single-family

housing type. In 1980, single-family homes were the predominant type of housing unit in all four regions of the country. In the Northeast, this represents a reversal of the pattern that existed in 1940, when multifamily units were the predominant housing type. Since 1940, the number of single-family units has grown each decade in every region, and the number of housing units in multifamily structures has done likewise, except in the 1950s in the Midwest and South. The fastest growing housing type overall, however, is the mobile home.

Since the 1960s, growth of single-family and multifamily units in metropolitan areas has far outdistanced growth of like housing types in nonmetropolitan areas. The growth of mobile homes has been fairly equally distributed between metropolitan and nonmetropolitan areas.

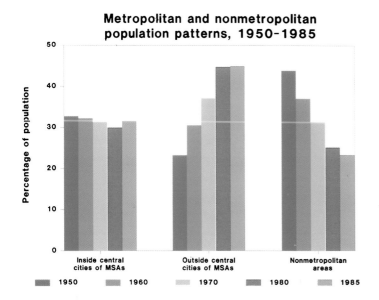

Metropolitan and nonmetropolitan population patterns, 1950-1985

Percentage of population

Inside central cities of MSAs · Outside central cities of MSAs · Nonmetropolitan areas

■ 1950 ■ 1960 ■ 1970 ■ 1980 ■ 1985

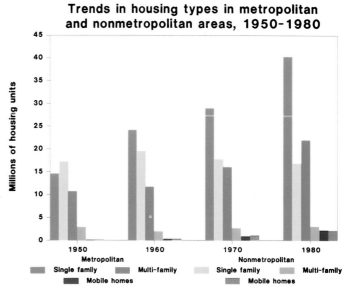

Trends in housing types in metropolitan and nonmetropolitan areas, 1950-1980

Millions of housing units

1950 · 1960 · 1970 / Metropolitan · 1980 / Nonmetropolitan

■ Single family ■ Multi-family ■ Single family ■ Multi-family
■ Mobile homes ■ Mobile homes

Trends in housing types, 1940-1980
Northeast

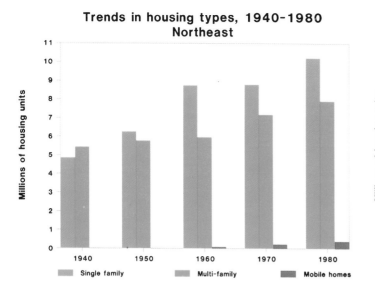

Trends in housing types, 1940-1980
South

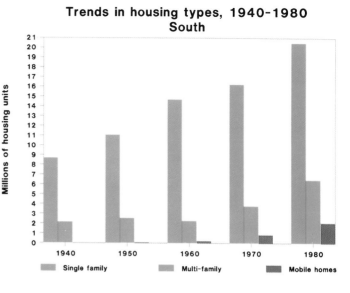

Trends in housing types, 1940-1980
Midwest

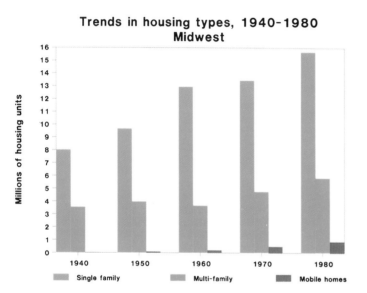

Trends in housing types, 1940-1980
West

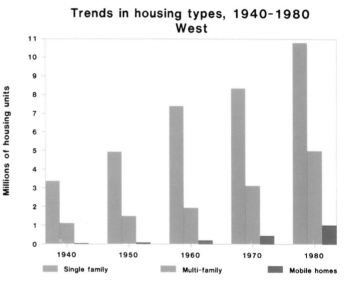

Housing units have grown larger in size and have more amenities than in 1940 when the first housing survey was completed. In 1986, new single-family units, on the average, had about 1800 square feet of floor space, and apartments in multifamily units had 900 square feet. In 1940, nearly one-half of the Nation's 37.3 million housing units had no plumbing, and a majority of them lacked central heating. Today, nearly all have plumbing and heating, and 59% have air conditioning. Despite these improvements, however, 8.9% of all occupied housing units were considered physically substandard in 1983.

Sources and technical notes

7-1
Population distribution in the United States

7-1
Population distribution in the United States, 1980

U.S. Department of Commerce, Bureau of the Census. 1981. *1980 census of population* (Washington, D.C.), satellite map.

7-2
Total population including armed forces overseas

7-2
Total population, including armed forces overseas, 1900–1987

U.S. Department of Commerce, Bureau of the Census. *Current population reports* (Washington, D.C.), series P-25, nos. 521, 802, 990, and 1022.

U.S. Department of Commerce, Bureau of the Census. 1987. *Statistical abstract of the United States, 1986* (Washington, D.C.), p. 5.

7-3
Population growth rate

7-3
Population growth rate, 1900–1986

U.S. Department of Commerce, Bureau of the Census. *Current population reports* (Washington, D.C.), series P-25, nos. 521, 802, 990, and 1022.

U.S. Department of Commerce, Bureau of the Census. 1987. *Statistical abstract of the United States, 1986* (Washington, D.C.), p. 5.

7-4
Components of population change

7-4
Components of total population change, 1940–1985

U.S. Department of Commerce, Bureau of the Census. *Current population reports* (Washington, D.C.), series P-25, nos. 802, 952, 990, and 1023.

7-5
Age structure of the total population

7-5
Age structure of total population, 1940–1986

U.S. Department of Commerce, Bureau of the Census. 1975. *Historical statistics of the United States: Colonial times to 1970* (Washington, D.C.), series A 30-37.

U.S. Department of Commerce, Bureau of the Census. *Current population reports* (Washington, D.C.), series P-25, nos. 311, 519, 917, and 1022.

7-6
Net population migration by region

7-6a
Net population migration by region, 1960–1985

7-6b
Population migration, 1980–1985

U.S. Department of Commerce, Bureau of the Census. *Current population reports* (Washington, D.C.), series P-25, no. 998.

7-7
Population density by county

7-7
Population density, 1984

U.S. Department of Commerce, Bureau of the Census. 1981. *1980 census of population* (Washington, D.C.), figure 19, Population density by counties, 1980 (updated), page 1-22.

7-8
Population density along major coasts

7-8a
Population density in coastal and noncoastal areas, 1940–1985

7-8b
Population density by coastal region, 1940–1985

7-8c
Changes in population density, 1940–1985

U.S. Department of Commerce, Bureau of the Census. 1982. *Statistical abstract of the United States: 1981* (Washington, D.C.), p. 7.

U.S. Department of Commerce, Bureau of the Census. 1987. *Statistical abstract of the United States: 1986* (Washington, D.C.), p. 19.

Coastal area covers 611 counties and independent cities that are entirely or substantially within 50 miles of U.S. coastal shorelines.

7-9
Metropolitan and nonmetropolitan population patterns

7-9
Metropolitan and nonmetropolitan population patterns, 1950–1985

U.S. Department of Commerce, Bureau of the Census. 1940, 1950, 1960, and 1970 censuses of population (Washington, D.C.).

U.S. Department of Commerce, Bureau of the Census. 1985. *Current population reports* (Washington, D.C.), series P-25, no. 976 (updated).

7-10
Trends in housing types

7-10a
Trends in housing types in metropolitan and nonmetropolitan areas, 1950–1980

U.S. Department of Commerce, Bureau of the Census. *U.S. census of housing: 1940, 1960, 1980* (Washington, D.C.).

7-10b
Trends in housing types, 1940–1980, Northeast

7-10c
Trends in housing types, 1940–1980, South

7-10d
Trends in housing types, 1940–1980, Midwest

7-10e
Trends in housing types, 1940–1980, West

U.S. Department of Commerce, Bureau of the Census. *U.S. census of housing: 1940, 1960, 1980* (Washington, D.C.).

Chapter 8
Transportation

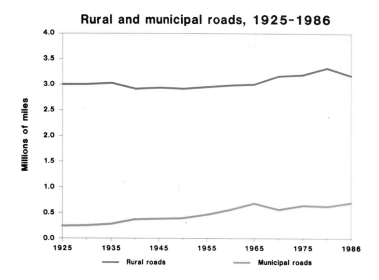

Rural and municipal roads, 1925-1986

8-1
Transportation networks

The major modes of transportation in the United States have changed dramatically since colonial times. Prior to 1800, transportation was characterized by the lack of mechanical power, and the movement of goods and passengers was slow and difficult. Transportation was mainly along the coasts, rivers, and streams, and the chief forms of transportation were boats propelled by humans, animals, wind, or water currents. The roads that existed were dirt and used by people traveling on foot or horseback. Animal-drawn carriage and wagon traffic was confined to local roads and a few main roads connecting centers of activity.

Water transportation networks helped shape the geographical development of the Nation. By 1850, an extensive system of canals had been built, miles of natural waterways had been improved for navigation, and the steamboat had become commercially successful. Between 1850 and 1900, however, water transportation lost its dominance, primarily because of the Civil War and the development of railroads.

Railroads were the first means of fast and efficient land transportation. Between 1830, when the first rail tracks were laid, and 1916, when the railroad network peaked at 250,000 miles of track, the railroad network grew from coast to coast and border to border. The result of this rapid growth was overexpansion and many miles of unprofitable track that were abandoned later in the 20th century. Since 1916, rail mileage has declined and little change in this trend is expected in the future.

With the development of railroads, natural barriers to the location of cities and towns no longer existed. Railroads could not satisfy all transportation needs, however, and in the early 1900s, water and road transportation reemerged as important modes of transportation. After World War II, 728 miles were added to the water transportation network when the inland coastal waterway system was constructed. Although the water network has the fewest miles of all the transportation networks, it reaches a large part of the Nation's population and represents the transportation backbone for a variety of large-volume, low-cost bulk freight.

Road construction and improvement followed the railroad era (1860–1920), and freight transportation by truck also emerged at this time. Initially, road improvements took place in and around cities when the automobile was introduced. Between 1925 and 1985, miles of rural and municipal roads increased steadily. It was not until after World War II that the interstate system of toll expressways and turnpikes was built.

Pipelines were introduced in 1865, initially as feeder lines to carry oil from the oil fields to water or railroad depots. Between 1900 and 1915, more than 40,000 miles of oil pipeline were laid. Today, over 200,000 miles of pipe form an extensive network.

Air transportation has been the most recent mode to be developed. From its beginnings in 1903, flying has evolved as a major, modern transportation mode. The air network consists of airports and airways (aerial highways). In 1940, the air network included approximately 37,000 miles. By 1984, the network had grown to 360,000 miles of aerial highways.

A major environmental impact of transportation networks is land disturbance. During the years of railroad network expansion, as much as 131 million acres of land was incorporated into the railroad system. Barriers to transportation, such as rivers, mountains, and forests, were overcome by engineering feats, often with impacts to the environment.

Modern expressways and roadways are fitted to the landscape according to very specific engineering standards. In the years preceding the passage of environmental protection legislation, environmental concerns often were not given much weight in applying these standards. In recent years, however, environmental concerns have been carefully integrated into the highway planning and design process to avoid, minimize, and compensate for adverse environmental impacts where possible.

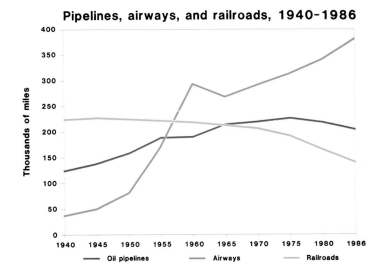

Pipelines, airways, and railroads, 1940-1986

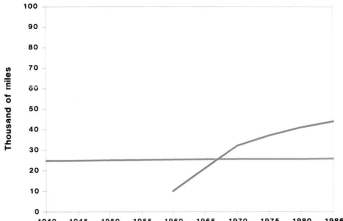

Inland waterways and interstate highways, 1940-1986

Automobiles and trucks, 1920-1986

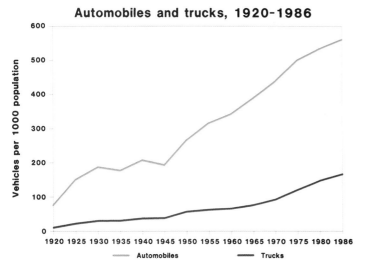

Buses and aircraft, 1930-1986

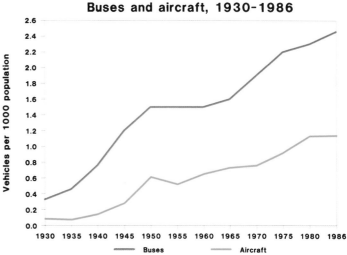

8-2
Transportation vehicles

Since 1920, transportation has matured into a five-modal system. In the first half of the 20th century, water, motor, air, rail, and pipeline modes competed to fill the economic niche for which each was best suited. Since then, a gradual stability in the role of each mode has occurred.

Between 1920 and 1985, the number of railroad cars in use declined, whereas the number of motor and air carriers increased dramatically, and the number of water transport vessels and oil pipelines grew at a steady rate.

Transportation has been recognized as one of the major sources of air pollutants since the 1960s. Mobile source emissions account for 70% of carbon monoxide, 35% of the hydrocarbons, and 40% of the nitrogen oxides identified in current emission inventories. The total quantity of mobile source emissions has declined steadily since 1970, however, because of emission control devices placed on the automobile. Further reductions are expected as older vehicles are retired from the fleet and as additional controls are placed on larger vehicles.

Transportation noise is a major environmental factor affecting the quality of people's lives. Reaction to noise is complex—it involves a combination of physiological and psychological factors that vary from person to person. Consideration of noise impacts and how they may be either avoided or attenuated has become an important element in planning, designing, and operating transportation facilities. For example, compatible land use planning is now an integral part of airport development and operations plans, and many new highways and highway expansions include noise barriers.

Other transportation impacts include runoff of deicing salts, heavy metals, and oil from highways and parking lots into surface- and ground-water systems. In addition, the disposal of abandoned and junked transportation vehicles and discard of spent motor oils and fuels contribute to the Nation's growing waste disposal problems.

8-3
Intercity passenger travel

Rail dominated the intercity passenger service industry until the beginning of the 20th century when electric railways invaded the railroads' traditional province. Soon, however, the automobile, the bus, and improved highways brought an end to the short-lived electric railway and encroached further on the railroads' passenger traffic. Excluding war-traffic related years, peak railroad passenger travel (on a per capita basis) was reached in 1914. By 1929, intercity bus service was estimated to be as much as 60% of rail coach.

Between 1929 and 1939, highway use increased significantly, despite the general depression. Rail passenger traffic was reduced still further. World War II, however, produced a sharp reversal in the 1930s trend and a fourfold increase in rail passenger miles traveled. The increase in rail usage occurred as a result of greatly increased levels of economic activity, heavy troop movements, increased private travel of military and related persons, and severe government restrictions on automobile use.

Highway traffic rebounded and modern air transportation began in the immediate postwar years (1946-1950). Since that time, a tremendous increase in these modes of transportation has occurred. Auto passenger-miles increased in response

Railroad freight cars, 1900-1986

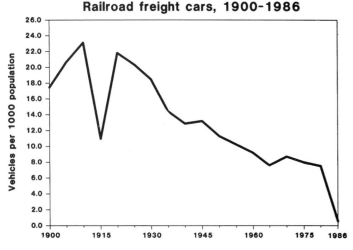

Railroad passenger cars, 1900-1986

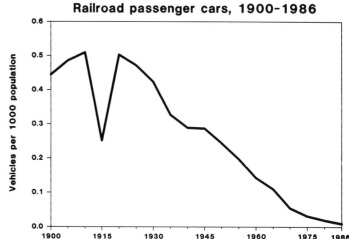

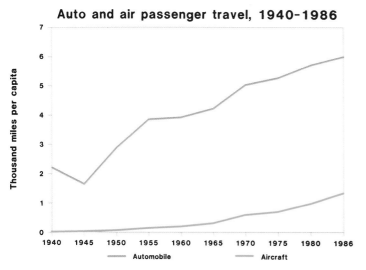

Auto and air passenger travel, 1940-1986

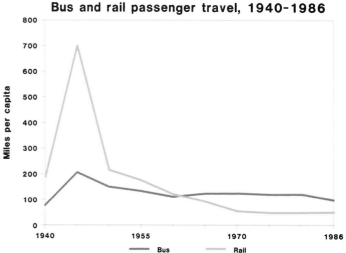

Bus and rail passenger travel, 1940-1986

to demands for personal mobility, improved and increasingly more efficient vehicles, and the construction of interstate systems. Higher per-family incomes also contributed by increasing automobile ownership and use.

Between 1940 and 1955, passenger air carrier mileage grew nearly one-hundredfold. This period included the introduction of high-speed, nonstop flights between even the most widely separated cities in the United States. Jet aircraft were introduced after 1955, and since then, air carriers have continued to expand their service.

8-4
Intercity freight transportation

All of the major modes of transportation in the United States (water, rail, motor, pipe, and air) play significant roles in freight movement. The best comparative measure of domestic freight movement is the ton-mile (one ton moved one mile) regardless of mode.

The domestic water network for freight movement consists of three systems: the Great Lakes (including the St. Lawrence Seaway), coastal waters, and

inland waters (rivers, canals, and inland waterways). Most of the freight moved by water is transported on inland waters and consists primarily of raw materials such as petroleum and petroleum products, grain and grain products, bituminous coal and lignite, sand and gravel, crushed rock, and iron and steel. Great Lakes and coastal freight traffic has stagnated since World War II because of competition from land pipelines and railroads. The inland component, however, has shown an opposite trend wherein ton-miles have increased more than sixfold since 1945.

Railroad freight transportation has declined in importance since the early 1900s, primarily because of competition from two new modes, truck and air, and the resurgence of water transportation. However, railroads still move more ton-miles of freight than any other mode. The products shipped by rail are primarily large-volume, heavy-weight raw materials, such as coal, grain, and chemicals. Railroads also ship automobiles, food, and other high-value products.

The growth of pipeline freight movement is directly related to the demand for petroleum products. Pipeline transportation has several characteris-

tics that set it apart from the other modes of freight transportation. It has a limited product mode—the only products that can be moved through a pipe are gases, liquids, and, to a limited degree, slurries. Oil pipelines have low public visibility and only a few users because of the concentrated structure of the oil industry. Pipeline transport is highly automated, energy efficient, and not a source of air or noise pollution. The trade-offs are land disturbance (including wetlands loss) during construction and maintenance, potential obstacles to wildlife movement of aboveground pipes, and the possibility of rupture.

Freight movement by truck did not become a significant part of the transportation system until the third decade of the 20th century because of lack of improved roads and dominance of the railroads. Just after World War I, about 1 million trucks were on the roads, but that number increased to more than 30 million by 1980. The rapid rise in truck movement of freight has been a contributing factor to the decline of the railroads. The primary reasons for the truck's success are its unique performance characteristics—speed and ability to perform as anticipated over time—and an extensive

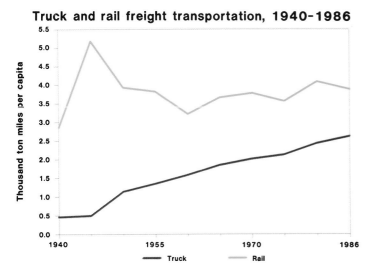

Truck and rail freight transportation, 1940-1986

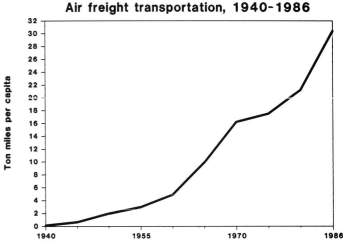

Air freight transportation, 1940-1986

road network. Trucks carry almost 25% of all ton-miles shipped, second only to railroads. They transport more than 70% of all meat and dairy products, textile mill and leather products, apparel and related products, fabricated metal products, industrial machinery, and transportation equipment. Trucks also move more than one-half of candy, beverage, tobacco, rubber, and plastic products transported domestically.

Air transport has recently gained an integral place in the overall freight transportation system. The growth of the air freight industry in terms of ton-miles has been dramatic even though shipments still account for less than 1% of the Nation's total. Although it had been forecast that air would become competitive with trucks, generally this has not happened. Aircraft are still best suited for transporting special high-value, low-weight, low-volume products, extremely perishable freight such as flowers and lobsters, and highly marketable manufactured products such as communication products and parts, instruments, and photographic equipment.

Increasing attention is being focused on the transportation of freight that is hazardous in nature because of the environmental and human health problems associated with spillage of these materials. Trucks carry more than 60% of all hazardous materials transported domestically and are responsible for the majority of hazardous spills. Corrosive substances have the highest accidental release rate, although gasoline truck accidents and releases are the most numerous and produce the greatest dollar damage. Most truck-related spills occur during loading and unloading of hazardous materials. Human error, including speeding and other basic traffic violations, is the leading cause of accidents and hazardous releases on the road. Freight cars also transport hazardous materials and, between 1973 and 1983, the total number of rail-related hazardous spills increased by 3% per year. Since that time, however, railroad cars carrying certain hazardous materials have been equipped with self-couplers, thermal insulation, and head shields, and few catastrophic rail accidents involving hazardous materials have occurred.

8-5
Principal means of transportation to work

Inner-city inhabitants represent the highest percentage of public transportation users. People

Pipe and water freight transportation, 1940-1986

Thousand ton miles per capita

Oil pipeline — Inland waterway

who live outside inner cities and in nonmetropolitan areas comprise the highest percentage of automobile users.

Nationally, more commuters still choose private transportation than any other means of transport to work. The proportion of workers using public transportation has declined by over one-half from 1960 to 1980. The percentage of people walking to work has declined also, but not as dramatically as that of those using public transportation. Carpooling is becoming more popular, however. Workers carpooling increased from none or a negligible portion of the domestic work force in 1960 to 20% in 1980. Over the same time period, the percentage of the work force relying on automobiles as their principal means of getting to work declined only slightly, from 67 to 64%.

Commuting distances are growing. In 1963, less than one-fourth of the domestic work force traveled 10 or more miles to work. By 1976, the proportion of 10-plus mile commuters had increased to more than one-third of the work force, and many of these commuters used the interstate highway system. By 1980, this proportion had increased to nearly one-half. As a result, the commuting distances around

major metropolitan areas are increasing and commuter routes are extending farther into non-metropolitan areas.

8-6
Automobile fuel economy

Fuel economy for new automobiles has improved steadily over the past 10 years. Increased efficiency is a function of motor vehicle design, lighter weight automobiles, and lower horsepower. Efficiency of new and older models also depends on other factors, including how the cars are driven, emissions control and safety equipment, vehicle maintenance and upkeep, passenger load, and the condition of the road surface.

Transportation uses over one-fourth of all energy consumed in the United States. These energy requirements vary according to transportation mode, speed, condition, load, and length of trip. Overall, the highway users—automobiles and trucks—consume the largest portion of the energy used for transportation, followed by air, water, rail, and pipeline. Because of the large loads and long distances traveled, water and railroads are the most energy

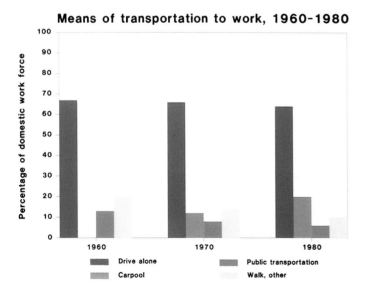

Means of transportation to work, 1960-1980

Percentage of domestic work force

Drive alone — Public transportation — Carpool — Walk, other

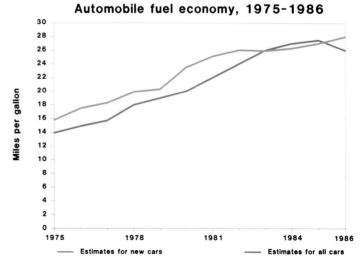

Automobile fuel economy, 1975-1986

Miles per gallon

Estimates for new cars — Estimates for all cars

efficient modes for freight transportation. Both consume less than 1000 Btu per ton-mile. Air freight transport, on the other hand, uses the most energy of the four freight transporters, consuming over 12,000 Btu per ton-mile. Trucks are intermediate in energy consumption, using about 2500 Btu per ton-mile. For local passenger travel, bus and rail transit use about the same amounts of energy—3000 Btu per passenger mile—whereas automobiles use over 4000 Btu. Buses reduce Btu consumption by two-thirds on the highway, whereas automobiles and rail are only slightly more efficient in intercity passenger travel. Air transport is the least efficient for intercity passenger travel, consuming about 7000 Btu per passenger-mile.

Sources and technical notes

8-1
Transportation networks

8-1a
Rural and municipal roads, 1925–1985

8-1b
Pipelines, airways, and railroads, 1940–1985

8-1c
Inland waterways and interstate highways, 1940–1985

U.S. Department of Transportation, Federal Highway Administration. *Highway statistics,* annual issues (Washington, D.C.).

Transportation Policy Associates. 1986. *Transportation in America* (Washington, D.C.), p. 21.

Motor Vehicle Manufacturers Association. *Facts and figures,* annual issues (Washington, D.C.), p. 84.

Bowersox, D. J., P. J. Calabro, and G. D. Wagenheim. 1981. *Introduction to transportation.* Macmillan Pub. Co., Inc. (New York).

8-2
Transportation vehicles

8-2a
Automobiles and trucks, 1920–1984

8-2b
Buses and aircraft, 1930–1985

8-2c
Railroad freight cars, 1900–1985

8-2d
Railroad passenger cars, 1900–1985

U.S. Department of Transportation, Federal Highway Administration. *Highway statistics,* annual (Washington, D.C.).

U.S. Department of Transportation, United States Coast Guard. 1985. *Boating statistics* (Washington, D.C.), p. 11.

Association of American Railroads. 1985. *Railroad facts* (Washington, D.C.), pp. 48-52.

U.S. Department of Commerce, Bureau of the Census. 1986. *Statistical abstract of the United States: 1985* (Washington, D.C.), p. 617.

U.S. Department of Commerce, Bureau of the Census. 1987. *Statistical abstract of the United States: 1988* (Washington, D.C.), p. 595.

8-3
Intercity passenger travel

8-3a
Auto and air passenger travel, 1940–1985

8-3b
Bus and rail passenger travel, 1940–1985

Transportation Policy Associates. 1986. *Transportation in America* (Washington, D.C.), p. 8.

Healy, K. T. 1985. *Performance of the U.S. railroads since World War II.* Vantage Press, Inc. (New York).

8-4
Intercity freight transportation

8-4a
Truck and rail freight transportation, 1940–1985

8-4b
Air freight transportation, 1940–1985

8-4c
Pipe and water freight transportation, 1940–1985

Transportation Policy Associates. 1986. *Transportation in America* (Washington, D.C.), p. 6.

Bowersox, D. J., P. J. Calabro, and G. D. Wagenheim. 1981. *Introduction to transportation.* Macmillan Pub. Co., Inc. (New York).

Library of Congress, Office of Technology Assessment. 1986. *Transportation of hazardous wastes* (Washington, D.C.).

8-5
Principal means of transportation to work

8-5
Principal means of transportation to work, 1960–1980

Executive Office of the President, Council on Environmental Quality. 1981. *Environmental trends* (updated) (Washington, D.C.), p. 64.

8-6
Automobile fuel economy

8-6
Automobile fuel economy, 1975–1986

U.S. Department of Energy, Oak Ridge National Laboratory. 1988. *Transportation energy conservation data book* (draft) (Oak Ridge, Tenn.).

Chapter 9
Environmental Risks and Hazards

9-1
Waste generation and disposal

Solid, liquid, and gaseous wastes are inevitable by-products of our advanced technological society. Each year billions of tons of virgin materials are extracted from mines, forests, farmlands, and waterbodies throughout the United States. Before these materials leave the extraction sites, several billion tons of residue, such as mine tailings and spoils, tree limbs and roots, and crop and animal wastes, are discarded. One million tons or more of waste are generated when the extracted materials are cleaned, chemically processed, or physically transformed into finished products. This processing requires large amounts of water and energy, and it generates large volumes of solid, liquid, and gaseous wastes. The finished products may be short-lived consumer goods, such as food or clothing, or long-term capital goods, such as automobiles, appliances, or buildings. Sooner or later, these goods become waste products as well and are returned to the land, water, or atmosphere by some form of disposal method, such as burial in landfills, land application, deep well injection, waste-water effluent discharge, ocean dumping, or incineration or are recovered as reuseable materials or energy.

The problem of waste disposal in the United States is not new but it has reached a critical dimension in recent years. Not only are quantities of waste increasing but also hazardous and toxic materials associated with these wastes. The impacts of waste storage and disposal are far-reaching, potentially affecting air and water quality, land use, and public health.

People are becoming more aware of the problems associated with waste storage and disposal. In many instances, the effects of past indiscriminate or improper waste disposal practices have taken years to surface as threats to health and the environment. Hazards that have lain unrecognized for years are now surfacing in alarming numbers and present serious environmental and human health problems.

The four most significant current waste disposal challenges are municipal and industrial solid waste and sludge disposal, uncontrolled hazardous site cleanup, control of newly generated hazardous waste, and radioactive waste disposal.

9-2
Municipal solid waste generation, recovery, and disposal

Every locality in the United States faces the problem of where and how to dispose of its ever increasing amount of municipal solid waste. In 1984, United

General flow of materials

(million tons per year)

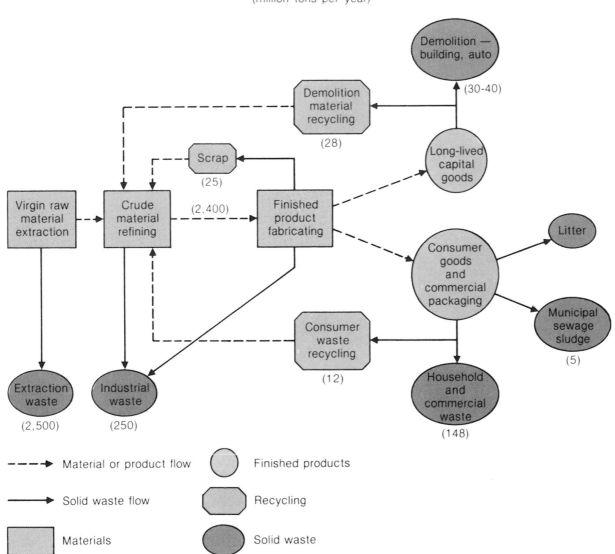

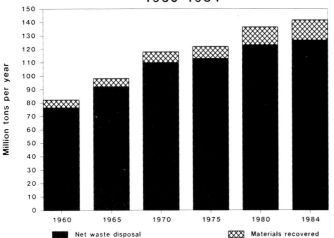

Municipal solid waste generation 1960-1984

Million tons per year

■ Net waste disposal ▨ Materials recovered

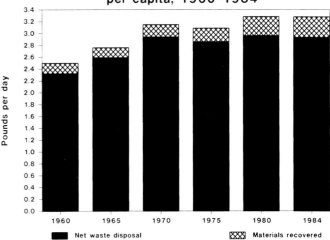

Municipal solid waste generation per capita, 1960-1984

Pounds per day

■ Net waste disposal ▨ Materials recovered

States consumers in the residential and commercial sectors generated over 148 million tons of solid waste, and most of it (over 126 million tons) ended up as municipal trash and garbage. Around 15 million tons or 10% of this municipal waste was recovered through recycling, material conversion, and energy conversion. (Excluded from the residential and commercial solid waste category are industrial wastes from mining, agricultural and industrial processing, demolition and construction wastes, sewage sludge, junked automobiles, and obsolete equipment.)

The amount of municipal waste generated in the United States has increased in the past 25 years. Some of the increase resulted from growth in population, but much has come from an increase in material consumption and the wasteful consequences of the packaging revolution. In 1960, each person in the United States generated approximately 2.5 pounds of waste per day. By 1984, the amount of waste generated per capita had increased to over 3.4 pounds per day.

The composition of discarded solid waste has changed over the past 25 years. There has been a significant increase in the proportion of paper, glass, and plastics in municipal waste and a decrease in metal, food, and yard waste. Paper always has been the largest category of consumer solid waste, accounting for 32% of the net discards in 1960 and 37% in 1984. Plastics, however, jumped from 0.5% of net discards in 1960 to 7.2% in 1984. This overall trend reflects the growth in the use of plastics in packaging materials and nonreturnable containers and as substitutes for other materials.

A reduction in metal waste has occurred, partly a result of increased recovery. The amount of aluminum recovered, for example, increased from 1.2% of gross discards recovered in 1970 to about 30% in 1984, and ferrous metal recovery increased from 0.5% of gross discards recovered in 1960 to 2.8% in 1984.

The amount of glass, paper, and paperboard recovered from gross discards has also increased over the past 25 years, although there were slight

declines in the amounts of these products recovered between 1966 and 1975. Demand for wastepaper by the paper industry has fluctuated over the last 25 years. Reductions in wastepaper recovery are associated with the increased costs of collecting, transporting, and processing the wastepaper and the increased efficiency and lower costs of harvesting and processing pulpwood (a primary source of paper fiber). Since 1975, paper and paperboard recovery has remained fairly stable at around 20% of gross discards recovered per year. Glass is 100% recyclable, and glass recovery has increased from 1.2% of gross discards recovered in 1970 to 7.2% in 1984.

Methods of storage, collection, and disposal of municipal wastes also have changed over the past 25 years. In the early part of the 1970s, there was a major emphasis on innovations to semiautomate the storage and collection of household refuse. In the 1980s, however, the emphasis has shifted to methods of disposal. Up until now, sanitary landfills have been the primary method of solid waste disposal for most localities. Yet, many of the existing

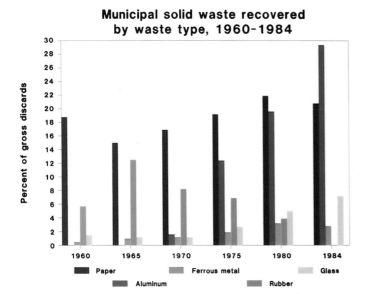

Municipal solid waste recovered by waste type, 1960-1984

Percent of gross discards

■ Paper ■ Ferrous metal ▨ Glass
■ Aluminum ■ Rubber

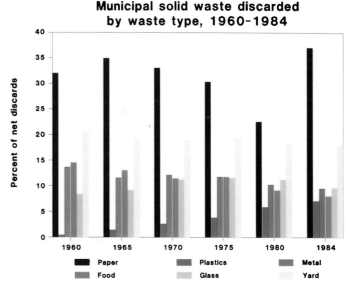

Municipal solid waste discarded by waste type, 1960-1984

Percent of net discards

■ Paper ■ Plastics ■ Metal
■ Food ▨ Glass ▨ Yard

Municipal solid waste recovered 1960-1984

Percent of gross discards

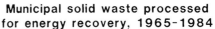
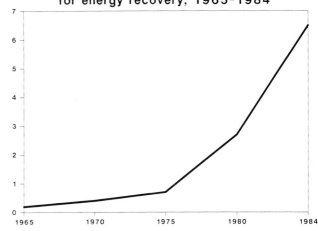

Municipal solid waste processed for energy recovery, 1965-1984

Millions of tons

landfills have reached or are nearing capacity. Municipalities are searching for solutions and are looking for other methods of disposal. It has become more difficult to obtain land for landfills and licenses for incinerators, primarily because of increased public concern about the environmental threats of these waste disposal practices, and it is much more costly to develop new facilities because of required environmental safeguards.

For some time, it was hoped that resource recovery, energy conversion, and bioconversion or composting would prove helpful, but they have not caught on to any significant degree. Even though there is a lot of potential for these systems in the United States, there are also numerous obstacles and uncertainties that hinder their development. There have been problems with the operation of some of these facilities, particularly in the separation of materials. Lack of financial backing and a constant and readily available market for the product produced have also prevented systems from being constructed. It is still more economically feasible for some localities to dispose of their waste in landfills rather than to send it through a resource or

energy recovery process. In view of the problems associated with landfills, however, it is expected that more and more communities will be looking at resource and energy recovery alternatives.

9-3
Solid waste disposal by industrial sector

In 1979, the industrial sector of the United States discarded over 163 million tons of solid waste after resource recovery. Since then, national totals have dropped significantly to 89 million tons in 1983, the last year in which industrial waste data were reported. Some of the decline resulted from economic recession and some from increased recovery of reusable materials.

Metal, chemical, food, and nonmetal mineral industries produced the largest proportions of industrial wastes between 1979 and 1983. Trends in waste generation by these industrial sectors follow the overall national trend for the reporting period.

In 1983, 9% of the solid waste discarded by industries was hazardous. During that year, chemical manufacturers produced 3.6 million tons of hazardous wastes, and petroleum and metal manufacturers produced 1.5 and 1.0 million tons, respectively. Manufacturers of electronic equipment and transportation equipment each produced 0.3 million tons of hazardous wastes, and food, nonmetal minerals, fabricated metals, and machinery (excluding electrical) producers each generated 0.2 million tons of hazardous wastes.

Each industry has its own characteristic type of waste and its own problems of waste treatment and disposal. The chemical industry, in terms of quantity and diversity of contaminants generated, is the most difficult to manage in regard to meeting wastewater discharge and solid waste disposal requirements. Most large manufacturing plants have their own wastewater treatment facilities that empty into a river or pretreatment facilities that discharge to a municipal treatment plant where organic destruction can take place. Solid waste disposal options include landfill, land application of sludge and slurries, microbial destruction, and incineration.

Industrial solid waste disposal, 1975-1983

Million short tons

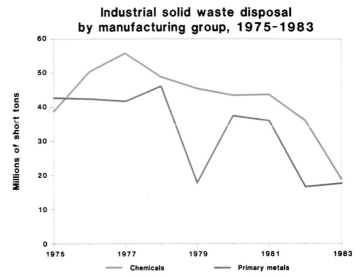

Industrial solid waste disposal by manufacturing group, 1975-1983

Millions of short tons

—— Chemicals   —— Primary metals

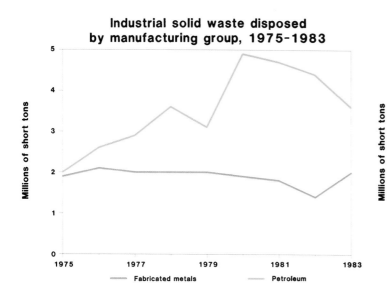

Industrial solid waste disposed by manufacturing group, 1975-1983

Millions of short tons

— Fabricated metals   — Petroleum

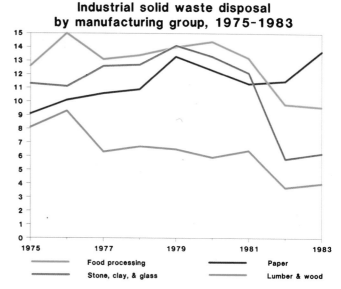

Industrial solid waste disposal by manufacturing group, 1975-1983

Millions of short tons

— Food processing   — Paper
— Stone, clay, & glass   — Lumber & wood

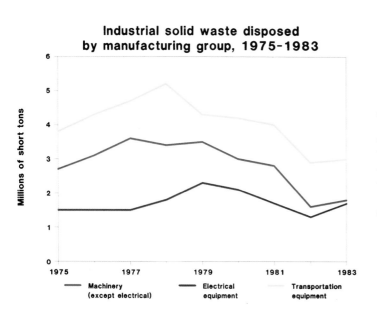

Industrial solid waste disposed by manufacturing group, 1975-1983

Millions of short tons

— Machinery (except electrical)   — Electrical equipment   — Transportation equipment

Industrial hazardous solid waste disposal by manufacturing group, 1983

Percent of net discards

Chemical | Petroleum | Fabricated metals | Machinery, excluding electronic | Electronic equipment | Transportation equipment

Industrial hazardous solid waste disposal by manufacturing group, 1983

Percent of net discards

Food | Lumber & wood | Paper | Stone, clay, & glass | Primary metals

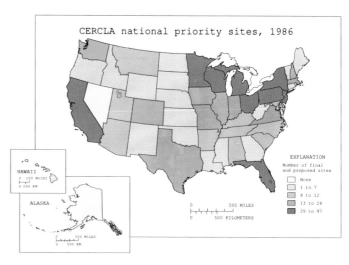

CERCLA national priority sites, 1986

HAWAII
0   100 MILES
0   100 KM

ALASKA

EXPLANATION
Number of final and proposed sites
☐ None
☐ 1 to 7
☐ 8 to 12
☐ 13 to 28
☐ 29 to 97

0   500 MILES
0   500 KILOMETERS

9-4
Hazardous waste sites

Thousands of abandoned or inactive waste disposal sites containing hazardous wastes have been discovered in the United States, and many more wait to be discovered. Many of these sites are located in environmentally sensitive areas such as floodplains and wetlands, and some have been found in densely populated residential areas (Love Canal, for example). At sites containing hazardous wastes, surface and underground soil layers may be contaminated, and rain and melting snow seeping through the sites can carry chemicals into underground waters and nearby rivers and streams. At some sites, the air is also contaminated as toxic vapors rise from evaporating liquid wastes or from uncontrolled chemical reactions. Some pollutants, such as metals and organic solvents, are known to damage vegetation, endanger wildlife, and threaten the health of people who unknowingly drink contaminated water.

Most of the hazardous waste sites were created by the chemical and petroleum industries. A smaller number of sites were once municipal landfills that may have become hazardous as a result of accumulated pesticides, cleaning solvents, and other chemical products discarded in household trash. A few sites are the result of transportation spills or other accidents, and others are the final resting place of persistent toxic pollutants contained in industrial wastewater discharges or air pollution emissions. "Midnight dumping" of illegal waste continues to create hazardous sites. The majority of hazardous waste sites are found in the industrial regions of the Nation.

The federal government can require the "responsible parties" who generated or transported the wastes or owned or operated the disposal site to clean up the hazardous site. If there appears to be no responsible party able or willing to clean up the site quickly enough, the federal government may proceed with cleanup using funds from a special fund called "Superfund" financed mainly by a tax on chemical production. States must contribute 10% of the costs of Superfund-financed cleanups. Later, the federal and state governments may seek reimbursement by the responsible parties under the cost recovery provision of the law.

To be eligible for a long-term remedial action under Superfund, a site must be listed on the national priority list for hazardous sites. Starting in 1980, efforts have been made to identify all uncontrolled hazardous sites and to determine whether the sites present a hazard and, if so, what cleanup actions are appropriate. By 1986, over 24,000 uncontrolled hazardous sites had been inventoried. Of these, 703 sites qualified for the national priority list and another 185 sites were in the proposed category, for a total of 888 sites. Some sites required emergency action because they represented an immediate threat. By 1986, 726 removal actions had been initiated, including 177 at national priority sites where initial cleanup measures were required.

9-5
Production of selected industrial chemicals

It is estimated that over 58,000 different chemical compounds are in use in the United States, and the number is growing. Ten times more chemicals were in use in the mid-1980s than in 1970, and many of these chemicals are toxic under certain conditions. At least 363 chemical (organic and inorganic) substances from a wide range of industrial sources are listed as being hazardous because they are ignitable, corrosive, reactive, or toxic.

Comprehensive federal regulation of commercial chemical products and chemical wastes became a major undertaking in the United States beginning in 1976. Until then, only chemical pesticide products were systematically regulated. Growing concern over the possible links between exposure to even small amounts of chemical substances and human cancers provided the impetus for tightening federal regulatory control over the chemical industry and associated handling of hazardous wastes.

Among the most common toxic chemicals produced and used by industries are acrylonitrile, benzene, vinyl chloride, phthalic anhydride, and polychlorinated biphenyls (PCBs). Acrylonitrile is used as a chemically manufactured resin that is used in the production of plastic bottles, acrylic fibers, and textiles. Combined with butadiene and styrene, acrylonitrile forms a polymer, ABS, which is widely used in appliances, luggage, telephones, and many other common industrial and household products. Current production of acrylonitrile is far in

excess of current and projected domestic demand, and an average annual growth rate of 3% is expected after 1986. Acrylonitrile is primarily released at the workplace. It is a suspected carcinogen and releases the toxic chemical hydrogen cyanide when burned.

Benzene is an organic compound that is derived from petroleum. It is an intermediate in the production of plastics, dyes, nylon, food additives, detergents, drugs, and fungicides. It is also used as a gasoline additive. Production of benzene has increased rapidly in the past 25 years, although some large benzene manufacturers have been periodically idled over the past several years because of weak demand or poor economics. Production peaked in 1979 when over 12 billion pounds of benzene were produced. Long-term demand for benzene is predicted to remain flat. Benzene is implicated as a cause of anemia, bone marrow damage, and leukemia.

Vinyl chloride is a chemically manufactured gas that is used in the production of plastics. The production of vinyl chloride continues to grow, along with the use of plastics, in industrial and consumer products. With many mature outlets for vinyl chloride, the long-term outlook for production growth will probably be moderate at an average annual rate of 2 to 3% for the balance of the 1980s. Vinyl chloride gas is released directly at the workplace, although small amounts are released as consumer products deteriorate and are disposed of. Human health effects from vinyl chloride include liver damage; birth anomalies; liver, respiratory, brain, and lymph cancers; and bone damage.

Phthalates are a class of intermediate synthetic organic chemicals that are used as a resin in the production of plastics, model cement, paints, and finishes. Use of phthalates, especially phthalic anhydride, is widespread and growing. Most phthalates are released at the workplace. They cause damage to the central nervous system in humans, accumulate in birds and cause eggshell thinning, and are toxic to fish.

Polychlorinated biphenyls were important industrial chemicals that were previously used in ink solvents, adhesives, textile coatings, and pesticides. Now PCBs are used only in electrical transformers and other closed systems, but many products containing PCBs remain in use. Production of PCBs was

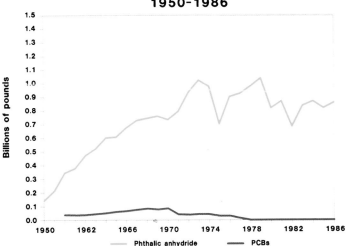

Production of selected industrial chemicals 1950-1986

Phthalic anhydride — PCBs

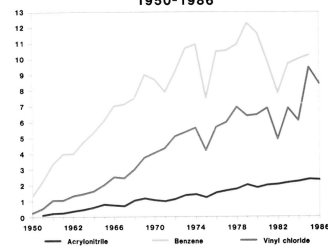

Production of selected industrial chemicals 1950-1986

Acrylonitrile — Benzene — Vinyl chloride

Benzene residues in human adipose tissue
1970-1983

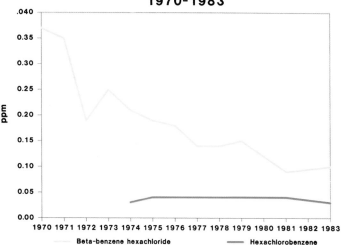

Pesticide residues in human adipose tissue
1970-1983

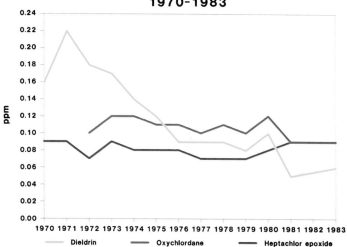

stopped in 1976 because of their environmental and health effects. The major environmental source of PCBs is through improper waste disposal, especially in waterbodies. The threat to human health is through the food chain—in fish, poultry, and meat. In humans, PCBs cause fatigue, vomiting, skin blemishes, abdominal pains, and temporary blindness. They are also suspected carcinogens and are implicated in causing stillbirths. PCBs also cause liver damage in mammals, kidney damage, eggshell thinning in birds, and suspected reproductive failure in fish.

9-6
Toxic residues in human adipose tissue

Humans are exposed to an increasing variety of toxic chemicals and other hazardous substances in the environment, largely because of the expanded production and use of chemicals today but also because of improper waste disposal methods of the past. Exposure of humans to toxic substances can

occur in varied ways, such as through inhalation of gases, fumes, mists, or dusts containing toxic compounds; ingestion of contaminated soil, water, or food; and absorption through the skin or mucous membranes.

Some of the substances are known to have mutagenic, teratogenic, or carcinogenic capabilities, whereas others are suspected of having similar potentials under adverse conditions. Many of the harmful effects occur long after the causative agents have been introduced to the environment, and long after exposure, which hinders early identification of potential health hazards. There is a long latent period for most chronic diseases to develop—15 to 30 years for most human cancers—after exposure to toxic chemicals, which also makes it difficult to pinpoint the causes of these diseases. Establishing cause-and-effect relationships usually requires epidemiologic studies where rates of illness in exposed populations are compared to rates in unexposed or reference populations.

The results of epidemiologic studies have shown that workers in the chemical industry tend to suffer

some serious effects of exposure to toxic forms of industrial chemicals. Cancer mortality for vinyl chloride workers, for example, is 50% higher than for the general population. Rates for biliary and liver cancers among vinyl chloride workers also are relatively high, and residents of communities with polyvinyl chloride plants have higher cancer rates than the general population. Recent studies of benzene workers have shown that they are several times more likely than the general population to contract leukemia.

Since 1970, there has been an annual program to collect and chemically analyze a nationwide sample of human adipose (fatty) tissue specimens for the presence of toxic substances in the general population. Quantitative data for a wide range of volatile and semivolatile organic compounds have been collected. The predominant volatile analytes and their frequency of detection (in 1982 samples) included chloroform (76%), 1,1,1-trichloroethane (48%), benzene (96%), tetrachloroethene (61%), toluene (91%), chlorobenzene (96%), ethylbenzene (96%), styrene (100%), 1,1,2,2-tetrachloroethane (9%),

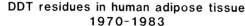

DDT residues in human adipose tissue
1970-1983

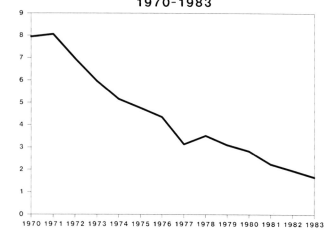

PCB residues in human adipose tissue
1972-1983

1,4-dichlorobenzene (100%), 1,2-dichlorobenzene (63%), xylenes (100%), and ethylphenol (100%). Quantitative data for organochlorine pesticides, PCBs, chlorobenzenes, phthalate esters, phosphate triesters, and polynuclear aromatic hydrocarbons (PAHs) are also obtained. The frequency of detection for some of the predominant compounds in this group in 1982 were dieldrin (31%), heptachlor epoxide (67%), DDT (55%), DDE (93%), and total PCBs (83%). Trends in the levels of detection with respect to age group and census region have been analyzed.

Concentrations of selected benzene compounds in human adipose tissue decreased from 1970 to 1983, the latest year in which data are available, yet the incidences of detection (in 1982) for all benzene compounds monitored were relatively high. One or more benzene compounds was detected in every age group and in every census region.

Concentrations of total PCBs in human adipose tissue also declined between 1970 and 1986. The frequency of detection for small amounts of PCBs (1 to 3 parts per million) was greater than that for larger amounts and declined at a faster rate. The detection of PCBs was widespread in 1982, occurring in every age group and in every census region of the United States.

Organochlorine pesticides are found in adipose tissues of virtually everyone in the United States, but in many cases the concentrations are declining. The levels are not acutely hazardous, although many individual poisonings, other acute illnesses, and chronic illness have been treated. Pesticides enter the human body through ingestion of contaminated food, inhalation of aerosols and dusts, and absorption through the skin. Residues of the parent compound and their metabolites are accumulated and stored in fatty tissue.

Dieldrin concentrations in fatty tissues have been declining since 1971, whereas oxychlordane and heptachlor epoxide, representative of the pesticides chlordane and heptachlor, have remained at relatively constant levels but with relatively high frequency. In 1982 samples, dieldrin was detected in every census region except Mountain, Pacific, New England, and Mid-Atlantic regions, and heptachlor epoxide was found in every region except Pacific. There has been a steady reduction in the concentration of DDT (and its principal metabolite DDE) in

human tissue samples since 1971. Use of DDT was banned in 1972, however, the occurrence of this persistent compound in human adipose tissue is still widespread throughout the Nation.

9-7
Radiation exposure

Radiation is a natural energy force that has existed on earth and in the universe since the beginning of time. Throughout the history of mankind, people have been exposed to natural sources of radiation from cosmic rays and radioactive elements in the earth's rocks and soil. In the past 86 years, however, exposures have come also from X rays and other nuclear medicine procedures, nuclear power plants and nuclear materials processing, nuclear bomb fallout, and a growing variety of low-level sources that range from communication equipment and electronic devices to microwave ovens and smoke detectors.

Ionizing radiation refers to the fact that this energy force can ionize, or electrically charge, atoms by stripping off electrons. There is sufficient energy in this force to change the molecular structure of things, including living tissue. Radiation takes several forms, none of which can be seen, heard, tasted, smelled, or felt. It may be either electromagnetic radiation (X rays and gamma rays) or particulate radiation, which may be either electronically charged (alpha and beta particles) or may have no charge (neutrons). Exposure to sufficiently high doses of radiation, either as high-frequency electromagnetic waves or as high-velocity particles, can result in cell damage ranging from genetic mutation and cancer for low-level exposure to serious burns and rapid death for high-level exposure.

Radiation exposure in humans is measured by the amount and kind of radiation that the body absorbs over time. One unit of absorbed radiation is a rem (roentgen equivalent man). A millirem, $1/1000$ of a rem, is the most commonly used measure for individual and population exposure. On the average, people in the United States receive 180 millirems per year, and most of it (67.6%) comes from natural sources of radiation.

Natural radiation exposure comes from 3 main sources: cosmic rays, which bombard the earth from the sun and from sources inside and outside our

galaxy; cosmogenic radionuclides, which are produced by cosmic ray interaction with air; and primordial radionuclides, which existed at the time of earth's formation and occur in the earth's crustal material. These natural radiation sources are all around us, although concentrations vary. Cosmic and cosmogenic radiation intensity increases with altitude, where the atmosphere is thinner. In Denver, Colorado, for example, radiation intensity is about double what it is in New York City. Cosmic ray intensity is also a function of latitude, being about 15% lower at the equator than at the poles. Primordial radionuclides of the major elements in the earth's crust (potassium, uranium, and thorium, for example) are widespread in distribution and can make a significant contribution to irradiation doses.

The most serious components of natural irradiation are the radium and radon decay products of uranium and thorium. Radium enters the body through food and drinking water and is deposited in bone. Radon, a gas, is believed to be a major cause of lung cancer. Reduction of air leakage from homes and buildings for energy conservation has resulted in increased indoor environmental concentrations of radon in structures throughout the Nation.

The discovery of radioactive materials and ways to make X rays pioneered a rapid growth in medical uses of radionuclides during the first half of this century. After World War II, natural radiation sources were augmented by man-made radionuclides produced by particle accelerators and nuclear reactors, and a larger number of radionuclides became available for medicine, industrial and defense applications, and research.

Medical uses of radiation include diagnostic X rays, radiotherapy, and other medical techniques involving exposure to or ingestion of radionuclides. In recent years, the average annual dose of radiation from these sources has declined, despite increasing uses of radiation in medicine. The reduction is attributed to the use of image intensifying X-ray screens, more effective radiation shielding, and lower dose-producing radionuclide-labeled compounds.

Global fallout from nuclear weapons testing since 1945 has added significantly to widespread radioactivity of the environment and accounts for about 0.6% of the average annual radiation dosage received. Intensive testing occurred in 1954–1958 and 1961–1962, with continued individual tests

Radiation exposure by source, 1986

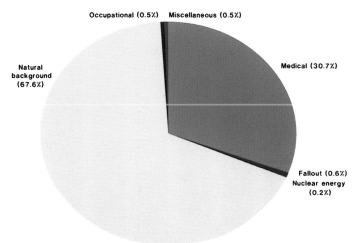

Strontium-90 in pasteurized milk, 1960-1986

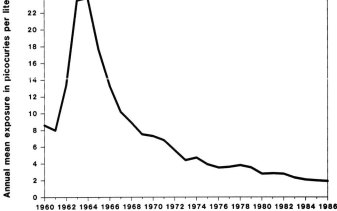

Cesium-137 in pasteurized milk, 1960-1986

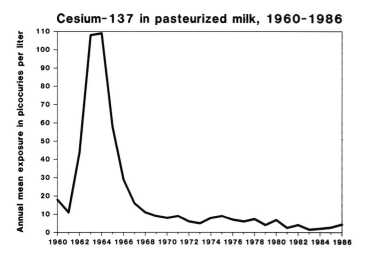

Krypton-85 in air, 1962-1983

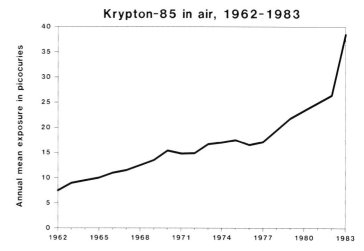

since 1964. Measured levels of two radionuclides deposited as fallout, strontium-90 and cesium-137, have declined significantly from the early 1960s. These radionuclides have been measured in pasteurized milk and become part of bone if they enter the body. The current level of exposure is the result of high-yield atmospheric tests conducted by the United States and Russia, and more recently, by the Peoples' Republic of China.

The nuclear fuel (energy) cycle constitutes a very small source of exposure to humans despite the potential large scale threat. The cycle includes the mining and milling of uranium ores; conversion, enrichment, and fabrication of fuel elements; production of power in nuclear reactors; reprocessing irradiated fuel and recycling recovered nuclides; and transportation and disposal of radioactive wastes. At each step of the cycle, small quantities of radioactive material may be released to the environment.

From an environmental concern, the most important products of the nuclear fuel cycle are tritium, carbon-14, strontium-90, iodine-131, cesium-137, cobalt-60, and krypton-85. Tritium and carbon-14 are not a hazard until they enter the body incorporated in food, air, and water; then they become part of body tissue. Iodine-131, like strontium-90

and cesium-137, can be taken up by dairy cattle and concentrated in milk. When ingested, iodine-131 is concentrated in the human thyroid. Krypton-85 is a long-lived radionuclide. This form of radiation exposure has increased along with the use of nuclear power to generate electricity.

Radiological monitoring stations in the United States are positioned to record ambient trends that would result from appreciable releases from nuclear reactor sites. Elevated concentrations of tritium and cobalt-60 have been recorded in surface water downstream from nuclear facilities, yet no increases in radioactivity have been detected in milk and airborne particles from the operation of domestic nuclear power reactors during the history of operation of the monitoring program. This includes the Three Mile Island accident in 1979. Elevated radionuclide concentrations were detected in the United States following the Chernobyl accident in 1986, however, and cesium-137 from this accident was measured in milk samples.

Other man-made sources of radiation exposure include occupational exposure and consumer product exposure. Workers in the nuclear power field as well as medical personnel, industrial workers, and researchers who are exposed to radiation fields

and/or radioactive materials in the course of their work are subject to occupational exposure. Airline personnel who are exposed to higher levels of cosmic radiation as they fly through the upper atmosphere also fall into this category. Average population exposure from consumer products, such as color televisions and other electronic equipment, watches with luminous dials, smoke detectors, and microwave ovens, varies widely but is about 0.5% of the total average annual dosage.

9-8
Radioactive waste

Radioactive waste disposal may be one of the most critical issues facing the United States. Radioactive waste originates from five major sources: the commercial nuclear fuel cycle; defense-related activities; institutions such as hospitals, universities, and research laboratories; industrial uses of radioisotopes; and mining and milling of uranium ore. The waste is broadly characterized as spent fuel, high-level waste, transuranic waste, low-level waste, and uranium mill tailings.

Spent fuel consists of irradiated fuel that has been permanently discharged from commercial and

Radioactivity accumulation from high-level radioactive waste, 1980-1986

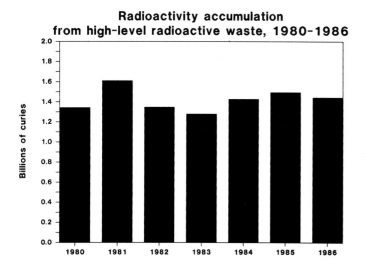

Radioactivity accumulation from low-level radioactive waste, 1980-1986

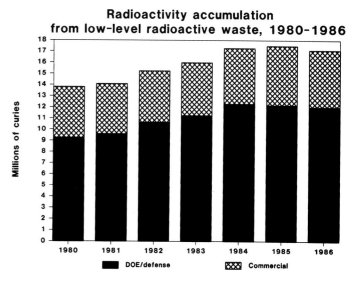

Radioactivity accumulation from nuclear reactor spent fuel, 1970-1986

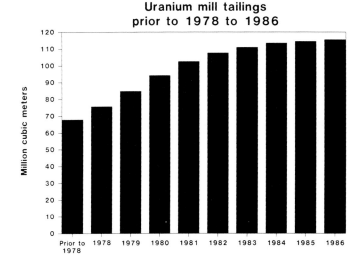

Uranium mill tailings prior to 1978 to 1986

one-of-a-kind nuclear reactors. Currently, most spent fuel assemblies are stored in pools at the reactor sites but ultimately will require geologic disposal. The remainder is already in storage at various Department of Energy (DOE) and commercial sites.

High-level radioactive waste results primarily from the reprocessing of spent nuclear fuel and consists mainly of liquids remaining from the recovery of uranium and plutonium, although it may also be in the form of sludge, calcine, or other products to facilitate their handling and disposal. High-level waste contains fission products that result in the release of considerable radioactive energy. For this reason, heavy shielding is required to control penetrating radiation and to dissipate decay heat. Most of the present inventory of high-level radioactive waste is the result of DOE/defense activities, although a small amount of commercial high-level waste has been generated. The inventories are in interim storage in tanks, bins, and capsules, and most will require incorporation into a stable, solid medium (glass, for example) for final disposal.

The term "transuranic" refers to elements with an atomic number greater than 92. Transuranic waste results primarily from fuel reprocessing and from the fabrication of plutonium weapons and plutonium-bearing reactor fuel. Most transuranic waste is trash (rags, coveralls, rubber gloves, equipment, and tools) that has been slightly contaminated during nuclear processing operations. Generally, little or no shielding is required for transuranic wastes, and they are buried at DOE and commercial sites.

Commercial uranium mill tailings are the earthen residues that remain after the extraction of uranium ores. Tailings are generated in very large volumes and contain low concentrations of naturally occurring radioactive materials. After being thoroughly washed, the tailings are pumped as a slurry to a tailings pond. Uranium production through conventional milling in the United States has declined since 1980, and, as a consequence, the quantity of mill tailings has declined each year.

Low-level radioactive waste is waste not classified as spent fuel, high-level, transuranic, uranium mill tailings, or mixed material (concentrations of low-level radioactive materials and hazardous waste). Radiation for low-level waste is sometimes high

enough to require shielding for handling and transport; however, low-level wastes are acceptable for disposal in a land disposal facility. There are currently three commercial shallow-land disposal sites for this type of waste. The commercial nuclear fuel cycle generates about 60% of the waste volume that is shipped to commercial burial sites; the remainder comes from industrial and institutional activities: radiochemical manufacturers, research laboratories, hospitals, medical schools, universities, other radioactive materials licensees, and some federal agencies other than DOE. DOE/defense low-level waste is buried at government sites. Prior to 1970, however, small quantities of DOE/defense low-level waste was mixed with cement, packaged in steel drums, and dumped at sea; and prior to 1983, some was mixed with cement and other additives and injected into shale at depths of 700 to 1000 feet.

9-9
Tornadoes

Of the violent windstorms, tornadoes are the most common. They occur most often along the eastern

and southeastern coasts, in the midwest, and across the central portion of the western states. A total of 764 tornadoes was reported in the United States during 1986, which was above the 33-year (1953–1985) national average of 749. The outstanding feature of the 1986 tornado season was the extremely low number of fatalities (15), the lowest since 1916. Total property damage was estimated to be in excess of 500 million dollars.

The climatology of tornadoes, like that of wind speed and direction, is determined by the global distribution of atmospheric pressure and the regional effects of topography, orography, geography, and meteorology. Tornadoes come quickly and provide little warning time, yet with information provided by a historical tornado data base on tornado track length, width, and location and tornadic intensity, tornado hazard assessments can be made to predict the probability of a tornado striking a particular geographic area. A high annual probability zone covers much of the Central Lowland, Interior Highlands and Low Plateau, and Gulf Coastal Plain regions of the United States, with smaller high hazard probability areas in southern New England and California.

Tornado risk zones

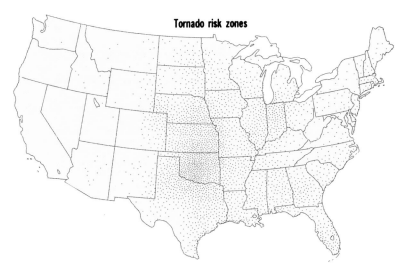

Each dot represents the approximate location of two occurrences during a 10-year period. An occurrence is defined as the first point of contact with the ground.

Average number of tornadoes and tornado days, 1953-1986

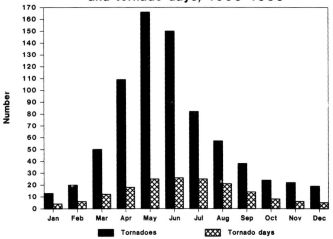

Number of tornadoes, 1916-1986

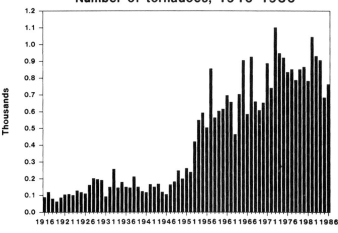

Lives lost in tornadoes, 1916-1986

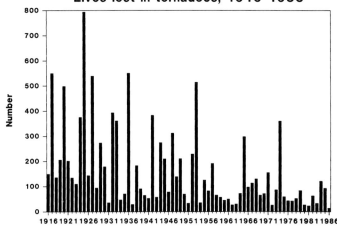

Tornadoes can occur at any time during the year, although March through August have the greatest number of tornadoes and tornado days. For the United States, the "typical" tornado is 0.98 mile long, 48 yards wide, and devastates 0.04 square miles. The weakest intensity tornado accounts for 23% of the tornadoes that have a severity estimate. For this class, the average length is 1.1 miles, the average width is 46 yards, the average winds are less than 73 miles an hour, and the mean area affected is 0.06 square miles. On the other end of the spectrum are the extremely violent tornadoes that make up less than 0.2% of the population. These tornadoes average 34.2 miles in length, 616 yards in width, have winds in excess of 261 miles per hour, and devastate 11.88 square miles.

The occurrence of tornadoes is not increasing over time, as the historical data on the number of tornadoes would imply. Many more small tornadoes than large tornadoes occur, yet early data compilations typically included only large, destructive tornadoes. Thus, early records probably underestimate the number of tornadoes because small size or weak

tornadoes had a much smaller chance of being reported.

Tornadoes may be of short duration, but their destruction can be long-lasting. Tornadoes destroy or damage structures, hurl debris, and overturn and destroy mobile homes and small aircraft. In 1986, tornadoes damaged or destroyed over 500 mobile homes in the United States. High concentrations of people and the siting of nuclear reactors and associated facilities in areas of high tornado hazard require special planning, including disaster preparedness and structural modifications to mitigate tornado effects.

9-10
Earthquakes

Earthquakes are vibrations of the earth that result from sudden internal movement along faults or breaks in crustal rocks. Earthquakes occur when forces that are caused by slow movement of the earth's inner crust build up to the point they exceed the strength of the rocks, and the rocks rupture or

fault. Aftershocks are common in most big earthquakes and are believed to be caused by readjustments to the main movement.

By vibrating the ground, earthquakes cause damage in a number of ways. They can set off landslides, produce seismic waves, cause uplift or subsidence, and damage or destroy structures. In urban areas, fires can be started by crossed electric wires and broken gas lines, and lines of communication can be disrupted. Damages caused by earthquakes in loss of lives and property are greater in densely populated areas. More than any other geophysical hazard, earthquakes are likely to produce almost complete social disruption, especially in urban areas.

The intensity of an earthquake is the violence of earthquake motion in any part of the perceptible area of the earthquake and is based on the effects observed on people and objects. Magnitude, stated according to the Gutenberg-Richter scale, is a measure of the energy release at the focus of an earthquake, as determined by amplitudes produced on a seismogram. Although the magnitude scale has no top or bottom values, the highest magnitude ever recorded was 8.9 and the lowest was about minus 3.

Most of the Nation is at some risk of earthquake occurrence, although earthquakes occur primarily along the West coast, especially in California. It is estimated that earthquakes in California and western Nevada represent approximately 90% of the seismic activity occurring in the conterminous United States. The principal fault in this area—the San Andreas—extends over 600 miles. Additional activity occurs in the sparsely populated Western Mountain region although less is known about this earthquake history. In addition, Montana and Utah have been subject to earthquakes of considerable severity.

Major earthquakes have also occurred in Missouri, Massachusetts, New York, and South Carolina. Usually, nonmountainous interior portions of continents are considered less earthquake prone than any other part of the earth, but this does not hold true in the central portion of the United States where the Upper Mississippi and Ohio River valleys experience relatively frequent earthquakes. Earthquakes in the Northeast may be explained by the readjustment of the earth's crust subsequent to the deformation caused by the ice load of the relatively recent Ice

Earthquake risk zones

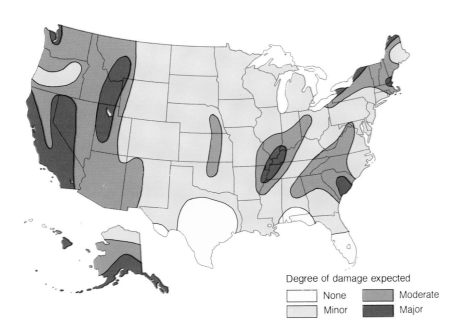

Degree of damage expected

None	Moderate
Minor	Major

Age. With the exception of the Charleston earthquake, the Eastern region of the United States has a moderate amount of low-level earthquake activity.

Alaska and the Aleutian Islands are part of the great seismic belt that circumscribes the Pacific Ocean. Although earthquake activity here is greater than in any other state, few shocks have caused severe damage because of the absence of large population centers. Hawaii, too, is an area of great seismic activity, where most of it is centered on the Island of Hawaii. Much of this activity is directly associated with volcanic processes, although the stronger shocks that are sometimes felt throughout the region are of tectonic origin.

9-11
Hurricanes

Since 1930, an annual average of ten named tropical cyclones develop in the South Atlantic, out of which six attain hurricane status. Of these, an average of two hurricanes hit the coast of the United States each year. Hurricane activity in the 1980s has been below normal, except for 1984 and 1985, which were near normal in terms of number of hurricanes forming, number of hurricane days, and

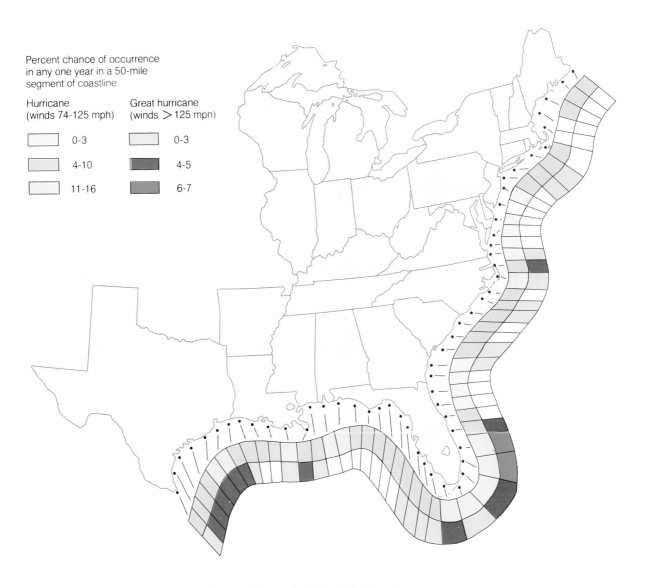

Percent chance of occurrence in any one year in a 50-mile segment of coastline

Hurricane (winds 74-125 mph)	Great hurricane (winds > 125 mph)
0-3	0-3
4-10	4-5
11-16	6-7

Hurricane risk along the Gulf and Atlantic coasts

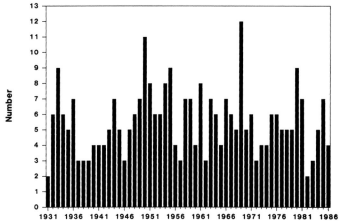

North Atlantic hurricanes, 1931-1986

number of hurricanes striking the U.S. coastline. In 1986, only two tropical storms and four hurricanes developed, but of these, two hurricanes made landfall in the United States. Not only were there fewer tropical cyclones in 1986, but they were also weaker.

Hurricane season is usually between the months of June and October. Efforts to discover and understand the factors controlling the seasonal variation in tropical cyclone activity are mired in statistics. However, there are indications that sea-level pressure patterns, high-level winds, and sea surface temperature are all related to tropical cyclone occurrence.

Hurricanes are divided into two categories. Tropical cyclones with reported winds of 74 to 125 miles per hour are considered hurricanes. Great hurricanes are those with sustained winds of 125 miles per hour or more. Throughout recorded history, there have been more hurricanes than great hurricanes.

The hurricane record for storms entering the coastal zone along the Gulf of Mexico and Atlantic coasts of the United States since 1886 has been used to predict the probability of occurrence within

a 50-mile strip of coastline. While this information cannot be considered a stable assessment of the risk of storm recurrence at any one locality, it is important for planning purposes. Because of the rapid shift in population to the coasts, especially the Gulf and Atlantic coasts, the population at risk is growing.

In general, the Gulf of Mexico coastline is more vulnerable than the Atlantic coast to early-season cyclones. This is to be expected, however, since the primary early-season hurricane genesis regions are the western Caribbean and the Gulf of Mexico. The location of the latest occurrences of late-season storms is shared by southwest Florida and the Cape Hatteras area. Other than this, late storms appear to be fairly well distributed along the Gulf of Mexico and Atlantic coasts. One particular feature of note is the concentration of high likelihood of great hurricane landfalls along the southeastern coast of Florida and most of the Texas coast.

Hurricanes do damage in two principal ways: the high winds and storm surge (increased height and volume of water) directly damage buildings and other man-made structures; and rains carried by

hurricanes cause extensive flooding along the coast and inland. The initial storm surge is responsible for 90% of the lives lost to hurricanes along the coast.

9-12
Floods

About 6% of the land area of the conterminous United States is prone to flooding by streams. Low-lying areas along the Nation's coastline are also subject to flooding by high tides associated with coastal storms and hurricanes. Floods become a hazard in floodplain areas where there is human occupancy and use. Floodplains serve to convey excess water during floods; however, because of their level ground, fertile soils, ease of access, and availability of water supplies, there are economic incentives for developing floodplains.

Many approaches have been used to reduce losses from flooding. Some efforts such as dam and reservoir construction are used to protect the occupants in flood-prone areas; other efforts are intended to keep development off the floodplains. There are trade-offs between upstream and downstream interests involved in virtually all flood-control activities. For example, levees may be built along the river banks to keep floodwaters in the channels, but this will limit floodplain storage of water and thus may exacerbate flooding downstream.

In addition to levees and reservoirs, other flood-damage mitigation strategies include "flood-proofing" of buildings in flood-prone areas, zoning to keep people and property out of the most hazardous areas, and development of flood warning systems. Timely forecasts and warnings can aid disaster preparedness and thus save lives and reduce property damage.

Complete protection from flooding is never achieved. Flood-control efforts may create a sense of security, encouraging development in partially protected areas. Flood protection in these areas may be achieved for most floods, but there is the potential for even greater losses during a very large flood when levees are overtopped or reservoir capacity is exceeded. This may provide a partial explanation of the observed long-term rise in flood damages.

Changes in land use generally affect the magnitude of floods downstream. Changes due to urbanization are the best documented, but other land-use

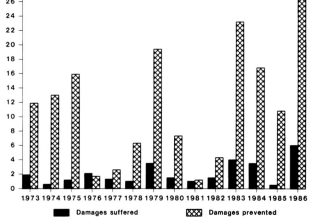

Flood damages and flood control, 1973-1986

■ Damages suffered   ▨ Damages prevented

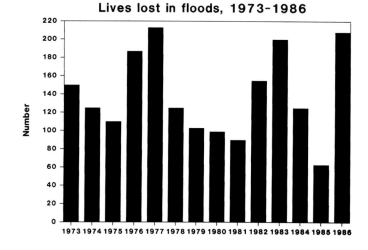

Lives lost in floods, 1973-1986

changes related to agriculture, forestry, and mining also have some effects, though more subtle and difficult to quantify. Urbanization results in the covering of parts of a drainage basin with impervious surfaces such as roads, parking lots, and roofs. This generally results in a greater volume of runoff from a given rainstorm than would have occurred prior to development. In addition, urban gutters, storm sewers, and natural channels, which have been straightened, deepened, or lined with concrete to move water away more efficiently, convey water into streams more quickly than natural drainage systems. The increased volume and rate of runoff commonly result in increased flood discharges, flood levels, and flood damage downstream. Some effort is being made to implement more comprehensive storm water management that uses innovative approaches such as detention ponds, restricted outlets from rooftops, porous pavement, and diversion of drainage from impervious areas to pervious areas.

Flood damages in 1986 were more than 6 billion dollars, the highest incurred since such records began and 3 times the yearly average during 1976–1985. Flood-related fatalities totaled 208, just above the national average of 200 lives per year. Flash floods accounted for 80% of the deaths.

Sources and technical notes

9-1
Waste generation and disposal

9-1
General flow of materials

Executive Office of the President, Council on Environmental Quality. 1981. *Environmental trends* (Washington, D.C.), figure 9-1, Flow of materials, products, and solid waste, 1977, p. 77.

9-2
Municipal solid waste generation, recovery, and disposal

9-2a
Municipal solid waste generation, 1960–1984

9-2b
Municipal solid waste generation per capita, 1960–1984

9-2c
Municipal solid waste recovered by waste type, 1960–1984

9-2d
Municipal solid waste discarded by waste type, 1960–1984

9-2e
Municipal solid waste recovered, 1960–1984

9-2f
Municipal solid waste processed for energy recovery, 1965–1984

Franklin Associates, Ltd., Prairie, Kansas. 1986. *Characterization of municipal solid waste in the United States, 1960 to 2000.* A report prepared for the U.S. Environmental Protection Agency (Washington, D.C.).

Bureau of the Census. 1988. *Statistical abstract of the United States* (Washington, D.C.), p. 193.

Regan, R. W. 1984. "Classification and properties of solid and liquid wastes," pp. 2-9, in *Solid and liquid wastes: Management, methods and socioeconomic considerations.*

S. K. Majumdar, and E. W. Miller (eds.). The Pennsylvania Academy of Science (Easton, Pa.).

9-3
Solid waste disposal by industrial sector

9-3a
Industrial solid waste disposal, 1975–1983

9-3b
Industrial solid waste disposal by manufacturing group (chemicals and primary metals), 1975–1983

9-3c
Industrial solid waste disposal by manufacturing group (fabricated metals and petroleum), 1975–1983

9-3d
Industrial solid waste disposal by manufacturing group (food processing, stone, clay and glass, paper, and lumber and wood), 1975–1983

9-3e
Industrial solid waste disposal by manufacturing group [machinery (except electrical), electrical equipment, and transportation equipment], 1975–1983

9-3f
Industrial hazardous waste disposal by manufacturing group [chemical, petroleum, fabricated metals, machinery (excluding electrical), electronic equipment, and transportation], 1983

9-3g
Industrial hazardous waste disposal by manufacturing group (food, lumber and wood, paper, stone, clay and glass, and primary metals), 1983

U.S. Department of Commerce, Bureau of the Census. *Current industrial reports,* annual (Washington, D.C.), series MA-200.

9-4
Hazardous waste sites

9-4
CERCLA national priority sites, 1986

U.S. Environmental Protection Agency, Office of Emergency and Remedial Response. 1986. *National priorities list fact book* (Washington, D.C.), pp. 19-20.

9-5
Production of selected industrial chemicals

9-5a
Production of selected industrial chemicals (phthalic anhydride and PCBs), 1950–1986

9-5b
Production of selected industrial chemicals (acrylonitrile, benzene, and vinyl chloride), 1950–1986

U.S. International Trade Commission. 1986. *Synthetic organic chemicals* (Washington, D.C.).

U.S. Environmental Protection Agency, Office of Pesticides and Toxic Substances (Washington, D.C.). 1986. Unpublished data.

Executive Office of the President, Council on Environmental Quality. 1981. *Environmental trends* (Washington, D.C.), pp. 90-91.

PCBs = Polychlorinated biphenyls. There has been no production of PCBs since 1978.

9-6
Toxic residues in human adipose tissue

9-6a
Benzene residues in human adipose tissue, 1970–1983

9-6b
Pesticide residues in human adipose tissue, 1970–1983

9-6c
DDT residues in human adipose tissue, 1970–1983

9-6d
PCB residues in human adipose tissue, 1970–1983

U.S. Environmental Protection Agency, Office of Pesticides and Toxic Substances (Washington, D.C.). 1986. Unpublished data from the National Human Adipose Tissue Survey of the National Human Monitoring Program.

Executive Office of the President, Council on Environmental Quality. 1981. *Environmental trends* (Washington, D.C.), p. 98.

9-7
Radiation exposure

9-7a
Radiation exposure by source, 1986

U.S. Department of Energy, Oak Ridge National Laboratory. 1986. *Understanding radiation* (Oak Ridge, Tenn.).

9-7b
Strontium-90 in pasteurized milk, 1960–1986

9-7c
Cesium-137 in pasteurized milk, 1960–1986

9-7d
Krypton-85 in air, 1962–1983

Environmental Protection Agency, Office of Radiation Programs (Montgomery, Ala.). 1986. Unpublished data.

Executive Office of the President, Council on Environmental Quality. 1981. *Environmental trends* (Washington, D.C.). pp. 110-115.

9-8
Radioactive waste

9-8a
Radioactivity accumulation from high-level radioactive waste, 1980–1986

9-8b
Radioactivity accumulation from low-level radioactive waste, 1980–1986

9-8c
Radioactivity accumulation from nuclear reactor spent fuel, 1970–1986

9-8d
Uranium mine tailings, prior to 1978 to 1986

U.S. Department of Energy, Office of Civilian Radioactive Waste Management. 1988. *Integrated data base for 1988: Spent fuel and radioactive waste inventories, projections, and characteristics* (Washington, D.C.), pp. 1-10, 31, 49, 60, 105-112, 114, and 115.

9-9
Tornadoes

9-9a
Tornado risk zones

Executive Office of the President, Council on Environmental Quality. 1981. *Environmental trends* (Washington, D.C.), figure 2-22, Frequency of tornadoes, 1953–1962, p. 41.

9-9b
Average number of tornadoes and tornado days, 1953–1986

9-9c
Number of tornadoes, 1916–1986

9-9d
Lives lost in tornadoes, 1916–1986

U.S. Department of Commerce, National Oceanic and Atmospheric Administration, National Climatic Data Center. 1987. *Storm data 1987* and earlier issues (Asheville, N.C.), p. 1-7.

9-10
Earthquakes

9-10
Earthquake risk zones

Executive Office of the President, Council on Environmental Quality. 1981. *Environmental trends* (Washington, D.C.), figure 2-23, Earthquake risk zones, p. 41.

U.S. Department of Commerce, National Oceanic and Atmospheric Administration and U.S. Department of the Interior, Geological Survey. 1982. *Earthquake history of the United States* (Boulder, Colo.).

9-11
Hurricanes

9-11a
Hurricane risk along the Gulf and Atlantic coasts

Executive Office of the President, Council on Environmental Quality. 1981. *Environmental trends* (Washington, D.C.), figure 2-21, Hurricane risk along the Gulf and Atlantic coasts, p. 40.

9-11b
North Atlantic hurricanes, 1931–1986

U.S. Department of Commerce, National Oceanic and Atmospheric Administration, National Climatic Data Center. *Storm data,* annual (Asheville, N.C.).

U.S. Department of Commerce, National Oceanic and Atmospheric Administration, National Climatic Data Center. 1984. *The federal plan for meteorological services and supporting research* (Asheville, N.C.).

9-12
Floods

9-12a
Flood damages and flood control, 1973–1986

9-12b
Lives lost in floods, 1973–1986

U.S. Department of Defense, Army Corps of Engineers, Office of the Chief of Engineers (Washington, D.C.). 1986. Unpublished data.

U.S. Department of the Interior, Geological Survey. 1984. *National water summary 1983—Hydrologic events and issues.* Water-Supply Paper 2250 (Washington, D.C.), pp. 163-167.

List of Figures and Tables